BIOLOGY OF PARASITES

Emphasis on Veterinary Parasites

Contributors to this Volume

DON R. ARTHUR

NORMAN F. BAKER

PAUL C. BEAVER

JAMES R. DOUGLAS

J. H. DRUDGE

S. M. GAAFAR

T. E. GIBSON

FRANS C. GOBLE

IRVING G. KAGAN

E. T. LYONS

G. A. MAEKELT

GILBERT F. OTTO

CLARK P. READ

R. F. RIEK

MIODRAG RISTIC

W. P. ROGERS

E. J. L. SOULSBY

M. A. STIREWALT

JOSEPH SZANTO

CLARENCE J. WEINMAN

PAUL P. WEINSTEIN

J. H. WHITLOCK

BIOLOGY OF PARASITES

Emphasis on Veterinary Parasites

Proceedings of the Second International Conference of the World Association for the Advancement of Veterinary Parasitology held at the University of Pennsylvania, Philadelphia, September 7th to 9th, 1965 in conjunction with Bicentennial Celebrations of Medical Education in the United States

Edited by E. J. L. SOULSBY

DEPARTMENT OF PARASITOLOGY
UNIVERSITY OF PENNSYLVANIA
PHILADELPHIA, PENNSYLVANIA

1966

ACADEMIC PRESS   New York and London

ACADEMIC PRESS, INC.
111 Fifth Avenue, New York, New York 10003

United Kingdom Edition published by
ACADEMIC PRESS, INC. (LONDON) LTD.
Berkeley Square House, London W.1

LIBRARY OF CONGRESS CATALOG CARD NUMBER: 66–17292

Second Printing, 1969

PRINTED IN THE UNITED STATES OF AMERICA

List of Contributors

Numbers in parentheses indicate the pages on which the authors' contributions begin.

Don R. Arthur, *Department of Zoology, University of London, King's College, London, England* (61)

Norman F. Baker, *Department of Veterinary Microbiology, School of Veterinary Medicine, University of California, Davis, California* (155)

Paul C. Beaver, *Department of Tropical Medicine and Public Health, Tulane University School of Medicine, New Orleans, Louisiana* (215)

James R. Douglas, *Department of Veterinary Microbiology, School of Veterinary Medicine, University of California, Davis, California* (155)

J. H. Drudge, *Department of Veterinary Science, Kentucky Agricultural Experiment Station, University of Kentucky, Lexington, Kentucky* (199)

S. M. Gaafar, *Department of Veterinary Microbiology, Pathology, and Public Health, School of Veterinary Science and Medicine, Purdue University, Lafayette, Indiana* (229)

T. E. Gibson, *Central Veterinary Laboratory, Weybridge, England* (1)

Frans C. Goble, *Research Department, CIBA Pharmaceutical Co., Summit, New Jersey* (237)

Irving G. Kagan, *U. S. Department of Health, Education, and Welfare, Public Health Service, Communicable Disease Center, Atlanta, Georgia* (277)

E. T. Lyons, *Department of Veterinary Science, Kentucky Agricultural Experiment Station, University of Kentucky, Lexington, Kentucky* (199)

G. A. Maekelt, *Departamento de Inmunologia, Instituto de Medicina Tropical, Facultad de Medicina, Universidad Central de Venezuela, Caracas, Venezuela* (321)

Gilbert F. Otto, *Abbot Laboratories, North Chicago, Illinois* (85)

Clark P. Read, *Department of Biology, Rice University, Houston, Texas, and Marine Biological Laboratory, Woods Hole, Massachusetts* (101)

v

R. F. RIEK, *Research & Development Laboratory, Merck Sharp & Dohme (Australia) Pty. Limited, Sydney, Australia* (15)

MIODRAG RISTIC, *College of Veterinary Medicine and Illinois Center for Zoonoses Research, University of Illinois, Urbana, Illinois* (127)

W. P. ROGERS, *University of Adelaide, Waite Agricultural Research Institute, South Australia* (33)

E. J. L. SOULSBY, *Department of Parasitology, University of Pennsylvania, Philadelphia, Pennsylvania* (255)

M. A. STIREWALT, *Naval Medical Research Institute, Bethesda, Maryland* (41)

JOSEPH SZANTO,* *Department of Veterinary Science, Kentucky Agricultural Experiment Station, University of Kentucky, Lexington, Kentucky* (199)

CLARENCE J. WEINMANN, *Division of Parasitology, University of California, Berkeley, California* (301)

PAUL P. WEINSTEIN, *U. S. Department of Health, Education and Welfare, Public Health Service, National Institutes of Health, National Institute of Allergy and Infectious Diseases, Laboratory of Parasitic Diseases, Bethesda, Maryland* (143)

J. H. WHITLOCK, *Department of Pathology, New York State Veterinary College and Division of Biological Sciences, Cornell University, Ithaca, New York* (185)

* Present address: CIBA Research Farm, Three Bridges, New Jersey.

Preface

In the last decade a tremendous amount of progress has been made in parasitology. A multitude of techniques and ideas from other disciplines have led to this progress; possibly we should not speak of other disciplines since each mode of thinking, be it biochemical, physiological, immunological, etc., is directed essentially at elucidating the complex interrelationship between host and parasite—the whole is a study of parasitism. However, it is still common to view the phenomenon of parasitism at one interval of time only. In many cases this is unavoidable because numerous host-parasite systems are intractable entities; however, in other areas the chronology of host-parasite association is being elucidated, and, as the picture becomes more complex and unique to each association, clear thinking becomes mandatory.

In the past few years there have been many publications dealing with all aspects of the "new" parasitology. Therefore, in planning its Second International Conference, the World Association for the Advancement of Veterinary Parasitology took the opportunity of asking authorities from several fields to discuss the current information available in their particular areas and to present a synthesis of the knowledge to those at the conference and to the readers of this volume. This work can serve as an authoritative guide for graduate workers in parasitology as well as a critical introduction for the experimental biologist who is drawn to the wholist, organismal, cellular, or molecular biological potentialities of the subject.

It is a great pleasure to acknowledge the cooperation of the contributors; their presentations have made my duties a delight rather than a task and I have learned much from their manuscripts. I am grateful to the publisher, who has spared no effort to produce an attractive volume in a minimum amount of time.

E. J. L. SOULSBY

Philadelphia, Pennsylvania
June, 1966

Contents

The Ecology of the Infective Larvae of *Trichostrongylus colubriformis*

T. E. Gibson

The Development of *Babesia* spp. and *Theileria* spp. in Ticks with Special Reference to Those Occurring in Cattle

R. F. Riek

Exsheathment and Hatching Mechanisms in Helminths

W. P. Rogers

Skin Penetration Mechanisms of Helminths

M. A. Stirewalt

The Ecology of Ticks with Reference to the Transmission of Protozoa

Don R. Arthur

Development of Parasitic Stages of Nematodes

Gilbert F. Otto

Nutrition of Intestinal Helminths

Clark P. Read

Pathogenesis of Migrating Stages of Helminths, with Special Reference to *Strongylus vulgaris*

J. H. Drudge, E. T. Lyons, and Joseph Szanto

Zoonoses, with Particular Reference to Parasites of Veterinary Importance

Paul C. Beaver

Pathogenesis of Ectoparasites

S. M. Gaafar

Pathogenesis of Blood Protozoa

Frans C. Goble

The Mechanisms of Immunity to Gastrointestinal Nematodes

E. J. L. Soulsby

Mechanisms of Immunity in Trematode Infection

Irving G. Kagan

Immunity Mechanisms in Cestode Infections

Clarence J. Weinmann

Immunity Mechanisms to Protozoa

G. A. Maekelt

BIOLOGY OF PARASITES

Emphasis on Veterinary Parasites

The Ecology of the Infective Larvae of *Trichostrongylus colubriformis*

T. E. GIBSON

Central Veterinary Laboratory, Weybridge, England

There is an extensive literature on the effect of external conditions on the development and survival of the preparasitic stages of trichostrongylid larvae and investigators' methods may be classified under four headings: laboratory observations, experiments on grass plots or boxes, field experiments, and observations on the seasonal and geographical distribution of species in outbreaks of disease. These several methods each have their attractions and their disadvantages. In laboratory experiments conditions can be controlled exactly and preparasitic stages can be exposed to constant temperatures, humidities, intensities of light, and so forth. The conditions of the laboratory are, however, quite removed from conditions to which eggs and larvae may be exposed in the field and the results of such experiments are of limited application to disease control. Experiments with grass plots and boxes allow the investigator to exert considerable control over the method and rate of contamination of the herbage while ensuring exposure to the weather conditions prevailing in the area concerned. Some attention must be given to the length of herbage grown on the plot for if it is allowed to become longer than the length which would be attained under normal grazing conditions the microclimate could be widely different from that under field conditions. Field experiments using animals infected with monospecific infections yield results nearest to those that might obtain under farming conditions, whilst still enabling the experimenter to retain a degree of control over contamination rates and some other features of the experiments. Observations on farms during disease outbreaks are the most difficult from which to derive information. The mixture of species usually present creates difficulties because of the uncertainties of identification of the eggs and larvae of different species.

1

NEMATODIRIASIS

The value of the plot type of experiment and the field experiment using small paddocks was well demonstrated in work carried out on nematodiriasis between 1951 and 1961. Gibson (1958) reported on a plot experiment in which was studied the development of the eggs of *Nematodirus battus* and *Nematodirus filicollis* when exposed to the weather conditions prevailing in the South of England. These observations demonstrated differences between the two species. With *N. battus* it was found that eggs passed in feces during April developed slowly during the summer and did not reach the infective stage until October. The eggs did not hatch, however, until March of the following year. These observations suggested that during the greater part of the year the larval population on pasture herbage would be low but that a rise would occur in March or April if eggs had been passed on to the herbage during the previous spring. Field experiments on the epidemiology of nematodiriasis described by Gibson (1963a) confirmed this deduction. The latter experiments suggested how grazing management could be used to control the disease and also that control by strategic anthelmintic treatment was possible. Further experiments (Gibson, 1963b) demonstrated the efficacy of the proposed treatment regimen in control of the disease.

Observations with eggs of *N. filicollis* demonstrated different behavior. Development is more rapid than with *N. battus* and some of the eggs voided in April will have hatched by the beginning of June, and clearly larvae would be expected to be present on the pastures for longer than was seen with *N. battus*. Field experiments (Gibson, 1963a) illustrated this point and showed that, following contamination of the pastures by eggs in the spring, larvae may be recovered from the herbage in large numbers from August to May of the following year. This does not make the epidemiology of the disease significantly different from that caused by *N. battus* because the controlling factor becomes the availability of young susceptible lambs rather than the presence of larvae on the pastures. The longer period of availability of larvae on the herbage does mean that disease caused by *N. filicollis* is not so strictly confined to the spring as that due to *N. battus* and outbreaks in late summer have been reported from time to time.

The success of the small plot experiments and field grazing experiments on small paddocks, in elucidating the epidemiology of nematodiriasis has prompted their use in the investigation of the epidemiology of trichostrongylosis. Although Turner *et al.* (1962) have shown some species of nematode influence the establishment of other species in lambs and consequently influence the level of infective larvae on the herbage, there is clearly a distinct advantage in having a series of observations carried out with monospecific infections. The first of these has been carried out using *Trichostrongylus colubriformis* and some of the preliminary results are described below.

ECOLOGICAL OBSERVATIONS ON THE INFECTIVE LARVAE OF *TRICHOSTRONGYLUS COLUBRIFORMIS* USING SMALL PLOTS

MATERIALS AND METHODS

The herbage upon which these observations were carried out was a long term ley specially sown on land that had been under the plough for a number of years and which on that account could be regarded as free from trichostrongylid larvae. Twenty six small plots, each 6 feet square, were marked out on this area and delineated by surrounds of galvanized iron sunk six inches into the ground and projecting one foot above. Observations began on 12 March 1962 and on that date feces containing eggs of *Trichostrongylus colubriformis* were first placed on the plot. Each day the total fecal output of a lamb infected with a pure strain of *T. colubriformis* was collected using a fecal collecting bag and then was spread on the plot. This was continued daily for one week. Two weeks after the first lot of feces was placed on the plot a sample of the herbage was collected by taking small random samples from 100 places on the plot, the aim being to collect about 100 gm of herbage. The herbage collected in this way was examined, by the technique described by Parfitt (1955), for the presence of the infective larvae of *T. colubriformis*. Feces were collected at the same time in order to study the development of the eggs but these observations are not relevant to the present discussion and will be reported elsewhere. Observations were continued until two consecutive collections were free from larvae. Every 4 weeks a plot was set up in a similar manner except that feces were spread for 2 weeks instead of one. At the end of one year when 13 plots had been set up a second series of plots was commenced. In this series feces were spread on each plot for one week only. This interval was adopted so that the results would have some relevance to conditions of rotational grazing when animals are kept in paddocks for a week before moving on to fresh grazing.

RESULTS

The results of the examination of material from the first series of plots is summarized in Fig. 1. It will be seen that infective larvae were not recovered from the herbage 8 weeks after eggs were placed on plot 1 but had appeared in a further 2 weeks. The larval population on this plot rose only to 100 larvae per kilogram of herbage and larvae could no longer be recovered by the end of November. On plot 2 development was quicker and by 6 weeks infective larvae were present on the plot. On this occasion the herbage larval count reached a level of 30,000 larvae

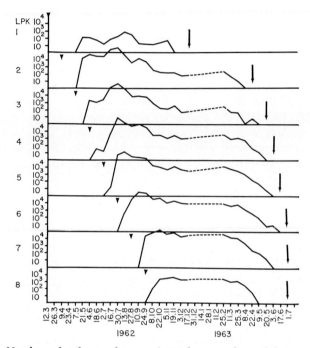

Fig. 1. Number of infective larvae of *Trichostrongylus colubriformis* per kilogram of herbage recovered from plots 1–8. LPK = larvae per kilogram of herbage. Plots 1–13 were set up during the year 1962–1963. Eggs in feces placed outside in October, November, December, Jaunuary, and February did not develop and no infective larvae were recovered from plots 9–13. The broad arrow indicates the date when feces were first spread on a particular plot. The long arrow indicates the cessation of observations on a particular plot. The broken line indicates a period of 12 weeks during which the presence of snow on the ground prevented herbage collection.

per kilogram of herbage. The larval population remained high during the summer and autumn, larvae finally disappearing in March of 1963. Broadly similar results were obtained during the months of May to September. As the season advanced larvae tended to appear more quickly and on most plots larvae were present on the herbage 2 weeks after feces were deposited on the plot. Although plots 3 to 8 were contaminated with feces at different times the larvae which developed died out on all plots toward the end of May 1963. No infective larvae developed on plots 9 to 13 upon which eggs were placed during the period October to February. After 17 December 1962 it was not possible again to examine herbage until 25 February 1963 owing to the presence of deep

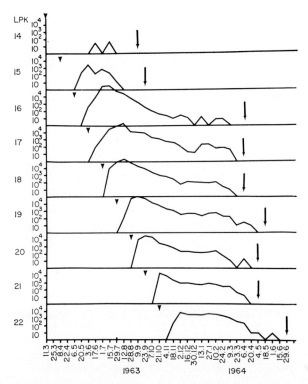

Fig. 2. Number of infective larvae of *T. colubriformis* per kilogram of herbage recovered from plots 14–22. LPK = larvae per kilogram of herbage. Plots 14–26 were set up during the year 1963–1964. Eggs in feces placed outside in November, December, January, and February did not develop and no infective larvae were recovered from plots 23–26. The broad arrow indicates the date when feces were first spread on a particular plot. The long arrow indicates the cessation of observations on a particular plot.

snow on the ground during that time. It is noteworthy that the herbage larval counts before the snow and after it had melted were almost identical.

The results obtained on plots 14 to 26 during the year 1963–1964 are shown in Fig. 2 and are in general similar to those of the previous year. It is noticeable, however, that the rate at which larvae disappeared from the plots was more rapid although larvae finally disappeared at about

the same time from any given plot as in the previous year. This more rapid
disappearance of larvae in the second year was probably due to the
absence of snow. If one imagines the lines on Fig. 1 running from the
level reached on 17 December to the point when larvae finally disappeared the graphs would look very similar to those depicted on Fig. 2.

DISCUSSION

Under the conditions of this investigation larvae persisted at a high
level for periods as long as 20 weeks. This is in contrast to the findings of
Taylor (1938), who found a rapid fall in the numbers of larvae recovered
from grass boxes infected with suspensions of strongloid larvae. Crofton
(1948), using a similar technique to Taylor but working with *Trichostrongylus retortaeformis* larvae, arrived at rather similar conclusions.
Crofton found the initial death rate of the larvae to be high during
periods of hot weather but that in the autumn and winter the initial
death rate was lower. Both these workers studied the survival of larvae
obtained from laboratory cultures and pipetted on to the herbage. It
is not stated in either paper that the larvae were freshly hatched when
placed on the herbage and it is possible that the rapid initial death
rate followed a previous "aging" process which had taken place in the
larvae during storage in the laboratory prior to use. Whatever the explanation there is a distinct difference between the results obtained in the
present work and those of both Crofton and Taylor. Crofton also reported that in summer the time required for the complete disappearance
of larvae was short but that in the winter it was long. This again is in
contrast to the present findings, for in the majority of plots larvae disappeared completely at the end of April or beginning of May irre-
spectively of when eggs were placed on the plot.

It is interesting that the presence of snow cover on the ground prolonged the survival of the larvae. During the period of the snow the air
temperature was frequently as low as —10°C and was accompanied
by biting winds, and these conditions would have quickly resulted in
the death of the larvae. Soil temperatures taken under the snow revealed
that the reading rarely fell below 0°C so that the larvae were, in fact,
under good conditions for long survival. There is no doubt that during
the winter of 1962–1963 the larval population was kept at a higher level
during the winter than in the following year because of the protective
properties of the snow.

Although these experiments have shown that a considerable proportion of the larvae, which hatch from eggs placed on a plot during the
summer, survive for a long time they give no clue to the epidemiological

significance of such "aged" larvae. It may well be that such larvae are incapable of infecting sheep by which they may be ingested. This point is at present under investigation. Rose (1963), working with larvae of *Haemonchus contortus*, found that larvae that have survived on herbage for $8\frac{1}{2}$ months gave rise to patent infections when fed to housed worm-free lambs, so that it is evident that the residual infection present in the spring may play some part in the infection of the new season's lambs.

ECOLOGICAL OBSERVATIONS WITH THE LARVAE OF *TRICHOSTRONGYLUS COLUBRIFORMIS* UNDER CONDITIONS OF ROTATIONAL GRAZING AND OF SET STOCKING

The observations on grass plots just described would suggest that rotational grazing would have little advantage over set stocking in reducing the level of larvae on pasture herbage available to grazing lambs. This is dealt with in the general discussion below. In view of this deduction an experiment was set up to compare the number of larvae under conditions of set stocking with those obtained on similar pasture rotationally grazed.

MATERIALS AND METHODS

The work was carried out on a long-term ley sown on land which had previously been several years under the plough. The ley had for 2 years been used for other grazing experiments but just prior to the beginning of the present investigation the level of pasture larval infection had for some months been 10 larvae per kilogram of herbage or less. An area of 3 acres of this land was fenced and divided into 2 paddocks of $1\frac{1}{2}$ acres. One of these was to be used as the set stocked area and was designated paddock A whilst the other was divided into 6 paddocks of $\frac{1}{4}$ acre each designated paddocks B–G. In order to ensure that some infective material would be present when lambs were introduced on to the experimental area, six 5-month-old Dorset Horn lambs infected with *T. colubriformis* were turned out on paddock A on 6 April 1964 and a similar group was at the same time placed in paddock B. The latter animals were moved daily into paddocks C, D, and so on in order to spread infection as evenly as possible over the area to be rotationally grazed. On 5 May 1964 six ewes and their 7 lambs were placed in paddock A and a similar group into paddock B along with the 6 Dorset Horn lambs already there. After a week's grazing the lambs in paddock B were moved to paddock C and so on until all 6 paddocks had been grazed. On the 7th week the sheep returned to paddock B and the system of rotation began once more. On 14 May 1964 four additional Dorset Horn lambs, infected with *T. colubriformis*, were added to each of the two groups of sheep in the experiment. On 27 July when the rotationally grazing animals had completed 2 circuits of paddocks B–G the lambs were weaned and the ewes withdrawn. Six weeks later, on 7 September, six of the Dorset Horns were removed from each group, and all sheep were finally removed from the experimental area on 19 October 1964. The lambs were weighed weekly and fecal egg counts were carried out weekly on all sheep. These observations are not relevant to the present discussion and will be reported elsewhere. The number of larvae on the pasture herbage of paddock A was estimated each week by the technique described by Parfitt (1955). It would, clearly, have been desirable also to examine each of the paddocks B–G weekly as well but in order to reduce the labor involved only one of these was examined each week. Examinations were made on Monday of each week and the sample was collected from whatever paddock of the series B–G was to be grazed during that particular week.

RESULTS

The results of the herbage examinations are summarized in Fig. 3. The solid line represents the changes in numbers of larvae seen in the set stocked paddock A, whilst the broken line shows the number of larvae to which the rotationally grazed sheep were exposed at the beginning of each week. It will be seen that on paddock A the herbage larvae count began to rise on 25 May and remained at a level of 250 larvae per kilogram of herbage or more until 10 August, when a steep rise occurred, a level of 1400 larvae per kilogram of herbage being reached on 7 September. Subsequently the level tended to decrease and had fallen to 500 larvae per kilogram of herbage by the time the sheep were removed on 19 October. After that date a further fall in larval population occurred; the number having fallen to 200 larvae per kilogram of herbage when observations terminated in December 1964.

A broadly similar picture was observed on the rotationally grazed paddocks. Here the initial rise began a week later than on the set stocked plot but then followed a similar trend to that described for paddock A. The rise that took place in early August on the rotationally grazed paddocks reached 2300 larvae per kilogram of herbage and although the graph for the population of larvae on paddocks B–G follows a similar trend to that for paddock A the number of larvae present on any occasion was always several hundred larvae per kilogram higher on paddocks B–G than on paddock A.

Discussion

The results of this experiment show that larval populations on pasture herbage were not lower on a rotationally grazed area compared with a similar set stocked area. Taylor (1938) reported a rapid drop in the numbers of larvae on pasture herbage a few weeks after infection and Crofton (1948) supported this finding so far as the populations existing in the summer months were concerned. The experiments reported in the

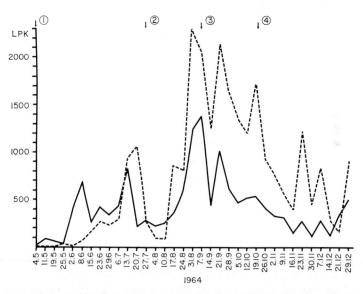

Fig. 3. Showing the fluctuations in the numbers of infective larvae of *T. colubriformis* under conditions of set stocking and rotational grazing. The broken line represents the changes on the rotationally grazed paddocks. The solid line represents the changes on the set stocked paddock. L.P.K. = larvae per kilogram of herbage. The small arrows indicate the occurrence of the following events: (1) Ewes and lambs entered paddocks; (2) ewes removed from paddocks; (3) 6 Dorset Horn lambs removed; (4) all remaining sheep removed.

first half of this paper suggested that larval populations of *T. colubriformis* remain at a high level for a longer period than the results of Taylor and Crofton would suggest. The length of herbage will clearly profoundly affect the microclimate to which larvae are exposed. On the rotationally grazed paddocks the herbage was long at the beginning of the week's grazing but usually short at the end. It may well be that at the end of the week's grazing, or soon afterward, the larval population on a small paddock was reduced to a low level but that the heavy contamination of eggs during the week's grazing restored a high larval level by the time the paddock came to be grazed again. It is unfortunate that weekly observations on each of paddocks B–G was not possible for they would have thrown light on this point.

GENERAL DISCUSSION AND CONCLUSIONS

Laboratory experiments of the development of infective larvae from eggs in fecal cultures show that development occurs within one week. If this happens in the field it is clearly a disadvantage to keep animals in a field for longer than one week and on this account a weekly rotational system has been proposed for the control of parasitic gastroenteritis. The work of Taylor (1938) supported to some degree by that of Crofton (1948) indicated that the life of the bulk of the larvae so produced would be short and so a 6 weeks rotation system has been advocated. The results obtained in the first part of the present investigation showed that larvae persisted in large numbers on herbage for much longer than six weeks and indicated that a 6 weeks rotational grazing system would result in sheep returning to a previously grazed paddock at a time when the larval population on the herbage was still high. This deduction that under British conditions rotational grazing would not control parasitic gastroenteritis was confirmed in the epidemiological experiment carried out in the second part of the investigation.

The technique of small plot experiments in the ecology of larvae followed by epidemiological experiments designed in the light of the results of the small plot experiments has yielded profitable results both with nematodiriasis and trichostrongylosis. It is proposed to carry out a series of similar experiments with other species which it is hoped will produce equally useful results. The small plot technique requires very little in the way of facilities, although it is rather laborious. It is therefore a technique which could be widely applied to elucidate the problems of gastrointestinal parasitism in sheep, particularly in countries with limited resources.

It is important that experiments of this kind be carried out in many localities rather than that the assumption be made that the results for one area are valid for another. This is clearly illustrated by comparing the results of Andersen et al. (1965) with those of the present author. These workers conducted similar grass plot experiments between April and August 1964 and carried on examination of herbage for the presence of larvae for 10 weeks after infection. They found that small numbers of larvae survived for 10 weeks only during early spring and that larvae could not be recovered for more than 5 to 6 weeks during the summer. Clearly under the latter conditions rotational grazing would have a greater chance of success than under the conditions under which the present writer's experiments were carried out. These differences are undoubtedly referable to the climatic conditions in the two areas.

Although climate has a profound influence on the ecology of nematode larvae, microclimate and the microhabitat in which the larvae live are more important, and similar microclimates can exist in widely different climatic conditions. The importance of microclimate on larval nematode populations is well illustrated by the work of Crofton (1952). He studied the larval populations on eight lowland sheep pastures where clinical signs of gastrointestinal parasitism had been seen in lambs and found 900–3900 larvae per pound of herbage in different grass samplings. On three farms where disease did not occur pasture populations were estimated monthly for three successive years. On all three pastures the number of larvae remained below 75 per pound of herbage during the May to October grazing season except for peaks which lasted for 4 to 6 weeks. The time when the peak occurred varied in different pastures. On one field grazed mainly by cattle a peak of 150 larvae per pound of herbage occurred in late August one year, a peak of 105 in early September in the next year, and a peak of 105 in late August of the third year. A second field grazed by sheep and cattle showed a peak of 180 larvae per pound of herbage in early July in the first year; a peak of 105 in late June in the second year, and a peak of 65 in late June in the third. On the third field sheep were grazed and a peak of 105 larvae per pound of herbage in late September was seen in the first year; a peak of 140 in late September in the second year, and a peak of 100 in early September in the third. The time of larval peak thus depends on the pasture and not on the climate since the fields observed were on farms within 2 miles of each other.

The importance of microclimate and its lack of relation to macroclimate was illustrated in the small plot of experiments of 1962–1963 described earlier in this paper. It was found that soil temperatures under the snow rarely fell below 0°C although air temperatures of —10°C were experienced above the snow. Beneath the snow a very satisfactory habitat for larval survival was created and this was reflected in the recovery of almost identical numbers of larvae from the herbage after the snow melted as were there immediately before its arrival. Without doubt the results would have been different under conditions of intense cold where frost penetrates deeply into the soil. It is important to realize, however, in countries where deep snow persists for several months without freezing of the surface layers of the soil larval survival may be encouraged and spring pastures thought to have been sterilized by the cold may be carrying a considerable residual larval population. It may well be that in countries like Norway and Iceland mountain pastures may retain a residual larval population in the spring which is responsible for the initial infection of young lambs sent to the mountain pastures in early summer.

The significance of larvae which survive over winter as infective agents for animals in the spring is difficult to assess. Microscopic examination shows these larvae have few granules in their cells and are often sluggish. Rogers (1961) has shown that in aged larvae the fat stores are used up and larvae with depleted fat reserves are not so motile or so infective as young larvae with large amounts of fat. Rose (1963) found that larvae of *Haemonchus contortus* that had been on herbage for $8\frac{1}{2}$ months were capable of infecting worm-free lambs, 303 worms being recovered after a lamb was dosed with 2000 larvae. It is possible there may be a rapid decline in infectivity of surviving larvae during the rapid fall in numbers which precedes their final disappearance from the herbage.

SUMMARY

The survival of infective larvae of *T. colubriformis* on small grass plots was studied for 2 years. It was found that in early spring infective larvae appeared on the herbage some 12 weeks after the deposition of eggs but the period decreased as conditions for development improved so that in August larvae were present one week after deposition of feces. Larval populations persisted at a high level for several weeks but a gradual decline in numbers followed. Larvae finally disappeared from the herbage of most plots in May of the year following the original infection. These observations also demonstrated that the microclimate under a blanket of snow was conducive to prolonged larval survival.

A second experiment comparing the larval populations on the herbage of set stocked paddocks with those on a similar area rotationally grazed revealed no significant difference between the larval numbers available to sheep under the two systems. This is a result which was predicted from the results of the first experiment.

The value of these techniques for the study of the ecology of infective larvae and the epidemiology of parasitic disease is discussed, as well as some of the factors which influence the ecology of trichostrongylid larvae on pastures.

REFERENCES

Andersen, F. L., Boatman, P. A., and Levine, N. D. (1965). Development and survival of the free-living stages of *Trichostrongylus colubriformis* on pasture. *J. Parasitol.* **51**, Suppl., 32.

Crofton, H. D. (1948). The ecology of immature phases of trichostrongyle nematodes II. The effect of climatic factors on the availability of the infective larvae of *Trichostrongylus retortaeformis* to the host. *Parasitology* **39**, 26-38.

Crofton, H. D. (1952). The ecology of immature phases of trichostrongyle nematodes IV. Larval populations of lowland pastures. *Parasitology* **42**, 77-84.

Gibson, T. E. (1958). The development and survival of the preparasitic stages of *Nematodirus* spp. on pasture herbage. *J. Comp. Pathol. Therap.* **68**, 338-344.

Gibson, T. E. (1963a). Experiments on the epidemiology of nematodiriasis. *Res. Vet. Sci.* **4**, 258-268.

Gibson, T. E. (1963b). The control of nematodiriasis by strategic anthelmintic medication. *Res. Vet. Sci.* **4**, 480-490.

Parfitt, J. W. (1955). Two techniques used for the detection and enumeration of the larvae of *Dictyocaulus viviparus* in faeces and herbage. *Lab. Pract.* **4**, 15-16.

Rogers, W. P. (1961). "The Nature of Parasitism: The Relationship of Some Metazoan Parasites to their Hosts." Academic Press, New York.

Rose, J. H. (1963). Observations on the free-living stages of the stomach worm *Haemonchus contortus*. *Parasitology* **53**, 469-481.

Taylor, E. L. (1938). Observations on the bionomics of strongyloid larvae in pastures. *Vet. Record* **50**, 1265-1272.

Turner, J. H., Kates, K. C., and Wilson, G. I. (1962). The interaction of concurrent infections of the abomasal nematodes, *Haemonchus contortus, Ostertagia circumcincta,* and *Trichostrongylus axei* (Trichostrongylidae), in lambs. *Proc. Helminthol. Soc. Wash., D.C.* **29**, 210-216.

Discussion

Dr. K. C. Kates: How do you account for the fact that *Nematodirus battus* was discovered in sheep in the United Kingdom only about a decade ago? Do you think it is a foreign importation and, if so, where did it come from?

Dr. Gibson: I consider it has been present in Britain in small numbers for a long time but about 1951, changes in husbandry resulted in an increase in its incidence and its presence was, therefore, at that time recognized. The egg is very distinctive, being coffee colored, and similar to eggs observed by Mr. H. V. Whitlock in South America.

Dr. Heath: The coffee colored egg would be *Nematodirus llamae*—not yet recorded.

Dr. Baker: It has been suggested that there is a minimal number of larvae which must be ingested before disease occurs. We have found with *Ostertagia circumcincta* that larvae given in a single inoculum or over 10 days result in much the same burdens. Dr. Gibson's data would indicate that at least 100,000 to 150,000 larvae were ingested daily; does he think that such exposure over a few days is responsible for disease and that continued exposure to lower intake is of little importance?

Dr. Gibson: This is not easy to answer. Experimentally, disease has been produced in sheep by single large doses of larvae or multiple doses of small numbers of larvae. In the field where animals may be exposed to high larval intake for a long period it has not been elucidated whether it is the initial dose which produces infection or whether multiple doses are required. It is certain, however, that large numbers of the larvae taken in do not develop into mature worms and presumably are destroyed by the host before they reach maturity.

The Development of *Babesia* spp. and *Theileria* spp. in Ticks with Special Reference to Those Occurring in Cattle

R. F. RIEK

Research & Development Laboratory, Merck Sharp & Dohme (Australia) Pty. Limited, Sydney, Australia

INTRODUCTION

Smith and Kilborne (1893) first described the blood protozoan parasite *Babesia bigemina*, which causes tick fever or red water in cattle, and established the role of *Boophilus annulatus* (Say) in its transmission. The transovarial transmission of this protozoan has been recognized for many years, but despite attention by many workers the developmental cycle in the invertebrate vector has not only remained incompletely known, but the observations and conclusions published by those different investigators are by no means in agreement.

Although various forms of *Babesia* spp. have been described in the blood of different animal species the significance of these forms and the cycle of development in the vertebrate host is still uncertain.

The life cycle of *B. bigemina*[1] in the tick vector was first studied by Koch (1906) in *"Boophilus (Margaropus) australis," "Rhipicephalus evertsi,"* and *"Hyalomma aegyptium."* In the gut of the tick Koch observed pear-shaped parasites which became amoeboid and extended long, straight, thornlike pseudopodia. These amoeboid forms were said to associate in pairs and to give rise to organisms possessed at first of two nuclei which later fused to form a single nucleus. This worker also recorded multiple division stages, but was unable to indicate how they were formed or their relationship in the developmental cycle. Ultimately, clavate parasites were observed both in the gut contents and in the ova. Rather similar stages with spiky pseudopodia have also been re-

---

[1] Except when otherwise stated the abbreviation *B.* in this paper always stands for *Babesia; H.* will always mean *Hyalomma.*

corded by Dschunkowsky and Luhs (1910), but no information was given about their subsequent development.

Crawley (1915) observed cigar-shaped bodies in smears from replete female *Boophilus annulatus*, and from crushed preparations of eggs which they had deposited. Although only a limited amount of material was available, Crawley considered these forms to be identical with the clavate parasites described by Koch.

Subsequently Rosenbusch (1927) described the development of this parasite in *Boophilus microplus* (Canes) in which he found numerous elongated forms in the intestines and hemolymph. Multiple division of these elongated clavate parasites occurred in the cells of the digestive and vascular organs. The salivary glands became infected, but transmission occurred only under defined conditions. Certain of these elongated forms invaded the cells of the genital tube and without any further division were ultimately found in the ova. Multiplication commenced again only after the subsequent larva fed on blood. Rosenbusch considered that the tick was the definitive host of this parasite, and that its transmission to cattle was not indispensable to its developmental cycle.

Dennis (1932) observed various stages in the development of the parasite in the gut and ova in engorged females of *Boophilus annulatus*, and concluded that the initial development was the union of "isogametes" in the gut contents to form a motile "ookinete" which passed through the thin wall of the gut and penetrated the contiguous reproductive organs. The ova of the tick were invaded by the "ookinetes" which formed "sporonts." The "sporonts" gave rise to multinucleate "sporokinetes" which migrated throughout the tissues of the developing tick. Some of the "sporokinetes" came to occupy the analgen of the salivary glands and finally underwent fragmentation to form minute infective "sporozoites."

Regendanz (1936) disagreed with Dennis's work and concluded that the development of *B. bigemina* in the intestinal wall of *Boophilus microplus* corresponded completely with that of *B. canis* in *Dermacentor reticulatus* (Fabricius) as described by Regendanz and Reichenow (1933). After numerous binary fissions, the protozoa formed a motile vermiform stage which ultimately invaded the ovaries. Regendanz (1936) found no evidence of sexual forms, and he did not attempt to investigate the cycle in the larval and nymphal instars of the tick.

More recently, Muratov and Cheissin (1959), who studied the developmental cycle of *B. bigemina* in *Boophilus calcaratus* Berula, also described the formation of the club-shaped bodies observed by previous workers. These club-shaped stages, formed by binary fission or schizogony, penetrated into the epithelial cells of the intestine where multiple division, characterized by segmentation into amoeboid or round "aga-monts," was observed. Some of the club-shaped stages entered the body cavity and ultimately penetrated all the organs of the female tick where further division occurred. These stages also penetrated the eggs of the tick where they continued reproduction by means of the binary or mul-tiple division as observed in the intestines. As a result of the reproduc-tion round or amoebalike "agamonts" were formed, which in turn de-veloped into club-shaped forms. These increased in number during the process of incubation and were distributed throughout the organs of the developing larva. No stages which indicated the presence of sexual forms were found either in the intestine or in other organs.

Riek (1964) described the life cycle of *B. bigemina* in its tick vector *Boophilus microplus*. Early development occurred in the epithelial cells of the gut and in about 72 hours mature vermicules were seen in the hemolymph and ova. A further process of multiple fission was also ob-served in the developing and unengorged larva. The final cycle occurred in the salivary gland of the nymph and forms infective to the vertebrate host were observed 8–10 days and longer after the larvae were applied to the animals. Multiplication was by means of multiple fission and al-though various forms that could be associated with a sexual cycle were observed, Riek was unable to present irrefutable evidence to this effect. Certain stages in the development of this parasite are shown in Plate 1, Figs. 1–14.

Petrov (1941), working with *B. bovis* in *Ixodes ricinus* (Linn), de-scribed a developmental cycle very similar to that reported by Dennis (1932) for *B. bigemina*. Petrov stated that the "isogametes" fused in the tick's intestine to form an "ookinete" which passed through the intestinal wall and entered a developing ovum. Here the "ookinete" became glob-ular and formed "sporoblasts" which in turn formed "sporozoites" which passed to the salivary gland. The larvae, nymphs, and adults of the suc-ceeding generation all transmitted the parasite. Polyansky and Cheissin (1959) found that *B. bovis* followed essentially the same pattern in *I. ricinus* as described by Muratov and Cheissin (1959) for *B. bigemina* in *Boophilus calcaratus*. They stated that it reproduced by binary fission or schizogony in the tissues of the tick and in the eggs of infected fe-males. They found no stages of sexual reproduction or sporogony.

The life cycle of *B. canis* in *Rhipicephalus sanguineus* (Laterille) was first studied by Christophers (1907) and later by Shortt (1936), while Regendanz and Reichenow (1933) and Brumpt (1937) described the development of the parasite in *D. reticulatus*. No evidence of sexual reproduction was observed by these workers although Christophers (1907) thought sexual stages occurred but did not see copulation. Regendanz and Reichenow (1933) stated that some of the ingested parasites entered the intestinal epithelial cells, where they multiplied by a series of binary fissions. These became vermiform and passed into the body cavity, where they entered the ovary and then penetrated the eggs. Here they became spherical and divided a few times to form very small round individuals. No further development occurred in the larval tick which hatched from the egg, but when it moulted these small round forms entered the salivary glands. Here, by a series of binary fissions, they gave rise to thousands of minute infective parasites.

Li (1958) also described clavate and oval forms in different developmental stages of *B. ovis* in *R. bursa* Canestrini and Fanzago. Li (1956) and Markov and Abramov (1957) had earlier described the presence of clavate parasites in the ovary and eggs of this tick.

A number of Russian workers (Tsaprun, 1952, 1957; Abramov, 1955; Kartashev, 1957) had also observed similar clavate parasites in the salivary gland and eggs of *D. marginatus* Sulzer, *D. pictus* Heron, and *Hyalomma plumbeum* (Panzer) infected with *B. caballi.* Tsaprun (1957) described the development of this parasite in *D. marginatus.* He was one of the few workers who reported anisogamic copulation in the invertebrate vector.

A number of small piroplasmas, *Theileria* spp., have been recorded from many species of animals. Neitz (1956) recorded the various species of ticks implicated by different workers in the transmission of these parasites. The majority of the vectors are three-host ticks and stage-to-stage transmission is the normal method of infection. However, Dodd (1910) reported that *Boophilus microplus* was capable of transmitting *Theileria mutans* and Reichenow (1935) stated that Miessner succeeded in transmitting *T. mutans* with the progeny of *Boophilus annulatus* adult ticks obtained from the United States. There are no reports of transovarial transmission of this parasite with any species of three-host ticks but Ray (1950) claimed that hereditary transmission of *T. annulata* (Dschunkowsky and Luhs, 1904) occurred through five generations of *Hyalomma savignyi* (Gervais) and Korienko and Shmuireva (1944) recorded that hereditary transmission also takes place in *H. turkmeniense* (= *H. excavatum* Koch). Delpy (1949), on the other hand, stated that there is no evidence of transovarial transmission with *Theileria dispar* (= *T. annulata*).

Theileria mutans, a nonpathogenic blood protozoan of cattle, has been reported from most countries of the world and a number of different species of ixodid ticks have been implicated in its transmission, *R. evertsi* Neum (Theiler, 1907), *Boophilus microplus* (Dodd, 1910), *Boophilus annulatus Say* (Reichenow, 1935), *R. appendiculatus* Neum (Neitz,

Plate 1

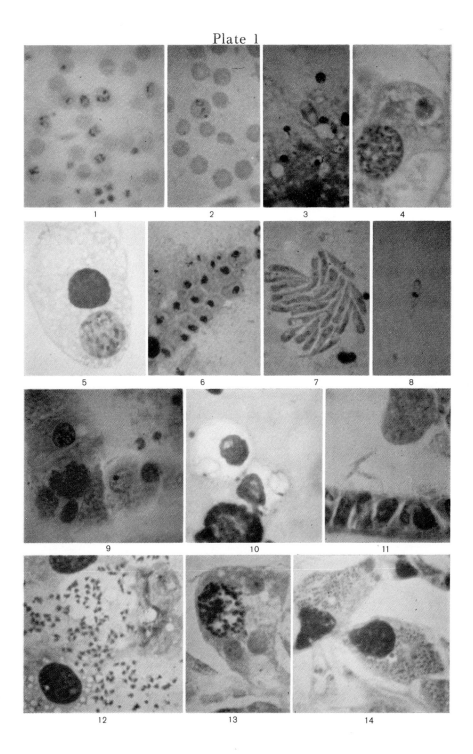

1

2

3

4

5

6

7

8

9

10

11

12

13

14

PLATE 1. Magnifications are 1200; Fig. 9 is 480.

FIG. 1. *Babesia bigemina:* parasites in bovine erythrocytes. FIG. 2. Paired pyriform parasites showing extrusion of second "nucleus." FIG. 3. Cigar-shaped body in gut contents of female *Boophilus microplus,* 18–24 hours after repletion. FIG. 4. Section of epithelial cell of gut showing very young fission body. FIG. 5. Intracellular fission body with chromatin spreading throughout the cytoplasm. FIG. 6. Fission body with discrete masses of chromatin and showing formation of vermicules. FIG. 7. Cluster of young vermicules. FIG. 8. Mature vermicule in the hemolymph. FIG. 9. Section of Malpighian tubule, showing fission bodies and vermicules within the cells. FIG. 10. Intracellular spherical forms in gut cells of the embryo. FIG. 11. Section of larva showing fission body in epithelial cells of the gut and vermicules in hemolymph. FIG. 12. Mature infective forms from salivary gland of the nymph. FIG. 13. Section of salivary gland of nymph showing young fission bodies. FIG. 14. Section of salivary gland of nymph showing mature fission bodies.

PLATE 2. Magnifications are 1200.

FIG. 1. *Babesia argentina* in bovine erythrocytes. FIG. 2. "Zygote" from gut contents of female *Boophilus microplus,* 24–36 hours on incubation. FIG. 3. Motile "ookinete" about 36 hours after commencement of incubation. FIG. 4. Spherical form, slightly older than the form in Fig. 3. FIG. 5. Multiple fission body in epithelial cell of the gut. FIG. 6. Immature vermicule showing red staining cap. FIG. 7. Mature vermicule showing typical hooked tail. FIG. 8. Multiple fission body and young vermicule in the unengorged larva. FIG. 9. Multiple fission body from salivary gland of the larva. FIG. 10. Mature fission body with forms infective to the bovine. FIG. 11. *Theileria mutans:* parasites in bovine erythrocytes. FIG. 12. *Theileria mutans:* immature multiple fission bodies in cells of the salivary gland of the nymph 24 hours after attachment. FIG. 13. *Theileria mutans:* mature fission body, with forms infective to cattle, in the salivary gland of the nymph 48–96 hours after attachment.

Plate 2

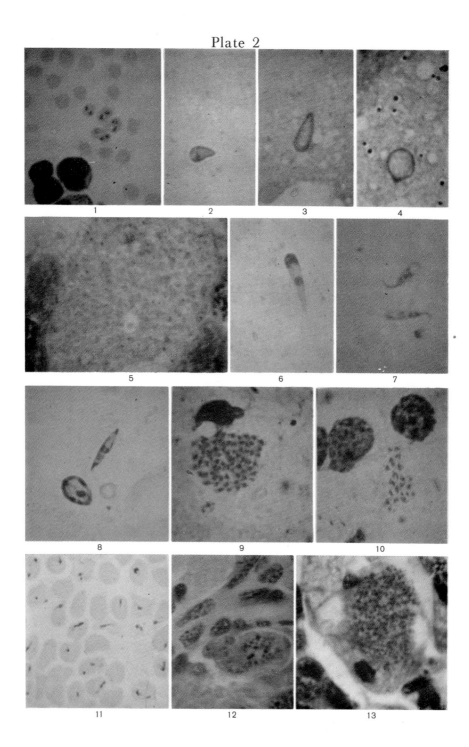

1956), *Haemaphysalis bispinosa* Neum (Ishii and Ishihara, 1951), and *Haemaphysalis punctata* Canestrini and Fanzago (Markov, 1957). Ishii and Ishihara (1951) obtained positive transmission with nymphs of *Haemaphysalis bispinosa*, the larvae of which had engorged on cattle infected with *T. mutans*. They were also successful with adults from infected nymphs and adults from infected larvae, the nymphs of which had fed on noninfected cattle. Neitz (1956) also recorded successful transmission of *T. mutans* with *R. appendiculatus* adults which had fed previously as nymphs on an infected calf. He also described the presence of schizogony in the lymph glands draining the area where the ticks had attached. Schizonts were first observed 9–22 days after attachment and 7–30 days later parasites were detected in the peripheral blood.

There are no reports of studies on the development of *T. mutans* in its tick vectors although the life cycle of *T. parva* in the arthropod vector *R. appendiculatus* has been studied by Gonder (1910, 1911), Cowdry and Ham (1932), Reichenow (1940), and Martin *et al.* (1964), that of *T. dispar* (= *T. annulata*) in *H. detritum* Schulze (= *H. mauritanicum*) by Sergent *et al.* (1936), and that of *T. dispar* (= *T. annulata*) in *Haemaphysalis neumanni*, and in *Hyalomma anatolicum* Koch by Laptev (1961).

The recent publication of Martin *et al.* (1964) reviewed the previous investigations on the cyclic development of *T. parva* in its tick vector, *R. appendiculatus*. They observed various forms, possibly developmental stages of *T. parva* in the gut contents, gut epithelial cells, and the cells of the salivary gland. The latter stages were the only ones that could definitely be considered a part of the normal life cycle. Multiplication occurred by multiple fission and no sexual stages were observed. Cowdry and Ham (1932) and Sergent *et al.* (1936) had reported the presence of sexual stages in the development of *T. parva* and *T. dispar* (= *T. annulata*), respectively, while Reichenow (1940) failed to observe any evidence of sporogony in his work with *T. parva*.

THE DEVELOPMENT OF *BABESIA ARGENTINA* IN *BOOPHILUS MICROPLUS*

PARASITES IN THE BLOOD OF THE BOVINE HOST

The parasites occurring in the bovine erythrocytes have been described as single spherical or paired pyriform bodies. The latter paired bodies are situated at an obtuse angle and measure about 1.5–2.2 μ by 1.0–1.5 μ (mean: 1.8 μ by 1.2 μ) (Plate 2, Fig. 1). Not infrequently much larger paired pyriform parasites are observed in the same blood film. On occasions paired pyriform parasites containing a second discrete red staining dot in the broad end of the parasite have been observed. These forms are similar to those described in B. *bigemina*. Multiplication in the erythrocytes appears to be largely by budding.

DEVELOPMENT IN THE REPLETE FEMALE TICK

The rate of development in the tick depends very largely on environmental temperature and the time of development is that occurring when engorged female ticks are held at 28°C and 80 percent relative humidity.

(i) Within the first 24 hours: Immediately on repletion and for the next several hours on incubation, the various erythrocytic forms seen in the bovine host were observed in smears of gut contents. Spherical bodies 3.0–5.3 µ in diameter with a single chromatin dot at the periphery or a linear band of chromatin extending partly around the periphery or with several red staining masses around the periphery were also observed during this period.

Spherical forms with a double nucleus, one elongated and extending around the periphery and the other spherical, similar to those recorded in B. *bigemina*, were observed in a small number of ticks within the first 24 hours on incubation. Smaller pyknotic forms with a small amount of cytoplasm but without any well-differentiated periphery were also seen. Irregularly shaped parasites, with varying amounts of cytoplasm which was invariably vacuolated, also occurred singly or as conglomerations of varying shape and size. The latter two forms are probably degenerating parasites.

(ii) At 24–48 hours: By about 36 hours developmental forms of the parasite appeared as blunt, cigar-shaped bodies 7.2–13.8 µ in length and 2.6–5.6 µ at their widest part (Plate 2, Figs. 2–3). These forms were similar to those described for B. *bigemina* but slightly larger. In some individual ticks they were numerous although in most instances only very small numbers were observed even though a replete female tick may have ingested many millions of parasites. It is as yet still not known which form observed in the bovine erythrocyte gives rise to this cigar-shaped body or whether a sexual process precedes this stage. The shape of this stage indicates mobility and this or slightly older forms have been observed within the cytoplasm of intact epithelial cells of the gut wall. These forms developed into spherical bodies between 5.8 µ and 8.2 µ in diameter (Plate 2, Fig. 4) with the chromatin located initially around the periphery.

(iii) At 48–96 hours: Further development of the fission body (Plate 2, Fig. 5) appeared to be similar to that described for B. *bigemina*, vermicules appearing in the hemolymph toward the end of the third day or early on the fourth day of incubation. The young vermicule had a red-staining cap on the broad anterior end, and the body was slightly curved and tapering (Plate 2, Fig. 6). The mature vermicule measured 14.3–16.9 μ by 2.8–3.5 μ with a mean value of 15.8 μ by 3.0 μ (Plate 2, Fig. 7). A large vacuole was almost invariably present at the anterior extremity and the nucleus was situated more toward the middle of the parasite. The posterior end was slender and tapered gradually and in the majority of specimens curved to form a hook. The vermicule of *B. argentina* was larger than that of *B. bigemina* and could readily be distinguished from the latter species.

The examination of sections from ticks indicated that only a very small proportion of epithelial cells became infected even though enormous numbers of parasites were ingested with the blood meal. The number of vermicules produced from a single infected cell was also smaller than that of *B. bigemina*, although comparatively large mature fission bodies 90 μ by 60 μ were observed. Development to the mature vermicule was about 24 hours longer in *B. argentina* than in *B. bigemina*.

(iv) At 90 hours and longer: In sections of replete ticks 4–5 days after incubation a small number of cells of the Malpighian tubules was infected with mature vermicules. It would appear that this infection occurred at the time of initial infection of the epithelial cells of the gut and was not a secondary cycle as proposed for *B. bigemina*.

The number of ticks showing vermicules in the hemolymph not only depended to some degree on the parasite density in the blood of the bovine host but also on the "strain" of ticks. The strains most susceptible to infection with *B. bigemina* were also most susceptible to infection with *B. argentina*.

DEVELOPMENT IN THE EGG AND LARVA

Development of this parasite in the egg and the growing larva followed that described for *B. bigemina*. The vermicules enter cells of the gut epithelium or presumably precursors of these cells and assume a spherical form with the chromatin distributed around the periphery. The chromatin breaks up into a number of discrete bodies around which cytoplasm condenses to form several individuals within the fission body. These masses develop into vermicules which are liberated into the hemolymph on rupture of the cell. These vermicules appear to be somewhat different from those observed in the hemolymph of the female tick, being smaller, of more uniform thickness, and pointed at both ends with the chromatin more centrally placed (Plate 2, Fig. 8). It is possible however that these are immature forms and may develop into vermicules similar to those in the female tick.

Further development of these vermicules occurred in the salivary gland of the larvae. This was again similar to that described for *B. bigemina* but the fission bodies were very much smaller (Plate 2, Fig. 9). The vermicule on entering the cells of the salivary glands become spherical with the chromatin remaining in a more central position. The body enlarges and the chromatin breaks up into a small number of dots. The cytoplasm becomes organized around these dots of chromatin to give rise initially to spherical bodies and later to the pyriform bodies similar to those seen in the bovine erythrocytes. In these studies only a very small number of salivary gland cells of an individual larva showed infection. The pyriform parasites resulting from these fission bodies measured about 1.5 μ by 1.0 μ and contained only a very small amount of cytoplasm (Plate 2, Fig. 10). These forms, which infect the bovine host, were observed from about 48 hours after the larvae were applied to the animal. This final stage of development is very rapid as no evidence of infection of the salivary gland has been observed in squash material or sections of unengorged larvae. Infection of the bovine host occurred about 2–3 days after the infected larvae were applied and parasites were usually observed in thick blood films 6–12 days later.

THE DEVELOPMENT OF *THEILERIA MUTANS* IN *HAEMAPHYSALIS BISPINOSA*

The development reported here is that occurring in the larva and nymph, for these instars were more convenient to section and to make squash preparations.

PARASITES IN THE BLOOD OF CATTLE

The parasites occurring in the red blood cells of cattle are described as rods, comma-shaped, pear-shaped, oval, round or anaplasma-like organisms and are usually less than 2.5 μ in length (Plate 2, Fig. 11). Occasionally rod-shaped forms extending across the erythrocytes were encountered. When division occurs, two or four chromatin granules, the latter arranged in a cross, are observed. With Giemsa stain the cytoplasm stained blue and the nucleus appeared as a deeply stained reddish-purple area situated at the broader end of the various forms. The nucleus may occupy more than half the area of the parasite.

Blood films taken at regular intervals failed to show any evidence of cyclic development or interrelationship between the various forms mentioned above.

Parasites in the Larva

Parasites similar to those observed in the bovine erythrocytes were observed lying free in gut contents immediately on repletion and for 24 hours later. Only comparatively small numbers were seen in squash preparations even though the parasite density in bovine blood was more than 10 percent. No intact erythrocytes were seen at any time in any of the preparations from engorged larvae.

Besides these comparatively normal parasites, similar forms with rather indistinct cytoplasm but well-stained nuclei were detected for 2–3 days. Occasionally clumps of these parasites were observed but it appeared as though these parasites were degenerating and undergoing digestion.

Small numbers of parasites were seen within intact epithelial cells of the gut wall from 24 to 48 hours but no signs of development other than slight enlargement and central vacuolation were observed.

Squash preparations of unmolted larva about 4 days after the commencement of incubation revealed the presence of spherical or elongated bodies between 3 and 4 μ in diameter and up to 5 μ in length. Only very few of these densely staining bodies were observed and their position in the development of *T. mutans* is in doubt.

At about 10 days incubation spherical bodies up o 15 μ in diameter with a homogeneous cytoplasm and a nucleus about 3 μ in diameter were observed on several occasions in squash preparation. These bodies were extracellular but appeared in the vicinity of intact gut epithelial cells. They were probably liberated from epithelial cells of the gut which were ruptured when the preparation was being made.

Parasites in the Nymph

No forms which could be definitely placed in the life cycle of this parasite were observed in squash preparations or sections of unengorged nymphs that had fed as larvae on an infected calf.

In the salivary glands of the nymphal and female *Haemaphysalis bispinosa* three distinct types of alveoli similar to those described by Till (1961) in *R. appendiculatus* were observed. Developmental stages of *T. mutans* were detected only in the granular secretory cells. However, only very few alveoli were infected and even in these only one or two cells were parasitized. These immature forms (Plate 2, Fig. 12) were seen in the nymph during the first 24 hours after attachment. Further development was by multiple fission which gave rise to bodies measuring about 40 μ by 30 μ in sections and containing large numbers of infective forms (Plate 2, Fig. 13). These infective forms were observed in the salivary glands of nymphs as early as 48 hours after application to the vertebrate host. In other specimens infective forms were still present on the 4th and 5th day.

Similar forms were seen on occasions in the salivary glands of the engorging female but it is not known whether these adult stages were also infective as nymphs after engorging as larvae on the infected calf.

DISCUSSION

Riek found that the infection rate of B. bigemina in replete female ticks depends to a large degree on the parasite density in the bovine erythrocytes (Riek, 1964). He also stated that the majority of parasites ingested by the tick die and only a very small number undergoes further development. This phenomenon has been reported by many workers with Babesia spp. (Dennis, 1932; Regendanz and Reichenow, 1933; Regendanz, 1936; Muratov and Cheissin, 1959; Polyansky and Cheissin, 1959). This observation presumes that the mature sexual forms, the gametocytes, are the only forms capable of surviving in the invertebrate host and that the asexual forms, which would normally constitute the major portion of the parasite population, rapidly perish when ingested with the blood meal. Although conclusive proof is lacking, the morphology of the parasites within the first 48 hours after repletion would suggest that the oval or spherical forms in the bovine erythrocytes appear to be the only forms which may survive in the tick.

The changes involved in the development of the "gametocyte" in the erythrocyte to the "ookinete" in the epithelial cells of the gut wall are still incompletely known. However, it is considered that the various intermediate forms observed and their sequence in appearance permit the following deductions to be made.

On liberation from the erythrocyte the "gametocyte" grows and the chromatin spreads to the periphery in the form of a dot or in a linear band. In some, the chromatin breaks up into three to four masses and it is suggested that these bodies may divide to give rise to the elongated parasites. The union of this elongated form with certain of the spherical bodies could give rise to a "zygote" or "ookinete." The developmental cycle to this stage would take place in the contents of the intestinal ceca. The initial shape of this "zygote" or "ookinete" suggests that it is motile. The "ookinete" then enters directly into the cells of the gut epithelium where it forms an "oocyst" or "sporont."

The subsequent development of B. bigemina in the epithelial cells of the gut to the infective forms in the salivary gland of the nymph was depicted schematically by Riek (1964).

Riek (1964) stated that in B. *bigemina* multiple fission was the normal method of multiplication in the adult tick and no evidence of binary fission was observed at any stage of development. Infection of cells other than those of the gut occurred about the 4th day, but only after the primary cycle in the gut. At 10–12 days, when oviposition was almost completed, infection was not observed in the gut, but only in the cells of the Malpighian tubules and hemolymph. Muratov and Cheissin (1959) observed division of round, clavate, and fusiform stages in the hemolymph, and stated that the clavate parasite penetrates into the internal organs of the tick where the agamous multiplication is continued by binary fission and schizogony. They further stated that the parasite (that is, the clavate form) undergoes the same changes in the salivary glands as in the other organs and produces small pyriform stages in addition. Rosenbusch (1927) also found that the salivary glands of some replete female ticks contained a multitude of the club-shaped forms and he concluded that invasion of this organ brings about infection of cattle.

Rosenbusch (1927) was unable to see parasites in the process of division in hatched larvae and considered that multiplication commenced only when the larvae began to feed on blood. There was an appreciable increase in the club-shaped forms and various small forms were also observed. Studies by Riek (1964) have shown that there is multiplication in the developing larvae even before it hatches. This cycle increases the number of vermicules which would be available to initiate the final cycle in the salivary gland of the nymph.

Neitz (1956) has indicated that transmission of B. *bigemina* by the two- and three-host ticks, H. *punctata*[2], R. *appendiculatus*, R. *evertsi*, and R. *bursa*, occurs not only via the egg, but also from stage to stage. The cycle of development in stage-to-stage transmission may differ from transovarial transmission and it may be difficult to relate the results of investigations using two- and three-host ticks to those with a one-host tick. However, a club-shaped parasite about 10 μ or more in length has been reported in the tick vector in almost every study on *Babesia* spp. There is little doubt that this is the stage which develops from parasites ingested with the erythrocytes of the vertebrate host and is responsible for infection in the ovum. Both Dennis (1932) and Muratov and Cheissin (1959) found parasites not only in the salivary glands of larvae, but also throughout the organs and muscles. It would appear from this observation that infection of the salivary glands may be incidental, but Riek (1964) concluded there was a definite sequence of events, with infection of certain tissues or organs at appropriate times. Each stage in the cycle had a predilection site and some change in development occurred in this site. The development in the invertebrate host tended to

[2] H. stands for *Haemaphysalis*.

ensure that at least some of the larvae would be infected and subsequently infective to the vertebrate host.

Rosenbusch (1927) did not observe the first phase of infection in the tick and suggested that the club-shaped forms recorded by many workers in several species of *Babesia* were sporozoites which ultimately invade the genital duct and transmit the infection to subsequent generations. He further stated that the salivary glands were infected only under certain conditions and that transmission to cattle was incidental and not indispensable to the developmental cycle. There is some support for the assumption that *Babesia* spp. are hereditary parasites of ticks as they may be transmitted from generation to generation when infected ticks are reared on refractory hosts.

However, Callow (1962) has obtained inapparent infections of *B. bigemina* in sheep, a goat, and a horse infested with *Boophilus microplus* carrying this parasite. Only small members of replete females were recovered, but the progeny of ticks from the goat and sheep were infective on most occasions, when applied to susceptible cattle. It is possible then that, when the infection persists after feeding on a host not normally infected with *Babesia*, the adult ticks become reinfected from the subclinical infection in the unnatural host and not through hereditary transmission as postulated by previous workers.

Dennis (1932) described sexual reproduction of *B. bigemina* in *Boophilus annulatus* by the union of isogametes to form motile club-shaped zygotes which pass through the intestinal wall and enter the ova. Petrov (1941) described a similar method of reproduction for *B. bovis* in *I. ricinus*. In both instances there is no report concerning any development in the epithelial cells of the gut or other tissues of the adult tick. Tsaprun (1957) working with *B. caballi*, detected anisogamic union in the tick *D. marginatus*. On the other hand, Regendanz (1936) and Muratov and Cheissin (1959) found no evidence of sexual reproduction in *B. bigemina* in either *Boophilus microplus* and *Boophilus calcaratus* respectively, nor could Polyansky and Cheissin (1959) for *B. bovis* in *I. ricinus*, nor Regendanz and Reichenow (1963) and Shortt (1936) for *B. canis* in *D. reticulatus* and *R. sanguineus* respectively. Riek (1964) was unable to present any conclusive evidence of sexual reproduction although various forms were observed which could indicate anisogany.

Rosenbusch and Gonzales (1923) stated that environmental temperature is of paramount importance in the transmission of infection by the tick, but even at relatively low temperatures infection is transmitted to the egg and larva. They believed that the tick is the definite host of the parasite *B. bigemina*, and that its transmission to cattle is incidental and occurs only if the ambient temperature rises above 29°C. The ticks, however, remain infected independently of external factors. Polyansky and Cheissin (1959) incubated replete female *I. ricinus* which had engorged on blood infected with *B. bovis* at 18°–20°C and noted that the maximal number of developmental stages occurred in the tick between 6 and 12 days, whereas at 16°–18°C they did not observe any corresponding stages by the 30th day.

The infection rate and degree of infection with *B. argentina* in replete female *Boophilus microplus* also depended to a large degree on the parasite density in the vertebrate host, the strain of tick, and the environmental temperature. However, with *B. argentina* very much smaller numbers of vermicules were observed in the hemolymph of infected ticks and the subsequent larval progeny. Death of heavily infected ticks occurred 5–7 days following incubation and this seemed to be associated with some alteration in the permeability of the gut wall which permitted hemoglobin to enter the hemolymph.

The development of this parasite in the replete female tick followed very closely that described previously for *B. bigemina*. Usually, however, a much smaller number of epithelial cells of the gut were found to be infected and infection of the cells of the Malpighian tubules was observed only on rare occasions.

Spherical bodies were observed lying free in the gut contents on repletion and for 48–72 hours subsequently. Many of these were larger than those observed lying within the intact erythrocytes in the gut contents. Intact erythrocytes were still present 4–5 days after repletion, but no parasites were observed within these cells. The blunt cigar-shaped bodies, "zygotes," occurred at about 36 hours, which was later than the appearance of similar forms in *B. bigemina*. On some occasions considerable numbers of these and later developmental forms were observed in preparations of the gut, but the forms that preceded them were not identified. The "zygote" showed marked variation in size and in the location of chromatin masses. Similarly the intracellular spherical bodies, "ookinetes," resulting from these "zygotes" varied considerably in size. These fission bodies gave rise to a smaller number of vermicules than observed in fission bodies of *B. bigemina*.

The comparative scarcity of fission bodies in the epithelial cells of the gut, as observed in both squash preparations and sections, would suggest that either only certain forms in the blood undergo further development in the tick or a sexual union occurs. A thorough examination of the intraerythrocytic forms failed to reveal any detectable differences in staining reaction which would indicate the presence of gametocytes. The shape of the cigarlike forms which entered the cells of the gut epithelium suggested they were motile but microscopic examination of fresh contents on a warm stage failed to reveal any evidence of motility. The scarcity of these bodies would, however, preclude the probability of seeing them in fresh preparations. No conclusive evidence has been forthcoming which would confirm the presence of a sexual stage in the life cycle in the tick vector.

The vermicules in the hemolymph of the replete female, incubated for 4–5 days or longer at 28°C, are very distinctive and can be identified readily from those of *B. bigemina*. They are usually longer, have a more slender tapering tail which is curved, and have a single large vacuole at the broad anterior end of the parasite. The chromatin mass usually lies close to the middle of the vermicule. It is possible that the morphological characteristics of the vermicule could help in the identification of the various species infecting cattle.

The vermicule undergoes development in the unhatched larvae to give rise to vermicules very similar to those seen in the hemolymph of the female tick. This multiplication has been observed only in the epithelial cells of the gut of the larvae. Although it was stated that in *B. bigemina* these vermicules were identical with the initial vermicules in the hemolymph of the engorged female, there appears to be some difference in the case of *B. argentina*. It is possible, however, that these forms are not mature.

No evidence of the final cycle of development in the salivary gland was detected in the unengorged larvae. However, fission bodies were observed within 48 hours after attachment. It was proposed that the ingestion of blood by the nymph initiated this cycle in *B. bigemina* but this is not so in *B. argentina* as larvae do not normally ingest blood. It is possible that the commencement of feeding by the larvae stimulates the further development of *B. argentina* in this instance.

The forms infective to the bovine host were evident in the salivary glands of the larvae 2–3 days after attachment. Only small numbers were observed in each of the infected larvae examined. The individual fission bodies gave rise to very small numbers compared with the very much larger numbers of infective forms from the fission bodies of *B. bigemina* in the salivary glands of infected nymphs. No hypothesis can be offered to explain these differences in the development of *B. argentina* and *B. bigemina* in the same tick vector.

Although a number of workers have described developmental stages of *T. parva* and *T. annulata* in the tissues of infected ticks, Martin *et al.* (1964) were unable to detect any stages of *T. parva* in the body cavity of *R. appendiculatus*. Except for a small number of early forms in the gut contents and a larger spherical body in the epithelial cells of the gut of the *H. bispinosa*[3] larva no stages of *T. mutans* were detected in the

[3] *H*. stands for *Haemaphysalis*.

unengorged nymph. Preinfective forms were observed in the salivary glands only after the infected nymph or adult instars had feed for 24 hours or more. Some stimulus appears to be necessary to induce the final stage of multiplication in the salivary gland. Development of this stage was by means of multiple fission and was extremely rapid, for cattle were infected within 48 hours after application of infected nymphs.

The erythrocytic forms which initiate the cycle in the ticks and the subsequent development are at present not known. The form which infects the salivary gland has not yet been observed. This stage has not been detected by any worker in studies involving other species of *Theileria*. These must be either in very small numbers or extremely small in size and escape detection. As mentioned by Martin *et al.* (1964) the use of fluorescent antibody technique seems to be the most promising in endeavors to elucidate this phase of the cycle in the invertebrate vector.

SUMMARY

Babesia argentina and *B. bigemina,* protozoan parasites causing tick fever of cattle in Australia, are transmitted by *Boophilus microplus.* The development of *B. argentina* in this invertebrate vector is very similar to that recorded by Riek (1964) for *B. bigemina.*

Many of the parasites occurring in the bovine erythrocytes are destroyed on ingestion but the early development in the lumen of the gut is uncertain. By about 24 hours in *B. bigemina* and 36 hours in *B. argentina* blunt, cigar-shaped forms, 7.2–13.8 μ by 2.6–5.6 μ invade the epithelial cells of the gut and subsequent development is by means of multiple fission. This leads by about 72 hours in *B. bigemina* and 96 hours in *B. argentina* to the production of mature vermicules which measure about 11.1 μ by 2.6 μ with a range of 9–13 μ by 2.0–2.9 μ and about 15.8 μ by 3.0 μ with a range of 14.3–16.9 μ by 2.8–3.5 μ, respectively.

At about this time vermicules enter the mature ova of the tick and a further cycle of multiple fission in the gut cells of the developing larva gives rise to vermicules similar to those produced in the adult tick. In *B. argentina* the final cycle takes place in the salivary glands of the larva and the forms infective to the vertebrate host appear 2–3 days and longer after larval attachment. Multiplication in this cycle is also by multiple fission and gives rise to comparatively small numbers of infective forms measuring about 1.5 μ by 1.0 μ. In *B. bigemina* the final cycle of development occurs in the salivary gland of the nymph and infective forms are observed within 8–10 days after larval attachment. These forms measure 2.2–2.7 μ by 1.0–1.5 μ and are very similar to the pyriform bodies observed in bovine erythrocytes.

Not all ticks develop an infection even after engorging on blood with a high parasite density. Certain "strains" of *Boophilus microplus* seem to be more susceptible to infection than others. Heavy mortalities occurred in many ticks after ingesting blood with a parasitemia of 5 percent or higher in *B. argentina* and about 20 percent in *B. bigemina* infections.

In certain parts of Australia, *Theileria mutans* is transmitted by the tick *Haemaphysalis bispinosa*. Stage to stage is the usual method of transmission. The development of the parasite in the tick prior to the appearance of immature fission bodies in the salivary gland of the nymph or adult is at present unknown. Stages infective to the vertebrate host were detected 48–96 hours after the commencement of engorgement of the appropriate instar.

REFERENCES

Abramov, I. V. (1955). About the period of retention of the causative agent of piroplasmosis of horses (*Piroplasma caballi*) in the tick *Hyalomma plumbeum*. *Veterinariya* **32**, 42-46; *Vet. Bull.* (*Commonwealth Bur. Animal Health*) **26**, 264 (1956) (abstr.).

Brumpt, E. (1937). Evolutional cycle of *Piroplasma canis* in Ixodines (Ixodidae). *Compt. Rend. Soc. Biol.* **124**, 928-931.

Callow, L. L. (1962). Studies on the infectivity of *Babesia bigemina* and *B. argentina*. Ph.D. Thesis, University of Queensland, Brisbane.

Christophers, S. R. (1907). *Piroplasma canis* and its life-cycle in the tick. *Sci. Mem. Med. Sanit. Dept. Govt. India* [N.S.] **29**, 1-83.

Cowdry, E. V., and Ham, A. W. (1932). Studies on East Coast Fever. I. The life-cycle of the parasites in ticks. *Parasitology* **24**, 1-48.

Crawley, H. (1915). Note on the stage of *Piroplasma bigeminum* which occurs in the cattle tick, *Margaropus annulatus*. *J. Parasitol.* **2**, 87-92.

Delpy, L. P. (1949). Studies in Iran on *Theileria annulata* Dschunkowsky and Luhs, and its natural and experimental transmission. *Bull. Soc. Pathol. Exotique* **42**, 285-294.

Dennis, E. W. (1932). The life-cycle of *Babesia bigemina* (Smith & Kilborne) of Texas cattle fever in the tick *Margaropus annulatus* (Say) with notes on the embryology of *Margaropus*. *Univ. Calif.* (*Berkeley*) *Publ. Zool.* **36**, 263-298.

Dodd, S. (1910). Piroplasmosis of cattle in Queensland. *J. Comp. Pathol. Therap.* **23**, 141-160.

Dschunkowsky, E., and Luhs, J. (1910). Entwickelungsformen von Piroplasmen in Zecken. *Trans. 9th Intern. Vet. Congr., The Hague, 1909* Vol. 7, pp. 1-5.

Gonder, R. (1910). The life-cycle of *Theileria parva*: The cause of East Coast Fever of cattle in South Africa. *J. Comp. Pathol. Therap.* **23**, 328-335.

Gonder, R. (1911). Die Entwicklung von *Theileria parva*, dem Erreger des Küstenfiebers der Rinder in Afrika. *Arch. Protistenk.* **22**, 170-178.

Ishii, S., and Ishihara, T. (1951). On the intermediate host of bovine small piroplasma. *Japan. J. Vet. Sci.* **13**, 344-345.

Kartashev, M. V. (1957). Observations of the infection of *Dermacentor* with *Piroplasma caballi* in various rural economy situations in central SSSR. *Tr. Vses. Inst. Eksperim. Vet., Vses. Akad. Sel'skokhoz. Nauk* **21**, 210-220; *Vet. Bull* (*Commonwealth Bur. Animal Health*) **29**, 121 (1959) (abstr.).

Koch, R. (1906). Beiträge zur Entwicklungsgeschichte der Piroplasmen. *Z. Hyg. Infektionskrankh.* **54**, 1-9.

Korienko, Z. P., and Shmuireva, M. K. (1944). On the possible transmission of *Theileria* to the progeny of the tick *Hyalomma turkmeniense* (Olenev, 1931). *Veterinariya* **4**, 24-25.

Laptev, V. I. (1961). The degree of infection of *Haemaphysalis neumanni* with *Theileria sergenti* and of *Hyalomma anatolicum* with *Theileria annulata* under experimental conditions. *Tr. Vses. Inst. Eksperim. Vet., Vses. Akad. Sel'skokhoz. Nauk* **27**, 80-82.

Li, P. N. (1956). Simplified method for the diagnosis of *Babesia ovis* in the tick *Rhipicephalus bursa*. *Veterinariya* **33**, 70-71.

Li, P. N. (1958). Developmental forms of *Babesiella ovis* in the larvae and nymphae of *Rhipicephalus bursa*. *Nauchn. Tr. Ukrain. Inst. Eksperim. Vet.* **24**, 283-287.

Markov, A. A. (1957). Blood parasites of livestock (piroplasmosis, babesiellosis, nuttalliosis, theileriosis, anaplasmosis) and principles of their control in SSSR. *Tr. Vses. Inst. Eksperim. Vet., Vses. Akad. Sel'skokhoz. Nauk* **21**, 3-33.

Markov, A. A., and Abramov, I. V. (1957). Peculiarities of circulation of *Babesiella ovis* (Babes, 1892) in the tick *Rhipicephalus bursa* Can. et Fanz. 1877. *Veterinariya* **34**, 27-30; *Vet. Bull.* (*Commonwealth Bur. Animal Health*) **27**, 569 (1957) (abstr.).

Martin, H. M., Barnett, S. F., and Vidler, B. O. (1964). Cyclic development and longevity of *Theileria parva* in the tick *Rhipicephalus appendiculatus*. *Exptl. Parasitol.* **15**, 527-555.

Muratov, E. A., and Cheissin, E. M. (1959). Development of *Piroplasma bigeminum* in tick *Boophilus calcaratus*. *Zool. Zh.* **38**, 970-986.

Neitz, W. O. (1956). Classification, transmission and biology of piroplasma of domestic animals. *Ann. N.Y. Acad. Sci.* **64**, 56-111.

Petrov, V. G. (1941). Development of *Babesiella bovis* in *Ixodes ricinus*. *Vestn. Sel'skokhoz. Nauki, Mosk. Vet.* **3**, 136.

Polyansky, Y. I., and Cheissin, E. M. (1959). Some data on the development of *Babesiella bovis* in tick-vectors. *Tr. Karel'sk. Filiala Akad. Nauk SSSR* **14**, 5-13.

Ray, H. (1950). Hereditary transmission of *Theileria annulata* infection in the tick *Hyalomma aegyptium* (Neum.) *Trans. Roy. Soc. Trop. Med. Hyg.* **44**, 93-104.

Regendanz, P. (1936). Ueber den Entwicklungsgang von *Babesia bigemina* in der Zecke *Boophilus microplus*. *Zentr. Bakteriol., Parasitenk., Abt. I. Orig.* **137**, 423-428.

Regendanz, P., and Reichenow, E. (1933). Die Entwickelung von *Babesia canis* in *Dermacentor reticulatus*. *Arch. Protistenk.* **79**, 50-71.

Reichenow, E. (1935). Uebertragungsweise und Entwicklung der Piroplasmen. *Zentr. Bakteriol., Parasitenk., Abt. I. Orig.* **135**, 108-119.

Reichenow, E. (1940). Der Entwickelungsgang des Küstenfebererregers im Rinde und der übertragenden Zecke. *Arch. Protistenk.* **94**, 1-56.

Riek, R. F. (1964). The development of *Babesia bigemina* (Smith & Kilborne 1893) in the tick *Boophilus microplus* (Canes.). *Australian J. Agr. Res.* **15**, 802-821.

Rosenbusch, F. (1927). Study of Tristeza (piroplasmosis). Development of *Piroplasma bigeminum* in the tick *Boophilus microplus* (Can.) *Rev. Univ. Buenos Aires* **5**, 863-867.

Rosenbusch, F., and Gonzales, R. (1923). Garrapatizacion y tristeza. Investigationes experimentales. *Anales Soc. Rural Arg.* **57**, 789-799.

Sergent, E., Donatien, A., Parrot, L., and Lestoquard, F. (1936). Étude morpholo-

32 R. F. RIEK

gique du cycle evolutif de *Theileria dispar* chez le boeuf et chez la tique. *Ann. Inst. Pasteur* **57**, 30-55.

Shortt, H. E. (1936). Life-history and morphology of *Babesia canis*, in the dog-tick *Rhipicephalus sanguineus*. *Indian J. Med. Res.* **23**, 885-920.

Smith, T., and Kilborne, F. L. (1893). Investigations into the nature, causation and prevention of Texas or southern cattle fever. *U.S. Dept. Agr., Bur. An. Ind. Bull.* No. 1.

Theiler, A. (1907). Further notes on *Piroplasma mutans*—a new species of *Piroplasma* in South African cattle. *J. Comp. Pathol. Therap.* **20**, 1-18.

Till, W. M. (1961). A contribution to the anatomy and histology of the brown ear tick *Rhipicephalus appendiculatus* Neumann. *Mem. Entomol. Soc. Southern Africa* No. 6, 1-124.

Tsaprun, A. A. (1952). Development of the agent of equine haemosporidiosis in the tick vector. *Tr. Vses. Inst. Eksperim. Vet., Vses. Akad. Sel'skokhoz. Nauk* **19**, 36-42.

Tsaprun, A. A. (1957). Material on the development of *Piroplasma caballi* in ticks of the genus *Dermacentor*. *Tr. Vses. Inst. Eksperim. Vet., Vses. Akad. Sel'skokhoz. Nauk* **21**, 221-240.

Discussion

Prof. Don Arthur: To what extent do males of *Boophilus*, or of most any tick which feeds as the male, transmit babesias?

Riek: *Boophilus* is a one-host tick and males would not be important vectors in the transmission of babesiosis. *Babesia argentina* is transmitted usually by the larvae whereas *B. bigemina* is transmitted chiefly by the nymphae. When the vector is a two- or three-host tick males could be involved in the transmission.

Mr. Sawyer: Are there any suggestions of motility of developing stages in ticks—is there any feeding of stages on host tissue?

Riek: The forms appearing in the gut contents around 24–36 hours after repletion appear to be motile but these have not been observed in unfixed material. The vermicules in the hemolymph are sluggishly motile.

There is no evidence of the various stages feeding on host tissue.

Dr. Paul E. Thompson: Have you noted a suggestion of agglutination occurring among blood forms of the babesias? We have observed suggestion of this in smears of *Babesia canis*.

Riek: Erythrocytes infected with *B. argentina* tend to occur in clumps although many infected cells also occur singly in blood films. This phenomenon is more characteristic of *B. argentina* infections and seldom seen in infections of *B. bigemina*. This clumping is not necessarily associated with antibodies as it may be seen soon after the injection of infected blood.

Dr. Marsden: What observations has the speaker made on the mortality of susceptible ticks, adults and nymphs, in relation to dose of *Babesia* parasites. I was struck by the envolvement of gut and Malpighian tubules of the adult tick. How do the ticks die?

Riek: The majority of female ticks engorging on blood with a parasitemia of 5 percent or more in *B. argentina* infections or of about 20 percent in *B. bigemina* die within 5–7 days after the commencement of incubation. However, proportions of replete female ticks succumb after engorging on blood with lower parasitemias. In these ticks there appears to be some alteration in the permeability of the epithelial cells of the gut. The hemolymph becomes red through the presence of hemoglobin from the ingested blood.

Exsheathment and Hatching Mechanisms in Helminths[1]

W. P. ROGERS

University of Adelaide, Waite Agricultural Research Institute, South Australia

INTRODUCTION

Attempts have been made to relate the hatching of infective eggs and the exsheathing of infective larvae to the general biology of parasitism. Thus it has been argued (Rogers, 1961) that the infective stage of parasitic animals is a resting stage in which development has been suspended. For infection to take place, the host, it was suggested, must provide a stimulus which restarts the development of the infective agent as a parasitic stage.

Within the framework of this hypothesis, then, infective mechanisms involved in the hatching of eggs or exsheathment of larvae may be regarded as taking place in three steps:

(1) The host supplies a stimulus that acts on a "receptor" in the infective egg or larva.

(2) As the result of the stimulus, changes take place in the infective stage which lead to the resumption of development and the first obvious indication of this is the secretion of a "hatching fluid" or an "exsheathing fluid."

(3) These fluids attack the layers of the egg shell or the sheath; the infective agent emerges and starts developing as the parasitic stage.

Some details of these processes have been obtained chiefly with ascarid eggs and larvae of trichostrongyles (see, for example, Fairbairn, 1960, 1961; Hass and Todd, 1962; Rogers, 1958, 1960, 1965a; Taylor and Whitlock, 1960; Silverman et al., 1964; Sommerville, 1964) and examples from this work together with more recent results on the mechanism of exsheathment and its relation to infection are given here.

[1] Paper read by Dr. Paul P. Weinstein.

METHODS

Infective larvae of *Nematospiroides dubius* were obtained from cultures of faeces of infected mice. Male mice, 20 gm in weight, were infected *per os* and the size of the infections was measured by counting fourth-stage larvae in the wall of the intestine 5 days after infection. When necessary, larvae were exsheathed artificially in 10 percent sodium hypochlorite.

Stock solutions of 0.1 M iodine were prepared in 0.18 M potassium iodide (Anson, 1941). Hydrogen sulfide–water, about 0.1 M, was prepared from iron sulfide.

The other methods that have been used are described in the papers listed above except that, unless otherwise indicated, reducing agents were omitted in the solutions used for stimulating exsheathment of larvae of *Haemonchus contortus*.

RESULTS

With the exception of the results on the inhibition of exsheathment and infection and its reversal by hydrogen sulfide–water, the results given below have been published and more detailed information may be obtained from the individual papers.

The Stimulus Provided by the Host

The Hatching of Infective Eggs

A number of species, *Ascaris lumbricoides, Toxocara mystax,* and *Ascaridia galli,* for example, have been examined, but most is known about the hatching of eggs of *Ascaris lumbricoides* (Fairbairn, 1961; Jaskoski and Colucci, 1964; Rogers, 1958, 1960). Dissolved gaseous carbon dioxide and (or) undissociated carbonic acid at 38°C seem to be the essential component of the stimulus for this species though strongly reducing conditions are evidently also necessary for hatching of eggs under physiological conditions. Moreover Rogers found that the range of concentrations of dissolved carbon dioxide is critical though, as might be expected, this is affected by the hydrogen ion concentration (Fig. 1). Jaskoski and Colucci obtained good results with solutions saturated with carbon dioxide but the eggs they used had been "de-shelled" with a solution of sodium hypochlorite.

Information about the hatching of infective eggs of the other species in less precise, though its seems that dissolved carbon dioxide at 38°C is again the essential component of the stimulus.

The Exsheathment of Infective Larvae

Larvae of *Haemonchus contortus, Trichostrongylus axei,* and *T. colubriformis* can be induced to exsheath in solutions containing dissolved gaseous carbon dioxide at 38°C, though the response of the different species varies somewhat. The other conditions for exsheathment seem to be related to the site at which exsheathment normally occurs in the host. Thus the stimulus for exsheathment of larvae of *H. contortus* and *T. axei* which normally occurs in the rumen of the host is usually most effective

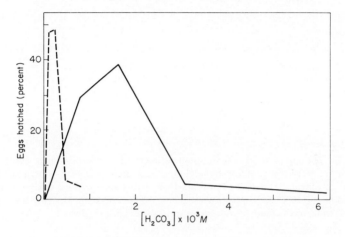

FIG. 1. The hatching of eggs of *Ascaris lumbricoides* at different concentrations of dissolved carbon dioxide and hydrogen ions. The medium was bicarbonate–carbon dioxide buffer at pH 7.3 (broken line) and pH 6.0 (continuous line) containing 0.02 M sodium dithionite under mixtures of nitrogen and carbon dioxide.

at hydrogen ion concentrations near neutrality, whereas *T. colubriformis*, which exsheaths in the abomasum, needs a low pH (Fig. 2).

In their studies with *H. contortus* Taylor and Whitlock (1960) found that the effect of carbon dioxide in causing exsheathment was enhanced when dilute solutions of salts were used. Reducing agents had no effect. Simple organic acids, in the absence of carbon dioxide, gave rise to exsheathment, but this procedure was relatively inefficient.

THE ACTION OF HATCHING FLUID

Infective eggs of *Ascaris lumbricoides,* after they have been stimulated, produce a hatching fluid which contains a chitinase and an esterase. There is some doubt as to whether a proteinase is also produced. Hatching fluid is produced only by infective eggs and only after they have been stimulated.

The enzymes in hatching fluid attack the lipid and chitin in the egg shells and so allow the embryo to escape. Normally the hatching fluid attacks the egg shell from within but the fluid isolated from eggs which

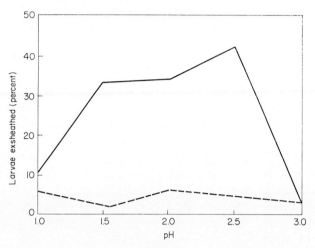

FIG. 2.   The effect of pH on the exsheathment of *Trichostrongylus colubriformis*. The medium consisted of dilute hydrochloric acid under nitrogen containing 20 percent carbon dioxide so that the concentration of dissolved carbon dioxide was about 4.80 to 4.85 $\times$ $10^{-3}\,M$ (upper curve). The results shown in the lower curve were obtained when no carbon dioxide was present in the gas phase.

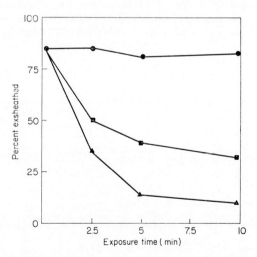

FIG. 3.   The reversible inhibition of exsheathment of *Haemonchus contortus*. The larvae were stimulated to exsheath in bicarbonate–carbon dioxide buffer, pH 7.3 at 38°C, under 40 percent carbon dioxide in nitrogen. Exsheathment was measured after 3 hours. Before stimulation the larvae were treated at 25°C for varying times as follows: Top line, control, $10^{-2}\,M$ potassium iodide; bottom line, 5 $\times$ $10^{-4}\,M$ iodine in potassium iodide; middle line, iodine, followed by 10 minutes in hydrogen sulfide–water.

have been stimulated will attack the egg shells of eggs that have not been stimulated from the outside.

The Action Exsheathing Fluid

The active substance is exsheathing fluid is extremely labile. It will attack sheaths from the inside only, and only in a special region so that the nature of the substrate in the sheaths which is attacked is unknown.

The enzyme concerned in the process is leucine aminopeptidase (Rogers, 1965a). This enzyme is present in the exsheathing fluid released as the result of stimulating infective larvae of *H. contortus* and *T. colubriformis*. Leucine aminopeptidases produced by *H. contortus* and *T. colubriformis* are highly specific and will attack the substrates in their own sheaths only. Moreover, leucine aminopeptidase prepared from mammalian tissue has little effect on sheaths of either species of nematode.

Reversible Inhibition of Exsheathment and Infection

The nature of the stimulus needed for exsheathment suggests that the receptors with which carbon dioxide reacts might be inhibited by certain oxidizing agents and this inhibition might be reversed by subsequent treatment with reducing agents. Indeed, it has been found (Rogers, 1965b) that treatment with low concentrations of iodine inhibited exsheathment of larvae of *H. contortus* and *T. colubriformis* and this inhibition could be reversed by subsequent treatment with hydrogen sulfide–water (Fig. 3).

Treatment of infective larvae of *Nematospiroides dubius* with 10^{-4} M iodine for 10 minutes at 25°C reduced the infectivity of these larvae to mice and the inhibition was reversed if the iodine-treated larvae were subsequently exposed to hydrogen sulfide–water for 10 minutes at 25°C (Table I). The effect of these reagents on the infectivity of the larvae

TABLE I

The Inhibition of Infection with *Nematospiroides dubius* with Iodine and Its Partial Reversal with Hydrogen Sulfide–Water

	Treatment		
Mouse no.	Water	10^{-4} M iodine	10^{-4} M iodine and H_2S-water
1	293	0	138
2	353	0	128
3	307	0	138
4	345	17	127
5	355	0	111

was not affected when larvae which had been artificially exsheathed with sodium hypochlorite were used.

DISCUSSION

For parasites which infect the host via the gut, dissolved gaseous carbon dioxide and (or) undissociated carbonic acid seem to be required as a major component of the stimulus which triggers the development of the parasitic stage. This applies not only for hatching of infective eggs and the exsheathment of infective larvae of nematodes but also to the excystment of metacercariae and sporozoites (Dixon, 1964; Jackson, 1962). Moreover, Sommerville (1964) has shown that carbon dioxide is necessary for inducing differentiation of the third-stage larvae of *H. contortus* in culture *in vitro*. This suggests that carbon dioxide sets in train a variety of developmental changes in addition to the more immediate processes such as hatching, exsheathment, and excystment.

This view is supported by the results of experiments on the reversible inhibition of exsheathment and infection described in this paper. Thus the same treatments which reversibly inhibited exsheathment also reversibly inhibited infection even with larvae from which the sheaths had been removed by artificial means.

It seems reasonable to suppose, therefore, that carbon dioxide reacts with a "receptor" in the infective stage (perhaps in the neurosecretory system) and this causes the release of substances which affect various target organs and tissues which are concerned in the general developmental processes of the parasitic stages.

ACKNOWLEDGMENTS

I am deeply indebted to Dr. Melvin Calvin of the University of California and Professor M. Atkinson of the University of Adelaide, who gave valuable advice on my recent work, which is described in this paper. This work was supported in part by a Public Health Service Grant, AI 04093-03, Institute of Allergy and Infectious Diseases. Parke, Davis & Co. also provided a substantial grant. To both these organizations I express my thanks.

REFERENCES

Anson, M. L. (1941). The sulphydryl groups of egg albumen. *J. Gen. Physiol.* **23**, 399-421.

Dixon, K. E. (1964). Excystment of metacercariae of *Fasciola hepatica* L. *in vitro*. *Nature* **202**, 1240-1241.

Fairbairn, D. (1960). *In* "Host Influence on Parasite Physiology" (L. A. Stauber, ed.), p. 50. Rutgers Univ. Press, New Brunswick, New Jersey.

Fairbairn, D. (1961). The *in vitro* hatching of *Ascaris lumbricoides* eggs. *Can. J. Zool.* **39**, 153-162.

Hass, D. K., and Todd, A. C. (1962). Extension of a technique of hatching ascarid eggs *in vitro*. *Am. J. Vet. Res.* **23**, 169-170.

Jackson, A. R. B. (1962). Excystation of *Eimeria arloingi* (Marotel, 1905): stimuli from the host sheep. *Nature* **194**, 847-849.

Jaskoski, B. J., and Colucci, A. V. (1964). *In virto* hatching of *Ascaris suum* eggs. *Trans. Am. Microscop. Soc.* **83**, 294-300.

Rogers, W. P. (1958). The physiology of the hatching of eggs of *Ascaris lumbricoides. Nature* **181**, 1410-1411.

Rogers, W. P. (1960). The physiology of infective processes of nematode parasites: The stimulus from the animal host. *Proc. Roy. Soc.* **B152**, 367-386.

Rogers, W. P. (1961). "The Nature of Parasitism: The Relationship of Some Metazoan Parasites to their Hosts." Academic Press, New York.

Rogers, W. P. (1965a). The role of leucine aminopeptidase in the molting of nematode parasites. *Comp. Biochem. Physiol.* **14**, 311-321.

Rogers, W. P. (1965b). Unpublished data.

Silverman, P. H., Poynter, D., and Podger, K. R. (1964). *In vitro* exsheathment of some nematode infective larvae. *Exptl. Parasitol.* **15**, 314-324.

Sommerville, R. I. (1964). The effect of carbon dioxide on the development of third stage larvae of *Haemonchus contortus in vitro. Nature* **202**, 316-317.

Taylor, A., and Whitlock, J. H. (1960). The exsheathing stimulus for larvae of *Haemonchus contortus. Cornell Vet.* **50**, 339-344.

Discussion

Dr. Davey: Some work which we have been doing may shed some additional light on the neurosecretory mechanism suggested by Rogers. We have used the nematode *Phocanema decipiens*, which undergoes its final molt in the intestines of seals. It is possible to duplicate this molt *in vitro*. We have found a group of neurosecretory cells in the ventral ganglion which undergoes a cycle of activity during molting. While it is very difficult at the moment to be specific, it appears that the neurosecretory cycle is most closely correlated with ecdysis or the shedding of the old cuticle. The neurosecretory cells in the ventral ganglion are closely associated with the excretory duct, which is the area that Rogers has demonstrated to be involved in the control of the production of exsheathing fluid.

Dr. Weinstein: Obtaining pertinent cytological information should certainly prove to be of great importance in contributing to an understanding of the mechanisms involved in molting and exsheathment of nematodes. It is obviously necessary to have cytological data to correlate with these gross changes. This aspect of the problem has received very little attention, and it is good to know that Dr. Davey and his colleagues are pursuing such an approach. It will be interesting to see how applicable the methods developed so successfully in the study of molting in arthropods as related to neurosecretion and endocrine function will be in the study of the comparable phenomenon in the nematoda.

Dr. Douvres: What are neurosecretory cells in a nematode?

Dr. Davey: A neurosecretory cell in any animal is a nerve cell that exhibits certain specific staining properties. In this particular case, the nerve cells contain granules which are stainable by a modified paraldehyde–fuchsin stain. To say that neurosecretory cells have an endocrine function requires experimental evidence.

Dr. Sawyer: A number of years ago Dr. Weller noted that a single larva of *Trichinella spiralis* grown *in vitro* would sometimes have three or four molted sheaths. More recently Meerovitch and Berntzen have reported that this condition may be manipulated experimentally with different mixtures of gases as CO_2, N_2, and air. Under conditions of multiple sheath formation could you expect large amounts of exsheathment fluid per larva? And, if secretory cells are demonstrable, shouldn't they be evident during such an active period? In short, wouldn't *T. spiralis* larva provide excellent material, under this condition, for both biochemical and morphological investigations of exsheathment?

Dr. Weinstein: Although it is certainly possible that an "exsheathing fluid" is responsible for the exsheathment of *Trichinella* larvae, so far as I know, there is still no experimental evidence for this. Both Meerovitch and Berntzen reported considerable difficulty in obtaining exsheathment *in vitro* of the great majority of molted larvae. Berntzen found it necessary to have molted larvae migrate through a desheathing apparatus in order for them to wriggle out of the enclosing sheath. It would appear that if "exsheathing fluid" normally takes part in this function *in vivo*, either it has not been formed *in vitro*, or it has appeared in quantities insufficient to function adequately. Further work comparable with that of Rogers and Sommerville on trichostrongylid larvae is definitely warranted, particularly extending the recent findings of Dr. Rogers which implicated leucine aminopeptidase in the exsheathing phenomenon.

Skin Penetration Mechanisms of Helminths[1]

M. A. STIREWALT

Naval Medical Research Institute, Bethesda, Maryland

INTRODUCTION

Invasion by way of skin is an important route of infection of hosts by parasites, but relatively few serious sustained investigations of the mechanisms involved have been published. Here is an open field for investigation. Not only is it challenging from the standpoint of interest, but it offers insight into possible means of inhibition of penetration or of termination of migration of the invaders, and thus may be expected to contribute basically to the development of prophylactic or therapeutic measures against parasitic invasion by way of skin.

Involved inherently in skin penetration by parasites are two distinct disciplines: dermatology and parasitology. This must seem a curious relationship since it has not at the present time been adequately explored in the thinking of either parasitologists or dermatologists.

Consideration of skin and its penetrators in close relationship offers a fruitful and rewarding exercise. The mechanisms used by skin penetrants are the adaptations made, in an evolutionary sense, by the parasites to the barriers to penetration presented by the skin. Possible examples are development of an oral cuticular armature; of adhesive mucous secretions and enzyme-containing secretions; and of pertinent sensory receptors. It is the purpose of this paper to explore briefly the relationship between skin and its invasion by helminths and to discuss our knowledge of penetration mechanisms.

SKIN-INVADING PARASITES

The parasites that invade vertebrate hosts through the skin number well over 50 species belonging to 30 or more genera in five larger taxa (Table I).

[1] From Bureau of Medicine and Surgery, Navy Department, Research Task MF .022.03.07-1001. The opinions and assertions contained herein are those of the author and are not to be construed as official or reflecting the views of the Navy Department or the Naval service at large.

41

TABLE I
PARTIAL CATALOG OF SKIN-PENETRATING PARASITES

Arthropoda	
Insecta and Arachnida	Adults and larvae
Nemathelmintha	
Nematoda	Adults and larvae
Platyhelmintha	
Cestoda	Larvae
Trematoda	Larvae

In an additional category, many more could be added which, while they invade hosts by another route, are capable of migration in skin and subcutaneous tissues. Although they might be expected to make use of similar migration mechanisms, this discussion must be limited to the skin invaders.

Tables II and III list examples of adult and larval arthropod skin invaders. While these are not helminths, the mechanisms they use in skin penetration should be pertinent to the general problem. They have not, however, been exhaustively studied. Relevant publications are at

TABLE II
EXAMPLES OF SKIN-PENETRATING ADULT ARTHROPODA

	Host
Itch or mange mites	
Sarcoptes scabei (all stages)	Man
Sarcoptes spp.	Various domestic animals
Psoroptes spp.	Sheep, cattle, rabbits
Notoedres spp.	Cats, rats
Chorioptes spp.	Horses, cattle, and other large domestic animals
Cnemidocoptes spp.	Poultry
Otodectes spp.	Dogs, cats
Sand fleas	
Tunga penetrans	Man and other mammals
Echidnophaga gallinacea	Fowl

TABLE III
EXAMPLES OF SKIN-PENETRATING (MYIASIS-PRODUCING) INSECT LARVAE

Warble or bot fly:	*Dermatobia hominis,* *Gasterophilus* spp. *Hypoderma* spp.
Tumbu fly:	*Cordylobia anthrophaga*
Screw worm:	*Callitraga hominovorax*
Flesh fly:	*Wohlfahrtia* spp.

hand only for *Hypoderma bovis* (Lienert and Thorsell, 1955) and for *Lucilia sericata* (Hobson, 1931) and *L. cuprina* (Waterhouse and Irzykie-wicz, 1957) in which collaginase activity was described. These adult and larval arthropods are mentioned here to relate them to the whole problem of skin penetration by parasites; to present the opportunities for investigation in this field; and to indicate a research problem. This is a question of host-parasite specificity. Some of these parasites are host specific. It seems probable that the reason for the specificity lies in the relationship of their penetration mechanisms to the skin structure of the host. This should be investigated.

Note that the arthropod invaders have armature: "chitinous" mouth parts, cuticular oral hooks or teeth, cutting tooth plates, backwardly pointing spines on the surface, and so on, suggesting the importance to them of abrasive action in their penetration of skin. Use of abrasive action and suction by *Sarcoptes* sp. has been described by Taylor and Murray (1946), who reported that this adult mite held onto the skin by means of suckers on the anterior legs, raised the hind end of the body on the bristles of the posterior legs until it was almost perpendicular, and then commenced to cut into the skin. Complete disappearance into skin occurred in $2\frac{1}{2}$ minutes.

Examples of skin-invading helminth adults and larvae are given in

TABLE IV
EXAMPLES OF SKIN-PENETRATING HELMINTHS

Nematoda	Cestoda	Trematoda
Adults	Larvae	Larvae
Gnathostoma spp.[a] mature and immature	Sparganum	Various cercariae causing swimmers' itch:
Dracunculus medinensis, penetrates from inside out		*Cercaria ocellata,* *C. pseudoarmata,* *Schistosomatium*
Larvae		*douthitti*[a], and others
Necator americanus		*Schistosoma*
Ancylostoma duodenale[c]		*haematobium*
A. caninum[a]		*S. japonicum*
A. braziliense[a]		*S. mansoni*[b]
Uncinaria spp.		
Nippostrongylus brasiliensis (*muris*)[b]		
Strongyloides stercoralis		
S. ratti[a]		
S. simiae[a]		

[a] Subjected to brief investigation.

[b] Subjected to more detailed investigation.

[c] Skin penetration in question.

Table IV. *Ancylostoma duodenale* has been questioned because in the past few years doubt has been cast upon its ability to penetrate skin. Several investigators have reported that these larvae invade through the mucous membranes, but not successfully through skin (Yamashita, 1958; Nishimura, 1959). Should this prove to be the case, comparison of these larvae with more effective skin penetrants should disclose informative differences.

The starred species in the list have been the subjects of at least some investigation. Surprisingly, the only two in which penetration mechanisms have merited serious attention are *Nippostrongylus brasiliensis* and *Schistosoma mansoni* (see reviews by Lewert and Lee, 1957; Lewert, 1958; Stirewalt, 1963). With the exceptions of statements that *N. brasiliensis* has been observed along hair follicles but does not seem to be restricted to this route of migration (Taliaferro and Sarles, 1939; Lindquist, 1950; Gharib, 1955), and of the description of entry of larvae of *Strongyloides ratti* into skin by way of hair follicles and their presence in sebaceous glands (Abadie, 1963), sites of entry and routes of migration in skin have been described only for cercariae of *Schistosoma mansoni* (Stirewalt, 1956, 1959a). The relationship of skin structure and penetrant behavior patterns will therefore be concerned essentially with the schistosome cercaria.

HOST SKIN AND PENETRATION MECHANISMS

MORPHOLOGY OF HOST SKIN

In spite of our long personal contact with our own skin, it is essentially an unknown tissue to us. Skin is the largest and most versatile organ of the body according to Montagna (1965). It is the very thin, continuous wrapping of the body, studied in recent years by several very excellent dermatologists. Of especial value in preparation of this paper were publications of Rothman (1954), Flesch (1962), Montagna (1962), Kligman (1964), and Kral and Schwartzman (1964).

Two general layers comprise skin: an avascular epidermis which lacks connective tissue, and a highly vascular dermis. The primary purpose of skin is protection of the body by prevention of both movement outward of vital fluids and movement inward of foreign material, either living or nonliving. Skin, then, is the outermost line of the body's defenses, and the first barrier against skin-invading parasites.

Because this is the medium through which the parasites of concern here invade the host's body, a clear picture of its histological and chemical characteristics is a necessity for the elucidation of the penetration mechanisms used by its invaders. Much of the fund of knowledge on the structure of skin must, of course, be omitted here, and emphasis must be placed on those details which appear at present to be pertinent to the problem of parasitic invasion. If hereby some structural details are not discussed which later turn out to be important, it may be because the entrance and migration patterns of only one parasite, *Schistosoma mansoni,* have been studied in detail.

The basic morphological plan of skin is essentially identical in all mammals; yet in detail it varies tremendously. Both the thickness and quality of the skin layers differ among the species and breeds of animals and with body regions, age, and sex (Kral and Schwartzman, 1964). For instance in man, Montagna (1965) states: "The skin areas of the chest, the pubic region, the scalp, the abdomen and the soles of the feet are as different from one another, structurally and functionally, as if they belonged to different animals." Such differences, related rationally to the behavior patterns of skin penetrants, could well be the stuff of which informative experiments relating to parasite entry and migration are made.

Cercarial Contact with the Skin Surface

Picture, then, a cercaria, less than 1 mm long, swimming in fresh water and coming in contact with host skin. It experiences contact first with sebum, the waxy film which covers the skin surface like a very thin greasy layer of hydrophilic ointment (Rothman, 1954). This film is a secretion, produced in part by the sebaceous glands and in part by epidermal cells. Liquid when secreted, it spreads quickly and thoroughly over the surface and solidifies at about skin-surface temperature. It is protective against atmospheric changes and against some exogenous infections, and incidentally contains the precursor of vitamin D. Its composition varies greatly. In man, the skin surface fats contain free fatty acids and fatty acids esterified with cholesterol, with wax alcohols, and with glycerol. It also contains free cholesterol and hydrocarbons, one of these being squalene (Rothman, 1954). By contrast, in sheep sebum, squalene is largely replaced by lanosterol, and in sebum of rats, mice, and guinea pigs, by 7-cholestanol (Wheatley and James, 1957). The fact that none of these variations is known to exert any observable influence on a parasite's entrance into skin suggests either that it does not present a variable barrier to cercarial entry or that the penetration mechanisms used by the parasite are broadly effective against it. There has been no investigation of this aspect of the problem. On the other hand, there is a little evidence that the human waxy surface material may be an attractant to schistosome cercariae (Stirewalt and Kruidenier, 1961), but this needs further study.

It has been customary for investigators to assay penetration and maturation as a single unit of data in terms, that is, of the percentage of worms recovered at autopsy of hosts exposed to known numbers of cercariae. It is possible, however, and highly desirable, to assay two phases of parasitic invasion accurately and separately, entry and migration. This is the custom in our laboratory and this discussion will present these two phases as separate information units, beginning with entry into skin.

CERCARIAL EXPLORATION AND ENTRY

Invading cercariae feel out the skin for varying lengths of time before attacking specific entry sites. By such exploration, these potential invaders make contact with the deeply sculptured skin surface characterized by the irregularities associated with hairs, bulbous outer ends of pilosebaceous follicles, loosened scales, wrinkles, sulci, furrows, ridges and folds.

This exploration of skin is the first penetration mechanism to be dis-

TABLE V

INVASIVE MECHANISMS OF CERCARIAE OF *Schistosoma mansoni*

I.	Exploration of skin surface for entry sites
II.	Secretion of mucus from the postacetabular glands for adhesion
III.	Muscular action of whole body in piercing the horny layer
IV.	Abrasion of host tissue by cuticular endings of acetabular gland ducts
V.	Secretion of alkaline mucus deposits from postacetabular glands for softening the horny layer
VI.	Secretion from the preacetabular glands, which presumably contain the invasive enzymes

cussed (Table V). It is an entry mechanism, involving sensory reception of the presence of skin and of the relative suitability of skin irregularities as entry sites. These vary in different types of skin, some of which have been analyzed for their influence on invading cercariae of S. *mansoni* (Stirewalt, 1956). In mouse tail skin with many hairs projecting from the joints between the hard horny scales which form an essentially impenetrable barrier, the hair-skin angles or the projections of the hairs themselves provide entry sites for the majority of the cercarial penetrants. Glabrous skin, such as many areas of human skin, is entered largely at wrinkle crevices. If this skin is tightly stretched, it is far less freely penetrated by cercariae. An intermediate type of skin such as hamster skin may be entered either along hairs or the bulbous projections of the pilosebaceous follicles, in wrinkles, furrows or flexure lines, under the upturned edges of loose scales, or through already used entry sites. Neither pilosebaceous nor sweat duct orifices are used for entry. Both are small and self-sealing in an aqueous environment (Kligman, 1964).

As cercariae explore the skin surface attaching alternately by the oral and ventral suckers, at each oral sucker attachment they deposit 6 minute droplets of secretion from the postacetabular glands. This mucus deposit swells in water, becomes sticky, and serves as adhesive attachment points for both suckers, the ventral being attached in it immediately after the oral is withdrawn from it and attached again at a new spot. With suitable preparation, it is demonstrable as a series of tracks marking the progress of an exploring cercaria (Stirewalt, 1959b). The secretion and use of this mucus for adhesion is the second entry mechanism to be mentioned (Table V).

If a cercaria hesitates long at a skin irregularity it is likely to be well anchored there in the mucus droplet which becomes progressively more sticky. It then orients itself perpendicularly to the skin surface and exhibits strenuous muscular activity both with the tail and in alternate contraction and elongation of the body (Stirewalt, 1956). These changes in body shape provide a means of enlarging the entry opening according to Gordon and Griffiths (1951) and they are considered by Stirewalt and Kruidenier (1961) to be a means of squeezing secretion from the postacetabular glands. This muscular action is the third important invasive mechanism (Table V). It is common to both entry and migration.

Schistosomular Migration through the Horny Layer

Simultaneously, the muscular oral sucker is alternately everted and withdrawn and in this way hammered into the crevice, bringing the cuticular tips of the acetabular gland ducts into contact with the skin, and thus depositing the secretions into the entry site (Cort, 1919; Faust, 1920). This abrasive action of the cuticular duct openings is the fourth invasive mechanism to be noted here (Table V). It also is common to both entry and migration.

In this manner the schistosomes gradually pierce the horny layer, the first real barrier to invasion of the host. This appears to be the most energy-consuming phase of skin penetration. As discussed by Kligman (1964) the horny layer is a thin but tough outer body wrapping, without which dry land life would be impossible for animals. This dermatologist has called it "miracle wrap." From fixed and stained sections it used to be thought of as "a loose, desquamating layer of scales permeated by large spaces and cracks, a mortuary of dead cells falling apart from each other" (Kligman, 1964). Recent study of the horny layer in the unfixed, more natural state has shown it to be otherwise. After application of a cantharidin, human horny layer can be lifted off as a tough resilient intact membrane, impermeable to water, a cellular fabric of hardy constitution resembling semitransparent plastic (Kligman and Christophers, 1964). It is generally about 11 to 15 microns thick. In many animals, such as deer, cattle, horse, and rabbit, it is too fragile to be separated as a continuous sheet. From rats and guinea pigs, it comes off as a delicate, easily ruptured membrane (Kligman, 1964).

Whatever the animal source, this layer is made up of dead epidermal cells which are moved outward gradually and continuously by the development of the living cells of the germinal layer of the epidermis, as they mature and die. Three major architectural components have been recognized: (1) a tough envelope consisting of the rugged cell membranes enclosing (2) packets of compact fibrous protein, all thought today to be embedded in (3) an adhesive cellular cement. About 50% or more of the horny layer is made up of consolidated fibrous keratin. This and the intercellular cement substance provide the tremendous cohesiveness of this layer (Kligman, 1964) and probably the tough barrier quality to parasitic invaders.

The toughness and protective quality of the horny layer of man appear to have developed with the loss of hair. Man's stratum corneum, for instance, is much thicker than that of an extreme example of hairiness, the sheep, in which the horny layer is very thin. Similarly, the horny layer of the nearly naked newborn rat is much thicker and stronger than that of the hairy adult (Kligman, 1964; Kral and Schwartzman, 1964). In this regard it is of interest that schistosome cercariae find the skin of these young rodents difficult if not impossible to enter (Stirewalt, 1956).

Cercariae, however, do appear to possess a means of preparing the horny layer for penetration. Dermatologists have known for a long time that keratin swells, is softened, and finally digested in an alkaline medium. They make use of this fact in the examination of skin scrapings for the identification of fungi by dissolving away the keratin with potassium hydroxide. Upon cercarial attack also, the horny layer swells and becomes soft. This, together with the fact that the postacetabular mucus-producing glands of schistosome cercariae give an alkaline reaction in phenol red, is strongly suggestive of a fifth penetration (entry) mechanism (Table V): the secretion of an alkaline mucus which is deposited, as described earlier, at each attachment of the oral sucker on a surface over which the cercaria is crawling, and the especial concentration of this mucus at the chosen entry site, thus providing for sufficient softening of the tough acid keratin to permit passage through it. Although this hypothesis has not been proven, the data at hand support it for cercariae. Further work along this line is in progress with cercariae as well as with filariform larvae of skin-invading nematodes.

With the exception of the horny layer of very young rats, cercariae of S. mansoni are able to pass through a wide variety of horny layers as shown by their maturation to adult worms in the hosts listed in Table VI.

Invasive efficiencies do vary, however, as shown in the variations in times spent in exploration and in the percentages of cercariae which are able to enter various types of skin (Stirewalt, 1956): over 90 percent in adult haired mouse tail; and only slightly less in adult human and monkey body skin; 78 percent in adult hairless mouse ear and hamster body skin; 73 percent in body skin of adult hairless mice and of baby mice; 60 to 65 percent in 1- to 2-day-old mouse body skin and adult hairless mouse tail skin; and 34 percent in 5-day-old rat body skin, as has already been mentioned.

TABLE VI

HOSTS SUSCEPTIBLE TO ENTRY, MIGRATION, AND MATURATION
OF *Schistosoma mansoni*

Infections patent	Infections nonpatent
Various primates	Rats, several species
Hamster	Rabbit
Mouse	Guinea pig
Cotton rat	Cat
Rice rat	Gerboa
Gerbil	Egyptian hedgehog
Jird	Mongoose
Bandicoot	Raccoon
Skunk	Chipmunk
Squirrel	Nutria
Opossum	Pig
Woodchuck	Shrew
Cow	Meadow vole
Armadillo	Anteater
Marmoset	

SCHISTOSOMULAR MIGRATION THROUGH THE HORNY LAYER

As the oral end of the parasite's body breaks through the horny layer, the cercaria or, as we should call it now, the schistosomule, turns to follow the keratogenous zone, or the stratum lucidum (Stirewalt, 1959a). The filariform larva of *Nippostrongylus brasiliensis* behaves similarly (Gharib, 1955).

Now the whole muscular activity of the schistosomule changes from the previous alternate elongation and contraction of the whole body to quivering contractions of the musculature around the preacetabular glands. Secretion from these is poured into the skin as can be dramatically demonstrated in purpurin-stained cercariae (Stirewalt and Kruidenier, 1961). This, then, is the sixth invasive mechanism (Table V): secretion of the contents of the preacetabular glands into the skin. It is a mechanism for migration only, not apparently being involved in entry.

By the time the body of the schistosomule is entirely through the horny layer and well within the keratogenous zone, the tail has usually been cast, both pre- and postacetabular gland secretion has been depleted and is not renewed (the degree of depletion being related to the difficulty of invasion and time spent in exploring and penetrating thus far), and the schistosomule often "rests" (Gordon and Griffiths, 1951). This resting period might logically be a period necessary for the cercarial secretion to permeate the epidermis and dermis as described by Lewert and Lee (1954), and for the secreted enzymes to "soften" or degrade the intercellular matrix of these tissues.

Once migration in the keratogenous zone is resumed, it is continued for varying lengths of time, sometimes as much as several days in mouse tail skin (Stirewalt, 1959a). Although this tissue might, therefore, be of especial significance to our understanding of the mechanisms of penetration, it is inadequately known. Dermatologists have not been in agreement concerning even its presence or absence in many types of skin. It is, however, identifiable in the volar skin of man and is probably present generally in skin. It is a hyaline transitional area subjacent to the horny layer. Its cells are incompletely keratinized, since this is the region in which they are changing to the cornified state. Activity of the skin enzymes is high here (Kligman, 1964). Evidently this is a structurally weak layer since the horny tissue can be lifted off along this region. Perhaps it is this weakness which makes it a favored route of migration for schistosomules and nematode invasive larvae.

SCHISTOSOMULAR MIGRATION ALONG THE DERMO-EPIDERMAL JUNCTION

By this time, largely by virtue of their relatively great diameters as compared with epidermis, but also probably with the help of cercarial secretions from the preacetabular glands in degrading the intercellular ground substance, the schistosomules have crossed the viable cellular epidermis. This consists of a variable number of cell layers embedded in intracellular cement, the outer layer composed of granular cells and the inner of germinal cells.

Most schistosomules then move along the dermo-epidermal junction subjacent to the germinal cell layers of the epidermis. This is the area of the epidermal basement membrane cited by Lewert and his associates (Lewert, 1958) as an important barrier to schistosomules. Although intermittently the existence of the basement membrane as a continuous cohesive sheet has been questioned, examination with the electron microscope by Porter and Bonneville (1964) has adequately demonstrated it. These investigators have identified two layers: one immediately subepidermal, a continuous sheet about 800 Å thick and composed of collagen, and the other next to the dermis, essentially a network of collagen fibers. All this is proteinaceous material secreted by epidermal cells. It is cleaved by trypsin and apparently by cercarial secretions (Lewert and Lee, 1954). Kral and Schwartzman (1964) stated, however, that basement membranes resist hydrolysis by hyaluronidase. It is of significance, however, that collagenases have been described by Lewert and his associates (Lewert, 1958) in secretions of living cercariae and in cercarial extracts.

PILOSEBACEOUS MIGRATION

The suggestion that the epidermal basement membrane is a substantial barrier to schistosomules (Lewert, 1958) is strengthened by the fact that schistosomules, unless present in overwhelming numbers, generally avoid crossing it, but follow along the epidermal side of it for the next few hours or days. They then turn inward along it as it surrounds the pilosebaceous follicles. This route leads into sebaceous glands in which many schistosomules remain for a considerable time (Stirewalt, 1959a). Although in sebaceous glands schistosomules are still extradermal, they have avoided the basement membrane of the surface epithelium and perhaps indeed any basement membrane. Pillsbury et al. (1956) stated that the basement membrane has been replaced around sebaceous glands by a connective tissue capsule within which lie small, flattened outer gland cells.

Several more facts may be of significance in consideration of the importance of sebaceous glands in the migration of schistosomules. One is that the usual path of absorption through the epidermis of soluble materials is, like the migration route of choice of schistosomules, not directly transcutaneous, but by pilosebaceous follicles into sebaceous glands and thus into the dermis. Another is that the sebaceous glands of various animal species or breeds and the various areas of their skin are morphologically similar (Kral and Schwartzman, 1964). Still another is that, while the invasive schistosomes are able to enter bird (pigeon) skin which lacks sebaceous glands (Mercer, 1961), they are completely barred from the dermis, and die and are sloughed off with the epidermis (Coutinho-Abath and Jampolsky, 1957). Unfortunately, the role of the secretion produced by the sebaceous glands in the entry or migration patterns of skin-invading parasites has not been adequately investigated. It would be interesting to know whether this sebum has a real attractiveness either on the skin surface to cercariae or in sebaceous glands and pilosebaceous follicles to schistosomules.

It should be added here that unknown variations in other types of skin also influence cercarial migration in them. *Schistosoma mansoni* cercariae die in varying percentages not only in the skin of pigeons (Coutinho-Abath and Jampolsky, 1957), but also in that of the dog (Pinto and Almeida, 1945), fox, and muskrat (von Lichtenberg et al., 1962). *Schistosoma japonicum* cercariae also die in skin of domestic fowl (Watarai, 1936), and several species of cercariae of the nonhuman schistosomes are destroyed in human skin. A clearer understanding of the influential features might give important clues to mechanisms of penetration of these parasites.

MOVEMENT THROUGH THE DERMIS INTO CIRCULATORY VESSELS

From the sebaceous glands most schistosomules move directly into the dermis, although sometimes they follow the dermo-follicular junction into deeper tissues. The dermis is composed of two regions: the papillary dermis subjacent to the basement membrane, and next inward, the reticular dermis. Both are composed of collagenous and elastic fibers, and numerous capillary meshes, all embedded in the ground substance, the semifluid, amorphous, gelatinlike intercellular cement, that we understand so poorly. This intercellular matrix material appears to be essentially a protein–mucopolysaccharide complex containing hyaluronic and chondroitin sulfuric acids in approximately equal ratio (Rothman, 1954; Montagna, 1962; Kral and Schwartzman, 1964). As presented to invading parasites, it would seem to be a viscous, jellylike material netted throughout by widely separated, relatively large collagen fibers, quite small reticulin fibers, and intermediate sized elastin fibers. Altogether the dermis must seem to schistosomules like a sort of random oriented tropical rain forest embedded in Jello.

Collagen fibers are about 20 to 40 microns in diameter, which is roughly about the same as a cercaria. The fiber texture is usually more dense in the papillary than in the reticular dermis. In man the reticular dermis is relatively thicker than in most other animals. Also, by way of comparison, it has a rich population of elastic fibers in contrast to most other animals. Finally, man has a highly vascular dermis, with extensive labyrinthine systems of blood vessels, and with complex subepidermal capillary loops. The dermis of other animals is relatively ischemic (Rothman, 1954; Montagna, 1962; Kral and Schwartzman, 1964). Yet through all these dermal regions so anatomically variable, schistosomules move relatively quickly. In general, they follow lines of tissue junctions, along fibers or blood vessels, and finally move into lymphatic vessels or veins.

The venous elements of the dermis are arranged in the form of three plexuses: the first of delicate vessels within or just beneath the elevation of the dermal papillae projecting into the epidermis, the second of somewhat larger vessels at the boundary of the papillary and reticular layers of the dermis, and the deepest with the largest vessels in the lower boundary of the dermis just as it merges with the subdermal tissue (Montagna, 1962). Schistosomules entering veins usually do so through the larger vessels. On rare occasions schistosomules have been observed as they entered venous vessels. Penetration of venule walls has always been followed by brief hemorrhage which appears to be stopped quickly by self-sealing of this tissue.

A few schistosomules have been observed instead of entering lymphatic or venous vessels in the dermis to move all the way through the skin into the subdermis, entering veins only in these deeper tissues or returning to the dermal plexuses.

Of course, the vascularization in the dermis is highly irregular, depending upon the region of the body, the animal under study, and the period of examination. Vascularization of the pilosebaceous follicles, for instance, is different at different times in the development of this appendage. In addition, at times various parts of the capillary system can be shut down for control of the skin temperature. The influence of these variations on schistosomular migration is not known.

Skin-Penetrating Enzymes

The penetration of skin by schistosomes then appears to be largely along the lines of least resistance: entry begun in crevices or other irregularities; migration along the keratogenous zone, the epithelial basement membrane in the dermo-epidermal junction, and inward along these same tissue junctions around pilosebaceous follicles; into sebaceous glands; through the interfibrous spaces of the dermis; and into lymphatic or venous vessels. It should be noted, however, that this route of invasion is not invariably followed. Several earlier investigators have recorded direct transepidermal migration and Lewert and Lee (1954) have described changes in the epithelial basement membrane in the vicinity of migrating schistosomules. Direct transcutaneous migration appears to occur most often when large numbers of migrants are moving simultaneously through host tissue.

In either case, the most important structural elements of skin to cercariae and schistosomules seem to be the secreted ones: the keratin or the intercellular matrix, as the cement substance of the horny layer and the viable cellular epidermis is known; the matrices of the tissue junctions; the ground substance of the dermis; and the cement substance of the venous walls. These are all probably lipid–mucopolysaccharide–protein complexes. It is, therefore, likely that once the horny layer has been penetrated with the aid of an alkaline cercarial secretion, enzymes are a necessity to degrade to a more liquid and thus yielding consistency these gel-like complexes. These enzymes are a part of the secretions from the cercarial acetabular glands which are depleted during skin invasion and are not renewed; that is, their activity is not demonstrable in schistosomules (Stirewalt et al., 1966, in press).

Evidences of the involvement of enzyme activity in entry and migration in skin by trematode cercariae, and also by the filariform larvae of nematodes, has been accumulating over the years to the extent that a sizable reference list now exists (Lewert, 1958; Stirewalt, 1963; Mandlowitz *et al.*, 1960; Gazzinelli and Pellegrino, 1964). Several types of evidence may be cataloged according to the experimental approaches employed in their study (Table VII).

TABLE VII

APPROACHES EMPLOYED IN THE STUDY OF SKIN INVASION BY PARASITES[a]

Cercariae	Lysis of tissue	Histochemistry of penetrated skin	Spreading factor effect	Enzyme-substrate systems
Schistosoma mansoni	X	X	X	X
Schistosomatium douthitti	—	X	—	—
Cryptocotyle lingua	X	—	—	—
Diplostomum flexicaudum	X	—	—	—
Cercaria spp.	—	—	X	X
Filariform larvae				
Ancylostoma caninum	—	—	X	X
Ancylostoma duodenale	—	X	X	X
Nippostrongylus brasiliensis	X	X	X	X
Strongyloides ratti	X	X	X	X
Strongyloides simiae	X	X	X	X
Insect larvae				
Hypoderma bovis	—	—	—	X
Lucilia spp.	—	—	—	X

[a] See the reviews of Lewert and Lee (1957), Lewert (1958), and Stirewalt (1963).

Undoubtedly, the most informative of these at present are the histochemical assessment of changes produced in skin by penetrating parasites, and the *in vitro* approach in which extracts or metabolic products of invasive stages of parasites are incubated with selected substrates and the degradation products identified. Information from the histochemical approach employed by Lewert and his co-workers (Lewert, 1958) has been cited earlier in this paper. The enzyme-substrate approach has been used by various investigators (see references for Table VIII). In Table VIII, the substrates chosen and the parasites studied are summarized.

No clear understanding of the enzymes used by skin-penetrating parasites is possible as yet from the information available. It appears that filariform larvae, insect invaders, and cercariae vary considerably in their enzymatic endowments but a great deal more work is required for definitive conclusions. Extracts of both the filariform larvae and cercariae studied have reduced the size of streptococcal capsules, indicating some

TABLE VIII

ENZYMES REPORTED IN SKIN-INVADING HELMINTHS[a]

Substrates tested	Schistosoma mansoni	Schistosomatium douthitti	Cercaria spp.	Nippostrongylus brasiliensis	Ancylostoma caninum	Strongyloides spp.	Insect larvae
Tissues	Yes	—	—	No	—	Yes	No
Hyaluronic acid	Yes; no	—	Yes	No	No	No	No
Streptococcal capsules	Yes	—	—	Yes	Yes	Yes	—
Chondroitin sulfuric acid	No	—	—	No	No	No	No
Heparin	Yes	—	—	—	—	—	—
Ovomucin	No	—	—	No	—	No	—
Mucopolysaccharide	Yes	—	—	—	—	Yes	Yes
Collagen	Yes	Yes	?	?; no	Yes	Yes	—
Elastin	Yes	—	—	—	—	—	—
Polypeptides	Yes; no	—	—	No	—	Yes	—
Gelatin	Yes	—	—	—	—	Yes	—
Casein	Yes	—	—	—	—	No	—
Hemoglobin	Yes	—	—	—	—	Yes	—
Lipid	Little	—	—	Yes	—	Yes	—

[a] See the reviews of Lewert and Lee (1957), Lewert (1958), and Stirewalt (1963), and the papers of Mandlowitz et al. (1960) and Gazzinelli and Pellegrino (1964).

type of mucopolysaccharidase. All the parasitic preparations studied have been inactive against chondroitin sulfuric acid. Some filariform larvae and insect invaders, and the two cercarial species tested show collaginase activity. Buffer extracts of as few as 1250 cercariae of S. *mansoni* per milliliter depolymerize urea-denatured hemoglobin, volume for volume (see references for Table VIII).

More information about the enzymatic activity of parasitic preparations against selected substrates *in vitro* is, of course, a necessity. It is advisable in such investigations to keep in mind the natural substrates in skin

TABLE IX

SUMMARY OF INFORMATION ON SKIN PENETRATION MECHANISMS

Skin-invading parasites	Information on skin penetration mechanisms		
	Behavior patterns	Histochemistry of skin	Enzymes
Adult itch and mange mites	0	0	0
Larval insects	0	0	Collaginase in 3 species[a]
Adult nematodes	0	0	0
Larval nematodes	0	Changes in 4 species[b]	Described in 5 species[b]
Larval cestodes	0	0	0
Larval trematodes			
Cercaria spp.	0	Changes in 1 species[b]	Described in 1 species[b]
Schistosoma mansoni	Described[c]	Described[b]	Described[b,d]

[a] Hobson (1931), Waterhouse and Irzykiewicz (1957), Lienert and Thorsell (1955).

[b] Lewert and Lee (1954), reviews of Lewert and Lee (1957), Lewert (1958), Stirewalt (1963).

[c] Stirewalt (1956, 1959a).

[d] Gazzinelli and Pellegrino (1964), Mandlowitz et al. (1960), Stirewalt (1963).

which are degraded *in vivo* by secretions of the invading parasites, and constantly to relate the two in our thinking. The action of demonstrated parasitic enzymes against specific peptide bonds should be clarified. A beginning has been made along this line by Mandlowitz et al. (1960) and in my own laboratory. Further information will be contributed by a clear understanding of the effect of inhibitors on parasitic enzymes.

A tantalizing research field thus lies before us. Collection of the presently available information (Table IX) reveals astonishingly comprehensive ignorance of the invasive mechanisms used by skin-penetrating parasites. It is hoped that this review may provide a little background and more stimulation for intensive study of the ways and means of parasitic invasion of host skin.

REFERENCES[2]

Abadie, S. H. (1963). The life cycle of *Strongyloides ratti*. *J. Parasitol.* **49**, 241-248.
Cort, W. W. (1919). The cercaria of the Japanese blood-fluke, *Schistosoma japonicum* Katsurada. *Univ. Calif. (Berkeley) Publ. Zool.* **18**, 485-507.
Coutinho-Abath, E., and Jampolsky, R. (1957). Comportamento das cercarias de *Schistosoma mansoni* na infestacao experimental de animais refractorios. I. Histopathologia das reacoes cutaneas observados no pombo domestico (*Columba livia domestica*). *Ann. Soc. Biol. Pernambuco* **15**, 93-125.
Faust, E. C. (1920). Criteria for the differentiation of schistosoma larvae. *J. Parasitol.* **6**, 192-194.
Flesch, P. (1962). The cementing substance of human horny layers. *J. Soc. Cosmetic Chemists* **13**, 113-118.
Gazzinelli, G., and Pellegrino, J. (1964). Elastolytic activity of *Schistosoma mansoni* cercarial extract. *J. Parasitol.* **50**, 591-592.
Gharib, H. M. (1955). Observations on skin penetration by the infective larvae of *Nippostrongylus brasiliensis*. *J. Helminthol.* **29**, 33-36.
Gordon, R. M., and Griffiths, R. B. (1951). Observations on the means by which the cercariae of *Schistosoma mansoni* penetrate mammalian skin, together with an account of certain morphological changes observed in the newly penetrated larvae. *Ann. Trop. Med. Parasitol.* **45**, 227-243.
Hobson, R. P. (1931). An enzyme from blow-fly larvae (*Lucilia sericata*) which digest collagen in alkaline solution. *Biochem. J.* **25**, 1458-1463.
Kligman, A. M. (1964). The biology of the stratum corneum. In "The epidermis" (W. Montagna and W. C. Lobitz, Jr., eds.), pp. 387-433. Academic Press, New York.
Kligman, A. M., and Christophers, E. (1964). Preparation of isolated sheets of human stratum corneum. *Arch. Dermatol.* **88**, 702-705.
Kral, F., and Schwartzman, R. M. (1964). "Veterinary and Comparative Dermatology," 444 pp. Lippincott, Philadelphia, Pennsylvania.
Lewert, R. M. (1958). Invasiveness of helminth larvae. *Rice Inst. Pam.* **45**, 97-113.
Lewert, R. M., and Lee, C. L. (1954). Studies on the passage of helminth larvae through host tissues. I. Histochemical studies on extracellular changes caused by penetrating larvae. II. Enzymatic activity of larvae *in vitro* and *in vivo*. *J. Infect. Diseases* **95**, 13-51.
Lewert, R. M., and Lee, C. L. (1957). The collagenaselike enzymes of skin-penetrating helminths. *Am. J. Trop. Med. Hyg.* **6**, 473-479.
Lienert, E., and Thorsell, W. (1955). Untersuchungen über die Aktivität von Autolysaten aus Wanderlarven (*Hypoderma bovis*) auf Elemente des Bindegewebes, *Exptl. Parasitol.* **4**, 117-122.
Lindquist, W. D. (1950). Some abnormal relationships of a rat nematode *Nippostrongylus muris*. *Am. J. Hyg.* **52**, 22-41.
Mandlowitz, S., Dusanic, D., and Lewert, R. M. (1960). Peptidase and lipase activity of extracts of *Schistosoma mansoni* cercariae. *J. Parasitol.* **46**, 89-90.
Mercer, E. H. (1961). "Keratin and Keratinization," 316 pp. Pergamon Press, Oxford.
Montagna, W. (1962). "The Structure and Function of Skin," 454 pp. Academic Press, New York.
Montagna, W. (1965). The skin. *Sci. Am.* **212**, 56-66.
Nishimura, T. (1959). Studies on the tissue-invading habit of hook-worm larvae in

[2] In the interest of brevity many of the references listed in the reviews of Lewert and Lee (1957), Lewert (1958), and Stirewalt (1963) are not repeated here.

various temperatures. 2. Observations in soil with larvae of *Ancylostoma duodenale* and *A. caninum*. *Japan. J. Parasitol.* 8, 189-195.

Pillsbury, M. A., Shelley, W. B., and Kligman, A. M. (1956). "Dermatology," 1331 pp. Saunders, Philadelphia, Pennsylvania.

Pinto, C., and Almeida, A. F. (1945). Penetracao das cercarias de *Schistosoma mansoni* na pele de *Canis familiaris* e do homen. *Rev. Brasil. Biol.* 5, 219-229.

Porter, K. R., and Bonneville, M. A. (1964). "An Introduction to the Fine Structure of Cells and Tissues," 2nd ed., Lea & Febiger, Philadelphia, Pennsylvania.

Rothman, S. (1954). "Physiology and Biochemistry of the Skin," 741 pp. Univ. of Chicago Press, Chicago, Illinois.

Stirewalt, M. A. (1956). Penetration of host skin by cercariae of *Schistosoma mansoni*. I. Observed entry into skin of mouse, hamster, rat, monkey and man. *J. Parasitol.* 42, 565-580.

Stirewalt, M. A. (1959a). Chronological analysis, pattern and rate of migration of cercariae of *Schistosoma mansoni* in body, ear and tail skin of mice. *Ann. Trop. Med. Parasitol.* 53, 400-413.

Stirewalt, M. A. (1959b). Isolation and characterization of deposits of secretion from the acetabular gland complex of cercariae of *Schistosoma mansoni*. *Exptl. Parasitol.* 8, 199-214.

Stirewalt, M. A. (1963). Chemical biology of secretions of larval helminths. *Ann. N.Y. Acad. Sci.* 113, 36-53.

Stirewalt, M. A., and Kruidenier, F. J. (1961). Activity of the acetabular secretory apparatus of cercariae of *Schistosoma mansoni* under experimental conditions. *Exptl. Parasitol.* 11, 191-211.

Stirewalt, M. A., Fregeau, W. A. and Minnick, D. R. (1966). In press.

Taliaferro, W. H., and Sarles, M. P. (1939). The cellular reactions in the skin, lungs and intestine of normal and immune rats after infection with *Nippostrongylus muris*. *J. Infect. Diseases* 64, 157-192.

Taylor, F. H., and Murray, R. E. (1946). "Spiders, Ticks and Mites," Serv. Publ. No. 6 (School of Public Health and Tropical Medicine). Australasian Med. Publ., Glebe, New South Wales.

von Lichtenberg, F., Sadun, E. H., and Bruce, J. I. (1962). Tissue responses and mechanisms of resistance in schistosomiasis mansoni in abnormal hosts. *Am. J. Trop. Med. Hyg.* 11, 347-356.

Watarai, J. (1936). Studies on the skin reaction caused by *Schistosoma mansoni* cutaneously applied on the animals, *Japan. J. Exptl. Med.* 14, 1-18.

Waterhouse, D. F., and Irzykiewicz, H. (1957). An examination of proteolytic enzymes from several insects for collaginase activity. *J. Insect Physiol.* 1, 18-22.

Wheatley, V. R., and James, A. T. (1957). The composition of the sebum of some common rodents. *Biochem. J.* 65, 36-42.

Yamashita, M. (1958). Experiment on mode of infection of hookworms in human body. *Igaku Kenkyu* 28, 2434-2439.

Discussion

Mr. James: Dr. M. J. Ulmer has studied the penetration of bird skin by bird schistosomes. You indicated that the schistosomes that infect mammals probably use the sebaceous glands as a point of entry. Since the birds have no sebaceous glands, and do have schistosomes, do you think that bird forms could penetrate mammalian skin more easily than mammalian forms.

Dr. Stirewalt: I would like to compare, enzymatically, the bird schistosome and human schistosome cercariae. It is possible that bird schistosome cercariae would not use the sebaceous gland approach; it is also possible that their enzymes are more effective against the basement membrane.

Mr. James: Do you think bird schistosome cercariae utilize an entirely different penetration mechanism?

Dr. Stirewalt: This is possible; this is of course speculation but it is possible the enzymes are specific for the composition of the basement membrane or cement substance of the particular skin. There may be enough differences in the bird skin so that bird schistosomes are not effective against mammalian skin.

Dr. Beaver: It can be demonstrated that bird schistosomes penetrate bird skin but the natural portal of entry appears to be mucous membranes of the mouth and nasal passage. I wonder whether Dr. Ulmer has in fact shown bird skin penetrated by bird schistosome cercariae?

Mr. James: Dr. Ulmer and some of his students are currently working on life cycles of some bird schistosomes. To my knowledge, skin penetration as an entry route has not been noted.

Dr. Whitlock: It is important to remember that bird skins are quite variable, both physiologically and morphologically in the summer. The molting and the reconstruction of pin feathers is quite prominent in many aquatic birds. I would suggest that before one could accept that schistomosomes may not be able to penetrate intact bird skin, that it would be important to examine the schistosome penetration at various stages of the molting cycle.

The Ecology of Ticks with Reference to the Transmission of Protozoa

DON R. ARTHUR

Department of Zoology,
University of London King's College,
London, England

THE SCOPE AND DIFFICULTIES OF THE PROBLEM

Piroplasmosis is widespread in Europe and Africa, but information on its detailed occurrence is lacking. The protozoan pathogen apparently exercises inimical effects only in the vertebrate host, and has a cyclical phase of development in the tick, although this does not appear to be obligatory since indefinite serial passage from one vertebrate host to another is possible. Any fundamental approach to the problem necessitates a knowledge of the behavior of the protozoan in the vector, as already carried out for *Babesia bigemina* in *Boophilus microplus* by Riek (1964), for example, and intensive investigations of the biochemical and biophysical factors of the protozoan environment within the tissues of the tick vector, which either stimulate or inhibit development, survival, or mobility of the parasite. Where transovarial transmission of piroplasmas by ticks has not been demonstrated it is also pertinent to question whether reservoirs for infection exist among wild vertebrates and, if so, what are the relationships among the wild vertebrate, the tick vector, and the domestic animal. Though the association of tick–pathogen–vertebrate host food-meshes appears well established, a number of features remain unexplained, for example, the capacity of one tick species to transmit a specific protozoan and the inability of closely allied species to do so. These then are problems requiring information on the biology and ecology of ticks. The present contribution attempts to highlight some of these features in relation to bovine and equine piroplasmosis in Eurasia and Africa. Within these limits, however, there is confusion in identification and nomenclature of both ticks and piroplasmas, revealing inadequacy of established criteria.

Babesias occur in both wild and domestic hosts, being probably more widely distributed among mammals than any other blood-inhabiting pro-

61

tozoan, with the possible exception of trypanosomes. Among wild hosts they have been reported from large herbivores and carnivores as well as from rodents and insectivores, but their specific status in many cases is questionable.

Shortt (1962) has maintained strains of *Babesia* from the mole *Talpa europaea,* the bank vole *Clethrionomys,* and the long-tailed field mouse *Apodemus* in Britain, and strains have been isolated from the shrew, *Sorex* spp., and the short-tailed vole *Microtus.* All appear to be morphologically identical and in laboratory animals their behavior leaves them indistinguishable. Previously it had been assumed that babesias either were almost specific to the mammals in which they occurred naturally or were not transmissible to mammals phylogenetically unrelated to their natural hosts. The natural infection of a splenectomized man with *B. bovis*[1] from cattle (Skrabalo and Deanovic, 1957), the contraction of *B. divergens* by two chimpanzees in Liberia following inoculation of heparinized blood containing *B. divergens* from England (Garnham and Bray, 1959), infection of a previously splenectomized *Macaca radiata* with babesias from a rodent, *Gerbillus indicus* (Shortt, 1962), and the extension of the host range of *B. divergens* by transmission to splenectomized moufflons, red deer, fallow deer, and the roe by Enigk and his coworkers all tend to contradict the earlier expressed opinion. Hence the concept of specificity may be replaced by that of an occult zoonosis. Owing to this the possibility of a number of species, including man, harboring such inapparent infections poses the question of their inimicality even in animals possessing spleens. On the question of protozoan specificity Garnham (1962) reported that *B. pitheci* of African monkeys has practically always been found after splenectomy, and suggested that the organism may be *B. divergens* of cattle—or possibly an allied species—which accidentally infected the monkey wherein a slight change in morphology occurred. Such commonly occurs when a change in host is involved.

Previously to the work of Neitz (1956) considerable divergence of opinion existed in the classification of *Babesia* spp., whereby synonyms such as *Piroplasma, Smithia, Nuttallia, Rosiella, Babesiella, Francaiella,* and so on had been proposed largely on shape, size, method of division in the red cell, and so forth. These can, however, be duplicated in many instances by strains other than those for which they are designated as having generic value. The need still remains for biological, epidemiological, pathological, and chemotherapeutical investigations on these protozoa, the results of which will probably establish the distinctiveness either of the species or of strains varying in virulence or immunogenicity.

It is relevant in the present connection to refer to the nomenclature

[1] In this paper the abbreviation *B.* always stands for *Babesia; H.,* for *Hyalomma.*

of *Babesia* species infecting bovines and equidae in Eurasia and Africa, as presently accepted. Those which have been described include the large piroplasma *B. bigemina* and four small species, namely, *B. bovis, B. major, B. divergens,* and *Babesiella berbera.* Of the small forms *B. major* is clearly differentiated morphologically, and Davies *et al.* (1958) distinguished between *B. divergens* from Britain and northern Europe and *B. bovis* from Yugoslavia. This agrees with Simitch *et al.* (1955), although earlier Simitch and Nevenitch (1953) and Sergent *et al.* (1945) had synonymized *B. bovis* and *B. divergens. B. bovis* was also synonymized with *Babesiella berbera* by Simitch *et al.* (1955).

Two species of babesias are associated with members of the family Equidae, namely, *B. caballi* (Nuttall, 1910) (= *Piroplasma caballi* Nuttall, 1910) and *Babesia equi* (Laveran, 1901) (= *Piroplasma equi* Laveran, 1901; *Nuttallia equi* Laveran, 1901; *Nuttallia asini* Dschunkowsky and Luhs, 1913; ?*Nuttallia minor* Sassuchin, 1933). Both were species with which Enigk worked intensively in Germany and Eastern Europe, but whose validity is questioned by Shortt (1962).

The ticks implicated in the transmission of these protozoa belong to the family Ixodoidea, with the exception of a suspected record of the argasid tick *Ornithodoros lahorensis* Neumann by Rastegaeva (1935) in Azerbaydzhan S.S.R. But just as there has been confusion in the nomenclature of the babesias so, too, have similar difficulties arisen in the vectors. The systematic distinctions between a number of species, as determined by earlier workers, are questionable, more particularly in respect of representatives of the genera *Dermacentor* and *Hyalomma* and with regard to the separation of *Ixodes ricinus* and *I. persulcatus* before 1934.

The presently approved species names are given in Tables I, II, and III and their synonymy in the text. The distribution data of ticks in Figs. 1, 2, 3, and 6 have been derived from a very large number of original sources, and the collection localities ascertained from the new "Times" atlas. In many instances the information on collecting sites in the original publications is insufficient, and these are omitted from the maps. Nor are duplicate records from the same locality included. But it is considered that the information is sufficient to make broad generalizations. The data for *Rhipicephalus evertsi, Boophilus decoloratus,* and *Rhipicephalus appendiculatus* in Fig. 5 are based on Theiler (1964).

TRANSMITTERS OF BOVINE PIROPLASMAS

In Table I the ixodid species implicated in the transmission of babesias to cattle, sheep, dogs, and representative species of the Equidae are presented.

TABLE I

TICK TRANSMITTERS OF EURASIATIC Babesia SPECIES

Tick species[a]	Cattle				Sheep		Equidae		Dogs
	B. divergens	B. bovis[b]	B. major	B. bigemina	B. motasi	B. ovis	B. caballi	B. equi	B. canis
I. ricinus	*	—	?	—	—	—	—	—	—
I. persulcatus	*	*	—	—	—	—	—	—	—
D. reticulatus	—	—	—	—	—	—	*	*	*
D. marginatus	—	—	—	—	*	—	*	*	*
D. silvarum	—	—	—	—	*	—	*	—	—
Haemaphysalis punctata	—	—	—	*	*	—	—	—	—
R. sanguineus	—	—	—	—	—	—	*	*	*
R. bursa	—	—	—	—	*	*	*	*	—
H. plumbeum plumbeum	—	—	—	—	—	—	*	—	*
H. excavatum	—	—	—	—	—	—	*	—	—
H. detritum scupense	—	—	—	—	—	—	*	*	—

[a] Synonymy: D. reticulatus Fabricius = D. pictus Herm. nec. D. marginatus (cf. Neitz, 1956); D. marginatus Sulzer is a valid species; H. plumbeum plumbeum = H. marginatum Koch; H. detritum scupense = H. volgense Schulze and Schlottke, 1929 = H. uralense Schulze and Schlottke, 1929.
[b] Babesiella berbera.

ECOLOGY OF IMPLICATED TICK SPECIES

Ixodes persulcatus has its eastern limit at about the longitude of Hamburg in north Germany (Fig. 1) and nowhere in Eurasia does it occur north of latitude 64°–65°N; southward in areas of continental climates it reaches to L. Balkhash, and under more maritime conditions of the east coast extends to 32°S, in the island of Kyushu (Japan). Its occurrence as a broad band across Eurasia is associated closely with the southern extension of the temperate and coniferous forests, while its northern limits

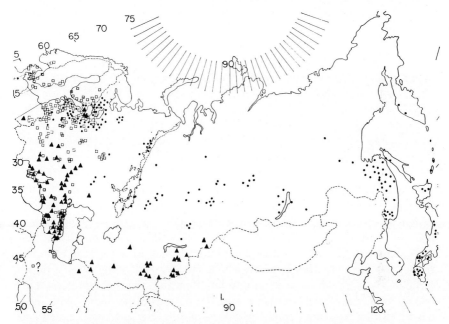

FIG. 1. The distribution of *Ixodes persulcatus* (●), *I. ricinus* (□), and *Haemaphysalis punctata* (▲) in Eurasia.

are imposed by low summer temperatures, early snowfall, the late thawing of snow, and the occurrence of tundra and pine forests growing on mire and rocky soils.

The eggs of *I. persulcatus* are the least resistant of the overwintering stages and like larvae survive the winter if the temperatures in the microhabitat do not fall below —7° to —8° C. Unfed nymphs and adults overwinter successfully if temperatures do not fall below —30° C, although engorged females are unable to survive these low temperatures. The length of the life cycle, varying from 2 to 3 years, is determined by climate.

Ixodes ricinus extends eastward to about 50°–55°E longitude (Fig. 1) and its southern boundary lies about 35°N latitude in Iran, passing westward through the mountains of Turkey, Bulgaria, Albania, Italy, Sardinia, and the Pyrenees (Fig. 2). The few available records from Spain and Portugal are questionable. Outliers occur on the coastal strip of Algeria and in Madeira, and it is reported from migrating birds in Egypt, but there is no evidence of establishment there. Westward the distribution is delimited by a north-south line from Madeira (longitude 16°E) along the western margins of the British Isles and Norway to about latitude 65°N, although some of the northernmost records may refer to *I. persulcatus*.

The ground distribution of *I. ricinus* is determined by its microclimatic requirements of saturated air (ca. 92 percent relative humidity) and the need for a temperature of 15° C for a period sufficiently long to permit development. In Britain these requirements are usually satisfied, except under marsh conditions and possibly on moss hags on the higher hill tops. The eggs and gorged stages of *I. ricinus* lose water rapidly in dry air and survive only short periods of exposure. Unfed stages lose water at the vegetation tips when questing, but generally attain equilibrium on retreating into the damp air of the vegetation layer. Death ensues when the microclimatic vapor tension falls below 80 percent at temperatures of 15° C and over for more than a fortnight. Hence the prime need is to overcome water loss, particularly in the summer, for during this period there is a lowering of the water table when evaporation from the soil cannot keep pace with the loss of water vapor from the vegetation to a macroclimate of high drying power. Consequently the humidity of the microclimate falls below saturation. Maintenance of a high relative humidity is achieved either by a thick mat of surface detritus or by a depth of field layer vegetation adequate to lengthen the moisture gradient. This occurs in field layers of woodland and scrub, in acid moorlands with moss cover, and in persistent mat vegetation associated with such species as *Nardus* and *Molinia*. More precarious survival conditions are provided by rushes, bracken, rough grazings, and deteriorating permanent pastures. Their effects are enhanced if the ground zone has a high water table as in peat soils or is sheltered from insolation by either a deep vegetation layer or canopy vegetation. The latter also provide a barrier for overwintering ticks against excessively low winter temperatures. These physiological necessities of *I. ricinus* are reflected in its European distribution for, broadly, the areas of high population correspond to those in which woodland and forest occupy more than 50 percent (cf. Fig. 6).

Ixodes persulcatus has a more northerly and easterly distribution than *I. ricinus* (Fig. 1), indicative of greater tolerance of temperature extremes and cold hardiness. Thus *I. ricinus* is unable to survive at −10° C for more than 70–80 days per annum, whilst *I. persulcatus* lives up to

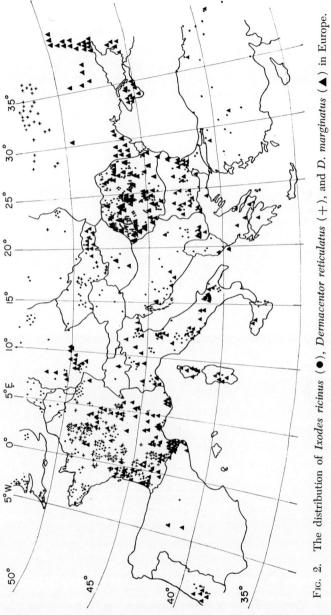

Fig. 2. The distribution of *Ixodes ricinus* (●), *Dermacentor reticulatus* (+), and *D. marginatus* (▲) in Europe.

150 days per annum under the same conditions. This does not imply that they are mutually exclusive within a broad geographical region, and there is considerable overlap at their boundaries (Fig. 1). Of interest in this connection are the distributions in the central zone of Karelo-Finnish S.S.R.; both *I. persulcatus* and *I. ricinus* infest cattle in small numbers in the vicinity of Lake Segozero, and more heavily in the western part of Medvezhlyegorsk (Fig. 3). In the eastern part of the latter and in Konopozhskiy region only *I. persulcatus* is found. In the central part of Suoyarv-

Fig. 3. The distribution of *Ixodes persulcatus* (●) and *I. ricinus* (○) in Karelo-Finnish S.S.R. (diagrammatic). N, C, S denote nothern, central, and southern zones respectively; %, infestation of stock; numbers in parentheses, number of ticks per head of stock.

skiy *I. ricinus* alone occurs. The southern zone has longer summers and more frost-free days in the autumn than do the northern and central regions, and both species are able to survive and develop, although in terms of distribution *I. ricinus* occurs almost exclusively in the western subregion and *I. persulcatus* in the eastern subregion, whilst both occur in a central subregion (Fig. 3). Distinct reproductive foci for these ticks occur (Lutta *et al.*, 1959): for *I. ricinus*, (a) the western shore of Lake Onezhskoye (Prionezhskiy region), (b) westward from Syamozero to Lake Suoyvari and north of Lake Shotozero and (c) north Priladozh'ye; and for *I. persulcatus*, (a) Pryazhinskiy, (b) Zaonezhskiy, northern part of Prionezhskiy, and southeast of Kondopozhskiy, (c) south of Pudozhskiy, and (d) southeast of Olonetskiy.

Their mosaic pattern of distribution is due to their ecological preferences. *Ixodes ricinus* occurs mainly in secondary small-leaved forests, (particularly of alder, aspen, and birch where tree felling occurs), shrub undergrowth, and pastures. *Ixodes persulcatus*, on the other hand, is associated with small-leaved forests in close juxtaposition to the primary coniferous forests, where spruce-basswood forests provide ideal conditions. Dry forests, open grassland, or marshland is quite unsuitable for this species. Primary forests no longer exist in the western subregion of the southern zone, but predominate in the eastern subregion. The central subregion is in an intermediate vegetal condition. Such biotic changes have far-reaching effects on the ecosystem, as can be illustrated by reference to a mechanical analog (Fig. 4). The disks represent factors: clockwise turn means increase. The central pulleys are the drive wheels and the peripheral pulleys are the pick-up. Z is a toothed idler wheel representing microclimate. Starting with a vegetation sere (G) involved in secondary succession, as this increases—either for natural reasons or more possibly through man's intervention—the proportion of taiga (O) must decrease necessarily, that is, the drive is toothed. Accordingly the environmental suitability for survival of *I. persulcatus* (T^1) decreases, and developing seral stages allow colonization by *I. ricinus* (T^2). If cattle (CA) are allowed to graze it they will reduce much rough cover which will also increase the number of herbivores (H). The introduction of sheep (S), which are selective feeders, permits seral development to continue in the direction of a climax, and this will increase cover for microfaunal elements such as rodents (R). Increase of herbivores and (or) rodents will augment carnivores (C), and together with cattle and (or) sheep contribute to increasing the density of *I. ricinus*. Reversion to taiga conditions implies recolonization by *I. persulcatus*.

Ixodes persulcatus and *I. ricinus* have many domestic and wild hosts in common, and the transfer of species from the habitat of one to that of

the other is possible. The role of birds in this connection has been emphasized by Russian workers in Europe and by Hoogstraal *et al.* (1963) in
Africa, although some species, for instance, *Emberiza citrinella* L. and
E. leucocephalus Gm, two bunting species, have an immunity to tick
saliva resulting in the death of immatures of *I. persulcatus* on them without feeding (Naumov, 1963). The ultimate success of such transfers from
one habitat to another depends on microclimatic conditions in the new
habitat and on the availability of suitable hosts.

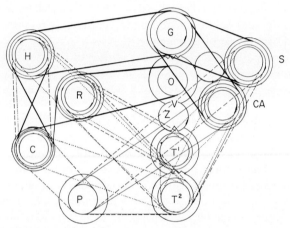

FIG. 4. Simplified diagram to illustrate the main strands of interrelationships in
the tick-vegetation-vertebrate-protozoa skein. Central pulley system represents tick
distribution in relation to vegetation in transient ecosystems (G = shrub vegetation;
O = taiga vegetation; Z = toothed idler wheel representing microclimate; $T^1 = I.$
persulcatus; $T^2 = I.$ *ricinus*). Dotted line: host relationships of ticks. Thick line:
distribution of wild hosts in relation to vegetation together with the territorial relationships of wild and domestic hosts (for explanation, see text). Dashed line: distribution of protozoa to their tick and wild vertebrate hosts. Solid line: distribution
of protozoa to their tick and domestic vertebrate hosts (indicated only for T_2 and CA).

   The overlap of bovine piroplasma-bearing ticks is nowhere better seen
than in South Africa. The larvae and nymphs of *Rhipicephalus evertsi
evertsi* feed on one host, with the engorged nymph detaching itself and
molting on the ground. The adults then feed on a second host. All stages
infest domestic or wild herbivores, particularly mules, donkeys, and wild
zebras, but adults commonly occur on domestic cattle, goats, and sheep.
Atypically the immature stages parasitize hares, elephant shrews, and
tree rats, but reasons for such outbreaks are unknown. *Rhipicephalus
evertsi evertsi* is widely distributed in the Ethiopian faunal region and
in South Africa is present regardless of altitude and frost, or summer or

TABLE II

Tick Transmitters of Bovine and Equine Piroplasmosis in Africa

Tick species	B. bigemina	B. bovis	B. caballi	B. equi
Boophilus decoloratus	✲	—	—	—
Rhipicephalus bursa	✲	—	—	—
Rhipicephalus appendiculatus	✲	—	—	—
Rhipicephalus evertsi evertsi	✲	✲	—	✲
Boophilus calcaratus	✲	✲	—	—
Hyalomma dromedarii	—	—	✲ a	✲ a

a Experimental transmission only.

winter rainfall, and its essential requirement in grassy areas is an annual rainfall of 10 inches (Fig. 5). The allied subspecies *mimeticus* replaces it in drier areas, as in Southwest Africa for example, but where vegetation does not form a grassy covering and rainfall ranges from 12 to 15 inches *R. evertsi evertsi* still manages to find a foothold. Dew at night

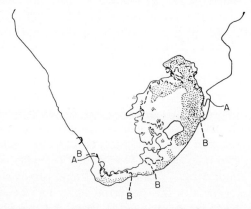

Fig. 5. The distribution of *Rhipicephalus appendiculatus* (stippled), *R. evertsi evertsi* (A-A), and *Boophilus decoloratus* (B-B) in the Republic of South Africa (after Theiler, 1964).

is a factor which prevents this and other species from critical water loss over several months, particularly in the larval stage. Where it extends into the deserts of the northern province (Kenya), the forested savannah and semidesert of the Sudan and the dry areas of Masai territory, that is, parts of Africa warmer than South Africa, a somewhat higher critical rainfall is necessary for its maintenance.

Boophilus decoloratus—a one host tick—occurs widely in most of the Ethiopian area, where a fair degree of shade and humidity is present, but is absent in open dry areas and in tropical forests. It is a more hygrophilous species than *R. evertsi evertsi* and does not reach as far west as the latter. The critical rainfall level for *Boophilus decoloratus* is 15 inches annually in the eastern half of South Africa, but in Southwest Africa these requirements are higher, possibly because of its erratic nature over long periods of time. In West Africa the isohyetal lines run parallel from east to west with the arid regions to the north; *Boophilus decoloratus* in most abundant south of the 20-inch isohyet, and occasionally between 10 and 20 inches. Most of the published information on hosts relates to cattle, although horses, sheep, and goats are parasitized to a lesser degree.

The allied *Boophilus annulatus* occurs south of the 30-inch isohyet in West Africa, extending into central Africa and certain parts of the southern Sudan near the periphery of East African biotic provinces. Brumpt (1920) and Sergent *et al.* (1945) referred to this species as *Boophilus calcaratus,* both implicating it in the transmission of *Babesia bigemina,* and the latter, of *Babesiella berbera.* The disease relationships and ecology of this tick in Africa are barely studied and are not dealt with further here. *Rhipicephalus appendiculatus,* a third transmitter of *B. bigemina,* reaches its northern limit in southern Sudan and southern Ethiopia and reaches into South Africa to just south of Pretoria, beyond which it has a coastal distribution. It is absent from areas lacking shrub cover, in deserts, and is probably absent in West Africa; its microhabitat is associated with tall grass and trees and where rainfall is over 30 inches, as in East Africa, is found between 4800 and 7500 feet. Whilst it is a three-host tick, it can produce either a single generation a year, corresponding to a single rainy season each year (Malawi), two or three generations a year where there are two rainy seasons (Kenya and Uganda), and two generations a year in South Africa. This implies a rapid turnover of tick populations. Cattle are generally the preferred hosts for the adults although other domestic hosts are parasitized. Larvae and nymphs may feed on these hosts and occasionally on cane rats and hares. The spatial overlap of the three species on South Africa (Fig. 5) suggests a reinforcing mechanism of infection by *B. bigemina* which should maintain it at a high rate in cattle. This mechanism is enhanced by the fact that all three aforementioned species transmit transovarially and can occur concurrently on the same host. Large numbers of *R. appendiculatus* are found on cattle, most commonly near the ear, although in cases of very heavy infestations they are present in fewer numbers around the base of the horns, eyelids, cheek, neck, tip of the tail, udders, scrotum, vulva, anus, and flanks. Immature stages of *R. evertsi* lie deeper in the ear and those of *Boophilus decoloratus* along the edge of the ear. Such an association doubtless increases the cross infection potential between the three species.

The vector involved in transmitting *B. major* in Eurasia is unknown, although the protozoan occurs in Yugoslavia. The somewhat doubtful occurrence of *B. bigemina* in Europe has been reported by Knuth and by Zeller and Helm, both quoted by Neitz (1956), and the vector given as *Haemaphysalis punctata*. This tick species is adapted to open terrain and has a southerly distribution in Europe (Fig. 1). It impinges on the south coast of the British Isles and has been found on exposed areas such as cliff tops. No detailed information is available on its incidence in any area of Britain and the possibility of incidental carriage by migrant birds cannot be entirely disregarded.

DISCUSSION—RELATION TO PROTOZOAL INFECTION AND TRANSMISSION

There are many references in the literature to transmission of *Babesia bovis* to cattle by *I. ricinus* but the specific identity of the piroplasma in most cases is dubious (Kossel *et al.*, 1904; Petrov, 1941; Polyanskii and Kheisin, 1959; Sudachenkov, 1941). Joyner *et al.* (1963) succeeded in transmitting *B. divergens* through larvae of *I. ricinus,* which is in agreement with Kossel *et al.* (1904), probably with the same piroplasma, and with Sudachenkov (1941) using the babesia *Babesiella bovis,* although not all females produced infective larvae. All three demonstrated nymphal transmission, but Sudachenkov and Joyner *et al.* reported that neither larval nor nymphal stages picked up the infection. This does not preclude the possibility of "pick-up" of infection by larvae or nymphs and delay of transmission until the immature stages of the next generation.

Transovarial and experimental transmissions of *Babesiella bovis* by larvae, nymphs, and adults of *I. persulcatus* were demonstrated by Sudachenkov (1937, 1941) and isolated cases of spontaneous babesiasis in *I. persulcatus*-infested localities have been reported (Khodakovskii, 1939; Sudachenkov, 1941; Chizh, 1939, 1949). Reservations on this issue are made by Lutta and Kheisin (1954), who state that babesiasis in the northwest of the Soviet Union occurs in spring and autumn in *I. ricinus*-infested areas and where it coexists with *I. persulcatus*. Since *I. ricinus* has a bimodal curve of seasonal activity in this area and *I. persulcatus* occurs only in spring, it seems by inference that *I. ricinus* is the likely transmitter. Further, they contend that infection in northern areas of *I. persulcatus* is low when compared with the incidence in comparable *I. ricinus* areas. Nevertheless, in more southerly areas where conditions favor the transmission of babesias by *I. ricinus,* the taiga tick, *I. persulcatus,* also transmits. Possibly toward the extreme northern limits of distribution, development of the piroplasma in the tick may be inhibited by low temperatures. Temperature had no effect upon the ability of *I. ricinus* to acquire or transmit *Babesiella bovis* according to Sudachenkov (1941), but differences of 2°C (that is, from 16°–18°C to 18°–20°C)

74 DON R. ARTHUR

delayed the appearance of the maximal number of developmental stages by 18–24 days in the same species in experiments by Polyanskii and Kheisin (1959). *Babesia bigemina* in one-host boophilid ticks is influenced by environmental temperatures and its transmission to cattle occurs only if the ambient temperatures rise above 29°C, although they remain infected irrespective of external factors (Rosenbusch and Gonzales, 1923). Their development in fully engorged ticks is inhibited if maintained continuously at 20°C, but infective forms are produced at 28°C. On the contrary, larvae held at a temperature of 5°C for 7–14 days were able to transmit *B. bigemina*. Field observations where the grass temperature approaches 5°–10°C indicate little or no development of the parasites within the tick, but those already present in larvae survive (Riek, 1964). Thus temperature effects not only influence development, survival, and behavior of all tick stages, but also the rate of development of the protozoa within their tissues, but not seemingly their survival. External temperatures also influence the transmissibility of pathogens to their vertebrate hosts by ticks.

Apparent infections of bovine piroplasms are readily recognized and Rosenbusch (1927) stated that transmission to cattle was incidental and not indispensable to the developmental cycle. Since transovarial transmission of *B. divergens* (Joyner *et al.*, 1963), *Babesiella bovis* (Sudachenkov, 1941), and *B. bigemina* (Neitz, 1956; Riek, 1964) has been demonstrated experimentally in a number of ticks it appears that these arthropods are their natural reservoirs. *Boophilus* lost infection with *B. bigemina* and *B. argentina* when reared on hosts other than cattle (Brumpt, 1920) but the more recent studies indicate that under natural conditions *Babesia* spp. are hereditarily transmitted when infected ticks are reared on refractory hosts. Inapparent infections of *B. bigemina* in sheep, a goat, and a horse infected with *Boophilus microplus* carrying this parasite were obtained by Callow (1962) but the tick progeny from goat and sheep were infective when applied to susceptible cattle. The possibility of adult ticks becoming infected in the field from subclinical infection in the unnatural host (Callow, 1962) is very possible in one-host ticks but less likely in three-host ticks. Nevertheless it must be recognized that the build-up of infective ticks, of domestic stock, and other wild fauna, will increase both apparent and inapparent protozoal populations.

The epizootiology of the disease has certain unexplained characteristics. Bovine blood continues to be infective long after subsidence of the clinical reaction, and since infection is egg-borne from one tick generation to the next, or hereditarily transmitted or subclinically acquired, expectedly in areas other than those of very recent infection, practically every tick on the pasture should be infected. Under such conditions epizootic disease should be rare, because the normal calf is tolerant and premunition established by its inapparent or benign first infection should be maintained indefinitely by superinfection. Yet outbreaks of clinical disease still occur (MacLeod, 1962).

Very few individuals in populations of *I. ricinus* taken from carrier animals are infected with *B. bovis* (Sudachenkov, 1941) and appear to be similar to infections of *Boophilus microplus* with *B. bigemina* (Riek, 1964). This has been attributed to the small number of suitably developed protozoal forms in bovine erythrocytes infective to the tick vector. The males of some genera (for example, *Ixodes*) do not feed, but those of others (including *Hyalomma, Dermacentor,* and *Boophilus*) do so in order to complete spermatogenesis, but we have no information on the role of males as transmitters of protozoa, either by feeding or by transference along with sperm. Now the majority of parasites ingested by ticks die (Dennis, 1932; Regendanz and Reichenow, 1933; Regendanz, 1936; Muratov and Kheisin, 1959; Polyanskii and Kheisin, 1959) and only a small proportion undergoes further development. To what extent this may be linked with the sex of the adults or the potential sex of larvae and nymphs has never been analyzed critically. Recent work in my department (Arthur and Snow, 1966) has shown that larvae and nymphs of ixodid ticks destined to become either males or females display different physiological feeding patterns. Hence the possibility of genetical factors either inhibiting development or increasing lysis of the protozoa in the "male" line should not be ignored in our present state of knowledge, for such a process, coupled with the work of Riek (1964), may partially explain the low natural infection rate of immature ticks with bovine babesias.

TRANSMITTERS OF EQUINE PIROPLASMAS

Neitz (1956) gave nine tick vectors of *Babesia caballi* and *B. equi* which, in the light of more recent taxonomic findings, have been renamed or synonymized as follows: *Dermacentor reticulatus* Fabricius (= *D. pictus* Herm); *Dermacentor marginatus* Sulzer (not a synonym of *D. reticulatus*); *Dermacentor silvarum* Olenev; *Rhipicephalus bursa* Canestrini and Fanzago; *Rhipicephalus sanguineus* (Latreille); *Hyalomma plumbeum plumbeum* (= *H. marginatum* Koch, and as in Neitz, 1956, = *detritum* of Delpy, *marginatum* of Feldman-Muhsam, and *H. marginatum* of Enigk, 1951); *Hyalomma excavatum* (= *H. anatolicum* Koch, of Neitz, 1956); *Hyalomma detritum scupense* (= *H. uralense* Schulze and Schlottke, cited by Neitz, 1956, and corrected to *H. detritum* by Delpy; = *H. volgense* cited by Neitz, 1956).

The individual vectors—all representatives of the genera *Hyalomma*, *Dermacentor*, and *Rhipicephalus*—for both babesias are given in Table I.

ECOLOGY OF IMPLICATED TICK SPECIES

Dermacentor marginatus is a western Eurasiatic species (Figs 2, 6) which also occurs rarely in Algeria, Morocco, Tunisia, and the Canary Islands and is present in the near east in Afghanistan, Iran, and Turkey. Eastward its limits are at about 85°E longitude and 60°N latitude. The closely allied *D. reticulatus* has been reported slightly further east (95°E longitude and 60°N latitude), but not in appreciable numbers.

Dermacentor reticulatus predominates north of 45°N latitude, with a broad southern extension along the west coast of France and on the French side of the Pyrenees. Its microhabitat is associated with primitive forests and its absence from Germany and Poland and occurrence in France are probably due to this. Survival is possible only in the protected conditions of the thick layer of plant litter, associated with mixed steppes and forests, maintaining a high relative humidity and a barrier against the inimical effects of temperature extremes. Thus unfed females can overwinter successfully at —42°F in January, at the bases of grasses and trees. Its range is determined by 400–1000 mm of rain annually and with average July temperatures of 60°–70° F.

Dermacentor marginatus is less hygrophilic than *D. reticulatus*, being found where the minimal annual rainfall is 200 mm, and average July temperatures 60°–80° F, with a preference toward the upper end of the scale. This explains its more southerly extension into the subtropical conditions of the Mediterranean area (Figs. 2, 6), its survival in more exposed formations, including herbaceous, bushy, and shrub vegetation, and its maintenance of a position on vegetation tips at temperatures which are inhibitory to *D. reticulatus*, that is, the temperature threshold of activity for *D. reticulatus* is lower than that for *D. marginatus*. Moreover, the relative humidity for the normal existence of the latter corresponds to that of the maximum for the former. Hence in temperate Europe, where the two species coexist, their environmental responses result in their being active at different times of the day. As in *I. persulcatus* and *I. ricinus*, their localized distribution in terms of overlap and mosaic are determined by microhabitats and this transition is illustrated in the Omsk region, by Alfianov and Netsky (1954). In the marshy taiga *I. persulcatus* is dominant (98.3%), with *D. reticulatus* (1.7%), but in secondary aspen birch forests there is a complete reversal of dominance, *D. reticulatus* being 95.8% and *I. persulcatus* some 2.9%, and further south on open steppe *D. marginatus* (97.6%) assumes dominance over *D. reticulatus* (2.4%). At intermediate points through the northern forest steppes and southern forest steppes, the respective percentage occurrence of *D. reticulatus* and *D. marginatus* is 76.7% and 23.3%; 16.2% and 83.8%.

Dermacentor silvarum, a third *Dermacentor* species implicated, is an eastern Asiatic form, occurring in the Primor territory, Amur, eastern Transbaikal, the vicinity of Irkutsk, Kemerov Province, and the eastern

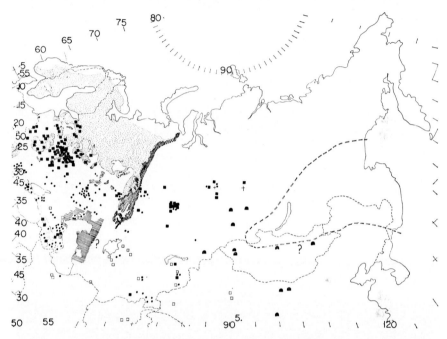

FIG. 6. The distribution of *Dermacentor reticulatus* (■), *D. marginatus* (●), *D. niveus* (□), and *D. nuttalli* (◢) in Eurasia. The possible range of *D. silvarum* is indicated by a broken line. Stippled area in Europe represents more than 50% wooded; horizontal lines represent arid areas; vertical lines represent Ural mountains.

Altai in Russia, and in Northern Mongolia (Fig. 6). Owing to misidentification this tick has been given a much wider geographical range than is really so. It is found in secondary bush country, and in a focus divorced from other known vectors of equine piroplasms.

Rhipicephalus sanguineus is probably one of the most widespread species in the world and inhabits practically all countries between 50°N and about 35°S. It is present everywhere in Africa except possibly under the most extreme conditions of the great deserts of northern and southwestern Africa, and perhaps in a few of the more isolated oases. It abounds in the mediterranean zone and in the Carpathio-Altaique steppes. In middle

Europe it is associated with litter in the temperate oak zone, as in many of the large towns of France. It is present in Bulgaria, Yugoslavia, and Rumania, Azerbaydzhan, Transcaucasia, and the Crimea. *Rhipicephalus bursa*, shown by Enigk (1943) to be an experimental vector of *B. caballi*, is a mediterranean species ranging into Palestine, Rumania, Turkey, and thence to Transcaucasia, the Crimea, and the Volga. In Africa it extends to Kenya, and is the most prevalent tick in Algeria, where it transmits *B. bigemina*. Its unfed stages live at the bases of herbaceous or bushy vegetation in either exposed or semiexposed sites, particularly in the mediterranean maquis; on dry steppes it lives in shrubby or bushwood formations where very localized relative humidities permit; in temperate Europe survival is possibly only where the relative humidity is high. Both these rhipicephalines thus overlap in their distribution with *D. marginatus* in southern Eurasia, and in part at least along the northern fringe of North Africa.

Vectors of the genus *Hyalomma* still pose problems of synonymy and nomenclature (Table III) because of their high degree of intraspecific variability.

Hyalomma plumbeum plumbeum is present north of the Caspian Sea, along the lower reaches of the Volga, in the Caucasus, and the Crimea. It has also infiltrated into the cultivated areas of the Nile delta, the Euphrates, and the Tigris. In the Caucasus a variety of microhabitats are occupied, it being abundant at 400–500 meters and higher altitudes (900–1000 meters). Most available biotopes, except the coniferous forests and the deserts, carry this species in the Crimea, whilst Feider *et al.* (1957) report it from sea level to 1000 meters in Rumania, inhabiting steppes, mixed brushland, and the oak forest zone. Sclerophyllous and steppe vegetation provide suitable microhabitat conditions in the mediterranean region and in the semidesert steppe of the near east. It is a two-host tick whose larvae and nymphs feed on one host and the adults on another.

The taxonomic status of *H. anatolicum*, referred to by Enigk (1943), is considered to be *H. excavatum* by Delpy (1949) and Feldman-Muhsam (1954), (cited by Neitz, 1956). The nomenclature, however, still remains controversial and in the present paper it is referred to by the latter name. It is common in Egypt, Palestine, and Asia Minor, and extends through South Russia to India; in southern Europe it is local and abundant in Greece and Maghreb. Being a xerically adapted species the association is with Mediterranean steppes, the semi-desert steppes of the Sahara and the Mediterranean, the Saharan desert steppes, and the tropical arabian persian steppes where it is localized in oases. Usually it is excluded from forested zones. The upper altitude limit is inversely proportional to the humidity and the amount of rainfall, and directly

TABLE III

Synonymy of European *Hyalomma* spp. Transmitting Equine Piroplasmosis

Original reference as a vector	Delpy, 1949	Delpy, 1952	Feldman-Muhsam, 1954	Accepted synonym in this paper
Hyalomma anatolicum Koch (Enigk, 1943)	*H. excavatum*	—	*H. excavatum*	*H. excavatum*
Hyalomma marginatum Koch (Enigk, 1943)	—	*H. detritum*	*H. marginatum*	*H. plumbeum plumbeum*
Hyalomma volgense Schulze and Schlottke (Enigk, 1944)	—	—	—	*H. detritum scupense*
Hyalomma uralense Schulze and Schlottke (Enigk, 1944)	*H. detritum*	—	—	*H. detritum scupense*

proportional to the height of the snow line during the summer. Hence it occurs in pastures at 6500 ft and at similar heights in Sinai, Yemen, Anatolia, and Eritrea. *Hyalomma excavatum* parasitizes a wide range of animals, but greatest population densities are associated with domestic stock.

Hyalomma detritum scupense, the third *Hyalomma* species implicated, is a one-host tick. It, too, is a southern form, being reported in the steppes and forests up to the 850 meters in Transcaucasia, and is common on deer and cattle in inhabited and cultivated areas on the forest edge at all altitudes in the Crimea, becoming more widespread in the dense undergrowth of valleys and in clearings in beech and oak associations. In central Asia thicket-covered steppes are the preferred microhabitat and because of its cold tolerance it replaces *H. detritum detritum,* which is more common in arid areas.

DISCUSSION—RELATION TO PROTOZOAL INFECTION AND TRANSMISSION

A consideration of the data makes it evident that south of the 45°–50°N latitude there is considerable overlap of *D. marginatus, H. excavatum, H. plumbeum plumbeum, H. detritum scupense, Rhipicephalus sanguineus,* and *R. bursa,* although doubtless each will occupy regions within its broad range according to the suitability of local microclimatic conditions and the availability of hosts. Coexistence of *D. reticulatus* with *Rhipicephalus* and *Hyalomma* species is restricted to high-altitude localities in the Crimea, Georgia, Armenia, Azerbaydzhan, Turkmen, Alma Alta, and Kirgiz, whereas north of about 43°N latitude there is a broad front of overlap of *D. reticulatus, D. marginatus* (Figs. 2, 6) and *R. sanguineus.* The successful transfer of ticks from one focus to another by vertebrates has been referred to earlier (p. 69). Such migrations enhance inapparent infections of wild hosts with *B. caballi* and *B. equi* and may extend the range of piroplasmosis for, as Enigk (1951) reported, the protozoa resist thermal deviations without loss of infective power.

The incidence of piroplasmosis in the Equidae, as in other domestic stock, is related too to the seasonal occurrence of feeding ticks on the host. Thus Enigk (1944) reported that *H. detritum scupense* (= *H. volgense*) parasitizes stock in winter and the seasonal incidence of piroplasmosis coincides with this although, as Enigk points out, temperature activation of other species brought into the stalls with hay may have induced this condition.

Babesia equi has been transmitted transovarially under experimental conditions by *H. excavatum, R. bursa,* and *H. detritum scupense* (Enigk, 1943, 1944) while under similar conditions only stage-to-stage passage has been demonstrated in *D. reticulatus, D. marginatus, R. sanguineus,* and

H. plumbeum plumbeum. Of these, both *Dermacentor* species and *R. sanguineus* are three-host ticks, *H. excavatum* may operate either as a two- or a three-host tick, *H. plumbeum* and *R. bursa* are two-host ticks, and *H. detritum scupense* is a one-host form. As already indicated under bovine piroplasmosis, ticks which transmit transovarially probably are reservoirs for the babesias, but those unable to do so require an alternative source of primary infection. Of these species the immature stages of *D. reticulatus, D. marginatus, H. plumbeum plumbeum,* and *H. excavatum* feed on rodents under natural conditions. *Rhipicephalus sanguineus* does so in varying degrees whilst the remainder feed on the same hosts as do their adults, in the case of one-host ticks, or ruminants other than equidae when they are two-host ticks. Hence, ticks feeding on three hosts could acquire such an infection as either larvae or nymphs from rodents and (or) insectivores and transmit either as nymphs or adults, when they could either infect new rodent hosts or representatives of the Equidae which they parasitized.

What sort of evidence do we have for this possibility? Shortt (1962) reported that very many species of rodents and insectivores harbor piroplasmas and that insectivores, for example, are hosts to one or more species of *Babesia.* Amongst domestic animals division of babesias to produce the "Maltese" cross is limited to *B. equi,* but it also occurs in *B. microtia* (= *Smithia microti*) in field mice, in *B.* (*Smithia*) *talpae* in the mole, and in *B.* (*Rosiella*) *rossi* in the jackal (Neitz, 1956). In syringe passage the "cross" pattern in *B. microtia* and in *B. rodhaini* has been established (Nowell, 1966), occurring with binary dividing forms.

Since (a) these rodent babesias conform to the comparable multiplicative pattern in *B. equi* and thus are phylogenetically closer to the latter than to those of other domestic hosts and (b) at least four of the seven implicated species feed on rodents or insectivores in their immature stages and natural transovarial transmission has yet to be demonstrated in them, the question of either rodents and (or) insectivores as sources of primary infection cannot be entirely disregarded. The situation in northern Europe and Russia is apposite in this connection. Enigk (1951) has shown that *Hyalomma* species are thermo- and xerophilous and reach their northernmost extension at 44°N latitude: *R. bursa* essentially belongs to warm climes, but being more hygrophilic extends a degree or so further north. Thus all the known transovarially transmitting species of *B. equi* do not extend beyond 45°N. But *B. equi* infections have been reported north of this by Pomerantzev and Matikashvih (1940), Zasukhin (1935), Pomerantzev (1950), and Enigk (1944). In these cases *D. reticulatus* and *D. marginatus,* as well as *D. niveus* and *D. nuttalli* are implicated. The two latter species, like the two former, feed in their immature stages on rodents and (or) insectivores and since transovarial transmission is not recorded, the feasibility of a wild host reservoir for *B. equi* requires investigation. Enigk (1943) has implicated *Hyalomma dromedarii* in the experimental transmission of *B. equi* and *B. caballi,* although Hoogstraal (1956) makes no reference to transmission under natural conditions in Africa.

ACKNOWLEDGMENT

The author is indebted to the trustees of the Wellcome Foundation for financial assistance in this inquiry.

REFERENCES

Alifanov, V. I., and Netsky, G. I. (1954). Ixodoidea ticks of the Omsk region. *Med. Parazitol. i Parazitarn. Bolezni* **23**, 270-271.

Arthur, D. R., and Snow, K. (1966). The significance of size in immature stages of the Ixodoidea. *Parasitology.* In press.

Brumpt, E. (1920). Les piroplasmes des bovidés et leurs hôtes vecteurs. *Bull. Soc. Pathol. Exotique* **13**, 416-460.

Callow, L. L. (1962). Studies on the infectivity of *Babesia bigemina* and *B. argentina.* Ph.D. Thesis, University of Queensland, Brisbane (cited by Riek, 1964).

Chizh, A. (1939). Piroplasmosis of cattle in Karelian ASSR. *Tr. Leningr. Piroplasmosis Sta.,* 1 (cited by Lutta and Kheisin, 1954).

Chizh, A. (1949). *Babesiasis of cattle.* Sel'khozgiz (Agricultural State Publishing House) (cited by Lutta and Kheisin, 1954).

Davies, S. F. M., Joyner, L. P., and Kendall, S. B. (1958). Studies on *Babesia divergens* (McFadyean and Stockman, 1911). *Ann. Trop. Med. Parasitol.* **52**, 206-215.

Delpy, L. P. (1949). Révision par des voies expérimentales du genre *Hyalomma* C. L. Koch 1844 (part 2). *Ann. Parasitol.,* **24**, 97-109.

Delpy, L. P. (1952). Role des *Hyalomma* dans la transmission de la theileriose bovine. Biologie et taxonomie des espèces en cause. *Rep. 14th Intern. Vet. Congr. London* 1949, **2**, 89-94.

Dennis, E. W. (1932). The life cycle of *Babesia bigemina* (Smith and Kilbourne) of Texas cattle fever in the tick *Margaropus annulatus* (Say). *Univ. Calif. (Berkeley) Publ. Zool.* **38**, 263-298.

Donatien, A., and Lestoquard, F. (1930). De la classification des piroplasmes des animaux domestiques. *Rec. Med. Vet. Exotique* **3**, 5.

Enigk, K. (1943). Überträger der Pferdepiroplasmose, ihre Verbreitung und Biologie. *Arch. Wiss. Prakt. Tierheilk.* **78**, 209-240.

Enigk, K. (1944). Weitere Untersuchungen Überträgerfrage der Pferdepiroplasmose. *Arch. Wiss. Prakt. Tierheilk.* **79**, 58-80.

Enigk, K. (1951). Der Einfluss des Klimas auf das Auftreten der Pferdepiroplasmosen. *Z. Tropenmed. Parasitol.* **2**, 401-410.

Feider, Z., Rauchbach, C., and Mironescu, I. (1957). Die Zecken der Rumänischen Volksrepublik. *Cesk. parasitol.,* **5**, 71-87.

Feldman-Muhsam, B. (1954). Revision of the genus *Hyalomma.* 1. Description of Koch's types. *Bull. Res. Council Israel,* **4**, 150-170.

Garnham, P. C. C. (1962). Discussion in "Aspects of disease transmission by ticks." *Symp. Zool. Soc. London* **6**, 257-258.

Garnham, P. C. C., and Bray, R. S. (1959). The susceptibility of higher primates to piroplasms. *J. Protozool.* **6**, 352-355.

Hoogstraal, H. (1956). *African Ixodoidea*, 1. Ticks of the Sudan. Res. Rept. N.M. 005,050,29. *U. S. Naval Med. Res. Unit Cairo* No. 3.

Hoogstraal, H., Kaiser, M. N., Traylor, M. N., Guindy, E., and Gaber, S. (1963). Ticks (Ixodidae) on birds migrating from Europe and Asia to Africa, 1959-1961. *Bull. World Health Organ.* **28**, 235-262.

Joyner, L. P., Davies, S. F. M., and Kendall, S. B. (1963). The experimental transmission of *Babesia divergens* by *Ixodes ricinus*. *Exptl. Parasitol.* **14**, 367-373.

Khodakovskii, A. (1939). Contribution to the ecology of the pasture tick *Ixodes persulcatus* applicable to conditions of the Belozersk area. *Tr. Leningr. Piroplasmosis Sta.*, **1** (cited by Lutta and Kheisin, 1954).

Kossel, H., Schütz, W., Weber, A., and Miessner, H. (1904). Uber die Haemogloburine der Rinder in Deutschland. *Arb. Kaiser Gesundh.*, **20**, 1-77.

Lutta, A. S., and Kheisin, E. M. (1954). Certain data of the relative role of different species of Ixodid ticks in spreading babesiasis in the north. *Zool. Zh.* **33**, 65-68.

Lutta, A. S., Kheisin, E. M., and Shul'man, R. E. (1959). On the distribution of ixodid ticks in Karelia. *Tr. Karel'sk. Filiala Akad. Nauk SSSR* **14**, 72-83.

MacLeod, J. (1962). Ticks and disease in domestic stock in Great Britain. *Symp. Zool. Soc. London* **6**, 29-50.

Muratov, E. A., and Kheisin, E. M. (1959). *Zool. Zh.* **38**, 970-986 (cited by Riek, 1964).

Naumov, R. L. (1963). Whether the taiga tick feeds on yellow and pine buntings *Emberiza citrinella* L. and *E. leucocephalus* Gm? *Zool. Zh.* **42**, 513-517.

Neitz, W. O. (1956). Classification, transmission, and biology of piroplasms of domestic animals. *Ann. N. Y. Acad. Sci.* **64**, 56-111.

Nowell, F. (1966). Unpublished data.

Petrov, V. G. (1941). The development of the piroplasm *Babesiella bovis* in the tick *Ixodes ricinus* L. and the method of examining ticks for its presence. *3rd Soveschch. Parasitol. Probl.*, 29-31.

Polyanskii, Y. I., and Kheisin, E. M. (1959). *Tr. Karel'sk. Filiala Akad. Nauk SSSR* **14**, 5-13 (cited by Riek, 1964).

Pomerantzev, B. I. (1950). Fauna of the USSR Arachnida. *Akad. Nauk SSSR* **4**, 1-224.

Pomerantzev, B. I., and Matikashvih, N. V. (1940). An ecological and faunistic outline of ixodid ticks occurring in Transcaucasia. *Parazitol. Sb. Akad. Nauk SSSR, Zool. Inst.* **7**, 100-133.

Rastegaeva, E. F. (1935). Un nouveau vecteur dans la transmission des hemoparasites des animaux domestiques: *Ornithodoros lahorensis* Neum, 1908. *Bull. Soc. Pathol. Exotique* **29**, 250-258.

Regendanz, P. (1936). Ueber den Entwicklungsgang von *Babesia bigemina* in der Zecke *Boophilus microplus*. *Zentr. Bakteriol., Parasitenk., Abt. I. Orig.* **137**, 423-428.

Regendanz, P., and Reichenow, E. (1933). Die Entwicklung von *Babesia canis* in *Dermacentor reticulatus*. *Arch. Protistenk.* **79**, 50-71.

Riek, R. F. (1964). The life cycle of *Babesia bigemina* (Smith and Kilbourne, 1893) in tick vector *Boophilus microplus* (Canestrini). *Australian J. Agri. Res.* **15**, 802-821.

Rosenbusch, F. (1927). *Rev. Univ. Buenos Aires* **5**, 863-867 (cited by Riek, 1964).

Rosenbusch, F., and Gonzales, R. (1923). *Rev. Med. Vet. Buenos Aires* **6**, 683-703 (cited by Riek, 1964).

Sergent, E., Donatien, A., Parrot, L., and Lestoquard, F. (1945). Études sur les piroplasmoses bovines. Alger. 816 pp.

Shortt, H. E. (1962). Ticks and piroplasms in "Aspects of disease transmission by ticks." *Symp. Zool. Soc. London* **6**, 157-174.

Simitch, T., and Nevenitch, V. (1953). *Babesiella bovis* (Babès, 1888) et *Babesiella berbera* Sergent, Donatien, Parrot, Plantureux et Rougebief, 1924, sont-ils synonymes? *Arch. Inst. Pasteur Algerie* **31**, 91.

Simitch, T., Petrovitch, T., and Rakovec, S. (1955). Les espèces de *Babesiella* du boeuf d'Europe. *Arch. Inst. Pasteur Algerie* **33**, 310.

Skrabalo, Z., and Deanovic, Z. (1957). Piroplasmosis in man. *Doc. Med. Geograph. Trop.* **9**, 11-16.

Sudachenkov, V. V. (1937). The role of *Ixodes persulcatus* P. Sch. in the transmission of bovine babesiellosis. *Sov. Vet.* **3**, 80-81.

Sudachenkov, V. V. (1941). Expérience de transmission de la babesiéllose bovine. *Nauk Vet.* **19**, 75-85.

Theiler, G. (1964). Ecogeographical aspects of tick distribution. *In* "Ecological Studies in Southern Africa" (D. H. S. Davis, ed.), pp. 284-300.

Zasukhin, D. N. (1935). "Ticks and the Problem of the Control of Piroplasmosis of Horses" (I. Saratov, ed.), 2nd ed., pp. 1-159.

Discussion

Dr. R. F. Riek: In view of what you say concerning the transmission of *Babesia equi* from rodents to horses, does not this invalidate the concept that babesias are essentially forms which occur in the tick?

Prof. Arthur: On the available circumstantial evidence it would appear that rodents may well be the reservoir for *B. equi,* for all the known transmitters in Eurasia at least do feed on rodents and (or) insectivores in their immature stages and on domestic stock as adults. When this is coupled with the possibility that certain established babesias, for example, *B. microtia* and *B. rhodiani,* are confined to rodents in natural conditions, and since these two species divide in the same way as does *B. equi,* the question of synonymy arises. But until we look at the problem as a whole I think it injudicious to state that babesias had their origin in ticks. This is substantiated by the fact that syringe passage of babesias in vertebrate hosts is possible without the intervention of ticks.

Development of Parasitic Stages of Nematodes

Gilbert F. Otto

Abbott Laboratories, North Chicago, Illinois

INTRODUCTION

One could dispose of this subject in its simplest form by noting that the normal process of infection is initiated with the second- or third-stage larvae, the so-called infective larvae, which progress successively through three or two additional molts, respectively, to the adults. This is the characteristic pattern for those nematodes that are acquired by the definitive host from the environment in the free-living state either by skin penetration or by ingestion, where the infective larva is the third stage. This appears to be equally true of those nematodes that are acquired by the definitive host from an intermediate host either through direct inoculation (and I use the term inoculation loosely) or by ingestion of the intermediate host. For those nematodes that establish in the definitive host when their embryonated eggs are ingested, the common pattern is for one molt to occur in the egg so that the resulting second-stage larvae hatch and may be termed the infective larvae. However, according to Chandler *et al.* (1941), Chitwood has found two molts in the egg of at least one such species, namely, *Enterobius vermicularis*. This opens up an interesting item for speculation. It may well be that in the evolution of parasitism the third-stage larvae is basically the infective stage for the definitive host. Thus the first two stages including the second molt to the third stage would be expected to take place in the egg, the external environment, or the intermediate host. It would be in keeping with this concept to find that in a well-established one-host species the first two molts must take place either in the egg, as in *Enterobius vermicularis,* or in the free-living environment after hatching, as in *Ancylostoma duodenale.* Such a form as *Ascaris lumbricoides* would be considered to be intermediate in its evolution from the two-host to the one-host cycle, with only one molt in the egg and the second stage penetrating the biological equivalent of the intermediate host and molting

85

to the third stage during its migration to its definitive site in the alimentary canal.

I would like to consider the role of the developing stages in relation to the host injury. Although I shall touch on the host immunological responses, I shall not develop the strictly immunological aspects since these are developed elsewhere in the chapter by Soulsby in this volume.

One approach is to consider the normal host for the parasite as the completely susceptible host, the host of a species which is accessible and acceptable to any given parasite species, provides the space and nourishment for the parasite, and does not include serious antagonistic elements. Actually such an environment does not exist for either any parasite or any free-living organism. The nearest approach to this for a parasite is the species of host to which the parasite has become adapted in its evolution and an individual of that species which is having its first encounter with the parasite in question. It is possible to further improve the environment by nutritional debilitation of the host. Even with the previously uninfected host of the appropriate species, we find that the ability of the parasite to become established may be inversely proportional to the age of the host, providing, of course, that the juvenile host in question did not receive some passive immunity from an infected mother. Winfield (1933) found that the decreasing susceptibility of rats to *Heterakis spumosa* followed an exponential curve. When rats were over 200 days old less than 1 percent of the worms matured, when they were 20 days old 45 percent matured, with intermediate rates at intermediate ages. It may or may not be biologically significant that, when the exponential curve was projected back, this projected line to the 100 percent development of worms fell on the day of conception.

DEVELOPMENT IN THE SUSCEPTIBLE HOST

OXYURATA

Among the nematodes that pass their adult stage in the alimentary canal, including those that live as free and unattached adults in the lumen, frequently there is either superficial penetration of the intestinal mucosa by the second-, third- or (and) fourth-stage larvae or even deeper penetration with migration in a "circle" via the liver and lungs back to the intestine. This migration through tissues may follow infection by skin penetration and in some cases even after infection by ingestion of eggs or larvae.

Among the Oxyurata that do not penetrate the tissues as adults, at least two are known to firmly attach to the mucosa during the fourth larval stage. Apparently, the stage (perhaps the third larval stage) that hatches from the egg on ingestion passes quickly down the alimentary canal to reach the cecum. The molt from the third to the fourth larval stage apparently takes place about the time that the worms reach the cecum. Wetzel (1930) demonstrated that the fourth-stage larvae of *Oxyuris equi* are firmly attached to the mucous membrane of the ventral colon of equines. The mouth parts are adapted to function as a buccal capsule. There is apparently, however, no blood sucking, but rather the tissues (the stratum glandulare) are drawn deep into the pharynx of the larvae and tissue fragments are apparently swallowed whole. Their attachment primarily or exclusively in the ventral colon suggests that one significant place where the life cycle is interrupted and parasites lost is in the subsequent migration back "upstream" to the cecum where the adults live briefly as lumen dwellers without any discernible injury to the host. Wetzel has called attention to the fact that the number of attached fourth-stage larvae in the colon far exceeds the number of adult worms seen in the cecum. Similarly Wetzel (1931) has reported the attachment of the fourth-stage larvae of *Dermatoxys veligera* to the mucosa, in this case in the cecum, of the hare. Both Dikmans (1931) and Wetzel described four conspicuous external larval hooks on these larvae for attachment, which disappear on molting to the adult stage. The fourth-stage larva of *D. veligera* further differs from that of *O. equi* in that the former does not ingest whole tissue or tissue fragments. On the contrary, there is extraintestinal digestion of the tissues so that the head end of the fourth-stage larva of *D. veligera* is surrounded by gelatinous or semifluid mass of host tissue on which it feeds. Thus the fourth-stage larvae of both *D. veligera* and *O. equi* directly produce greater injury to the host than does the adult stage of either. Relatively little attention has been given to the development of *Enterobius vermicularis* within the egg shell and most workers report that there is no larval molt within the egg, but, as already noted, Chitwood is certain there is at least one and perhaps two. Only Chitwood (in Chandler *et al.*, 1941) has reported the fourth-stage larvae attached to the mucosa, in this case the mucosa of the appendix. This needs confirmation and further exploration. It appears to be well established that there is little or no anti-mortem tissue penetration by the adults. Some of the earlier reports of tissue penetration in the appendix by adults quite evidently represent post-mortem penetration (Gordon, 1933). It is possible that the apparently bona fide penetration of tissues of the appendix by *E. vermicularis* reported may involve fourth-stage larvae rather than adult worms. In view of what is known about the life cycle of other oxyurids, post-mortem examination of pinworm appendices should include histopathological examination of adjacent tissues of the alimentary canal with particular attention to the upper colon.

Syphacia obvelata and *Aspiculuris tetraptera* in the mouse apparently do not normally penetrate the tissues either as larvae or as adults. *Syphacia obvelata* apparently quickly moves to the cecum where the remaining molts to the adult stage take place while the parasite is free in the lumen. However, *A. tetraptera* moves quickly through the cecum to the lower colon, where it molts to the fourth stage (Chan, 1955). The fourth-stage larvae or young adults migrate "upstream" to the upper one third of the colon, where the adults complete their development.

ASCAROIDEA

In the closely related Ascaroidea the tissue penetration by larval stages is much more aggressive and includes forms with complete cyclic migration. Ackert (1931) has shown that the second larval stage of *Ascaridia galli* penetrates the mucosa of the upper part of the small intestine and the resulting tissue destruction and hemorrhage are the most serious aspect of this infection in poultry. Chicks may be so seriously debilitated that they become easy prey to other infections; they actually starve owing to inability to move about or to feed. Only rarely do the larvae actually move through the intestinal wall or migrate beyond it. Apparently they emerge about the end of the second larval stage and thereafter establish themselves as third and fourth larval stages and adults in the lumen of the upper small intestine. Likewise, Wright (1935) and Sprent (1959) have shown that the second-stage larvae of *Toxascaris leonina* penetrate the tissues of the anterior intestinal wall. They emerge from the intestinal wall about the time they molt into the third stage and the third and fourth larval stages and the adults live free in the lumen of the upper half of the small intestine. The utilization of intermediate hosts will be discussed below.

Heterakis gallinae is of more than passing interest because of its role in the transmission of *Histomonas meleagridis*, the cause of "blackhead" in turkeys and chickens. The earlier workers including Danheim (1925), Chapham (1933), and Baker (1933) have all failed to clearly demonstrate tissue penetration by any stage and concluded that development was completed without any larval penetration of the tissues. However, Tyzzer (1934) has described and illustrated with photomicrographs of cecal sections, the penetration of the epithelium of the cecal glands. According to Tyzzer, shortly after hatching from the ingested eggs the larvae are found coiled "around the lumina of the glands." He stated that the head end may penetrate the epithelium, but his figure 2 illustrates deeper penetration, actually within the epithelium. He found no evidence, however, that they penetrated any deeper. He found little evidence of inflammatory response, but destructive mechanical injury. The larvae actually seem to grow out of the glands and come to lie free in the sulci between the folds of the mucosa. It is still not demonstrated that even transient tissue penetration is essential in the life cycle of *H. gallinae* and apparently it is not. What portion of the larvae may penetrate the tissue is not known and yet it may be significant in any interpretation of the phylogenetic relationship to other worms and of even greater importance in understanding precisely how the larvae transmit *H. meleagridis.*

The ascarids of mammals commonly have a cyclic migration through the lungs. *Ascaris suum* of swine will serve as the prototype. The first molt takes place in the egg and the second-stage larvae hatch and penetrate the intestinal wall to reach the portal vein and are thus carried to the liver. Despite the extensive damage with severe scars in the liver, the larvae move on to the lungs by the second or third day after the eggs are ingested. By the fifth day after ingestion of the eggs the molt (second molt) to the third larval stage begins and in the succeeding 2 or 3 days many of these third-stage larvae are coughed up or migrate up the trachea to be reswallowed. However, some of the larvae persist in the lungs beyond the tenth day after the eggs are ingested and these begin the next molt to the fourth larval stage. The fourth larval stages are equipped with broad fins that appear to aid in the migration up the trachea. Roberts (1934) believes that only the fourth larval stage is able to establish in the intestine. Since most of the larvae appear to leave the lungs in the third stage, this alone would explain why extensive scarring of the liver and debilitating pulmonary damage with fatal cases of thumps may be followed by the appearance of very few adult worms in the intestine.

Strongyloidea

The Strongyloidea usually hatch from the egg in the free-living environment or utilize obligatory or optional intermediate hosts for the early larval stages. Of the hookworms, *Ancylostoma caninum* of the dog has been the most extensively studied experimentally. The infection can be established in the normal host (dog) following either oral or cutaneous entrance into the host. In the canine host percutaneous or subcutaneous infection is followed by migration to the lungs, where the larvae grow slightly. However, they leave the lung while still in the third stage, at most beginning to show signs of the third molt. Under curcumstances that are not yet clearly defined, but must include debilitation of the host as one factor, some of them may go on to the fourth stage in the lungs and even a rare one may go on to the fifth stage in the lung (Otto and Schugam, 1940). It would appear, however, that the molt to the fourth stage is usually completed en route from the lungs to the intestine since even as early as the eighth day after infection fourth-stage but no third-stage larvae were found in the intestine.

Both *Gaigeria pachyscelis* of sheep and goats and the several species of *Bunostomum* in sheep and cattle also undergo the lung migration when infection results from skin penetration. However, in both of these genera the worms regularly molt to the fourth larval stage in the lungs before continuing on their way to the intestine.

All the hookworm species except *G. pachyscelis* apparently are capable of establishing in the normal host following the ingestion of the third-stage larvae. This appears to be the usual route of infection for the hookworms of domestic animals, as well as other Strongyloidea and Trichostrongyloidea. A higher percentage of worms usually develops from an oral infection than from a percutaneous infection. Ortlep's (1937) failure to produce infection with *G. pachyscelis* in the normal host following oral administration of the larvae appears to make this species unique among this group of worms. Infection following the oral administration of *Ancylostomum duodenale* or *Necator americanus* larvae has not been established unequivocally. Although these species appear normally to gain entrance into man by skin penetration, there is suggestive evidence that infection can be acquired by the oral route. Foster and Cross (1934) have clearly demonstrated that the pulmonary migration is not required and apparently is never initiated from the intestine, following oral administration of the third-stage larvae of *Ancylostoma caninum*, despite the evidence that it is essential following skin penetration. It is not even clearly established that the third-stage larvae of *A. caninum* even superficially penetrate the intestinal mucosa following oral administration in a completely susceptible dog.

Although most other Strongyloidea and Trichostrongyloidea gain entrance exclusively or primarily by ingestion, there are some forms that readily penetrate the skin. Among these is *Nippostrongylus braziliensis* of rats, which not only is normally a skin penetrator but also appears to be dependent upon some tissue migration, but not necessarily pulmonary migration, for further development (Twohy, 1956). Ingested larvae appear to have difficulty in penetrating the intestinal mucosa, since Schwartz and Alicata (1934) found that most of the ingested third-stage larvae were passed in the feces. Apparently, only the limited number which penetrated the intestine, migrated through the lungs, and returned to the intestine as fourth-stage larvae were able to complete their development.

On the contrary, *Haemonchus contortus* of sheep and cattle is apparently unable to penetrate the skin and even when the third-stage larvae are injected they fail to migrate either to the lungs or directly to the abomasum. Stoll (1943) found that following intraperitoneal injection of third-stage larvae they appeared to die in a few days and were walled off in nodules. However, following ingestion the third-stage larvae quickly penetrate the mucosa where they molt to the fourth stage and thereafter escape to the lumen.

So far, we have considered only the development of these forms in susceptible normal hosts. These and many other species in these and other groups, which time will not permit us to discuss, appear to go through very uniform development. The several stages are timed rather uniformly and delays or diversions in development are not common. Nevertheless, 100% development rarely occurs. The percentage loss increases both with increasing age of the host and increasing size of the inoculum. In the susceptible host, however, those larvae which fail to mature have not been associated with any unusual pathology or symptomatology.

DEVELOPMENT IN PREVIOUSLY INFECTED HOST

However, when the host pressures render the environment unfavorable, both the host response to the parasite and the host pressures on the parasite may produce quite a different situation. The so-called nodular worms of sheep, cattle, and swine (*Cooperia curticei* and the several species of *Oesophagostomum*) will serve as a good introduction to this aspect of the subject. The third-stage larvae of *Oesophagostomum* penetrate deep into the intestinal wall where the third molt occurs. In the initial infection, the resulting fourth-stage larvae may return to the lumen without inducing any appreciable host response. The comparatively small lesion may heal without any discernible scar. However, in animals that have been sensitized by previous exposure, a pronounced localized reaction takes place around the larvae in the submucosa. Eosinophilic and neutrophilic infiltration is followed by giant cells, caseation, and ultimately a fibroblastic encapsulation to form a nodule with a necrotic blood-filled cavity, containing the larva, and with a small aperture opening into the lumen of the intestine. Within the nodule the parasite may die but a few may escape to complete development. The most severe pathology characterizing the infection is this nodule formation with permanent scarring.

Similarly, *Cooperia curticei* in an initial infection produces even less injury than that produced by the several species of *Oesophagostomum*.

Unlike the latter, the third-stage larvae of *C. curticei* do not actually penetrate the wall of intestine. They come to lie in the crypts with little or no discernible tissue damage. In the animal sensitized by previous infection, there is an immediate inflammatory response. The larvae apparently do not penetrate the tissues but the resulting inflammatory response engulfs each larva. Ultimately a fibrotic capsule is formed and the resulting yellow nodule protrudes through the mucous membrane into the lumen of the intestine. Andrews (1939) reported that no nodules developed in a lamb from an initial infection of as much as 1,000,000 larvae whereas 319 to 32,000 nodules developed from an infection of 63,000 to 400,000 larvae administered to previously infected animals.

The genus *Strongylus* offers some interesting area for speculation. The available evidence indicates that third-stage larvae on ingestion penetrate the mucosa of the intestine, but hereon the details for three of the species vary. According to Wetzel (1940) the third-stage larvae of *S. equinus* come to lie in the subserosa where they are enclosed in nodules, escape as fourth-stage larvae in less than 2 weeks, and then leave the liver and migrate to the pancreas or remain in the peritoneal cavity where they undergo the next molt to the fifth (young adult) stage. The route and the time required for them to return to the colon are not yet established but Wetzel is certain that pulmonary migration is not involved. *Strongylus edentatus* apparently penetrates the intestinal wall, as third-stage larvae, moves to the peritoneal cavity, and lodges retroperitoneally in the abdominal area, where the larvae become encapsulated in hemorrhagic nodules and grow. Escaping from these nodules, they make their way back to the cecum or colon and penetrate the intestinal wall to become encapsulated again in a hemorrhagic nodule. Rupture of these nodules into the lumen releases the worms for maturation in the lumen. Occasionally, third and fourth larval stages and even adults are encapsulated in the liver and lungs and even adult worms remain in hematomas of the abdominal wall.

More data are available on *Strongylus vulgaris* and curiously enough as a result the situation is even more confused. Over three decades ago, Oldt reported pulmonary migration similar to that of *Ascaris* following the penetration of the intestinal wall by the third-stage larvae of *S. vulgaris*. He suggested that many aneurisms of the mesenteric arteries were produced by larvae that strayed from the normal course and penetrated the arteries at the sites of the thrombi and resulting aneurisms. Wetzel and Enigk (1938) and Enigk (1950) were unable to find any evidence of either hepatic or pulmonary migration and the latter developed evidence that the third-stage larvae penetrate the wall of the cecum and colon and thereafter molt to the fourth stage in the submucosa. According to

Enigk, the fourth-stage larvae enter the arterioles and migrate to the mesenteric arteries and penetrate the intima to form the well-known thrombi and resulting aneurisms. In the aneurisms they molt to the fifth stage, in 6 to 8 months escape into the lumen to be carried passively to the cecal or colon wall, then burrow into the walls, again causing nodule formation, before escaping into the lumen of cecum or colon.

As one reflects on what is actually known of the life cycles of these three species of *Strongylus*, one is impressed with the large gaps in our knowledge. The wide variety of tissues in which nodular formation takes place and the evidence of successive nodules induced by successive stages, particularly with *S. vulgaris*, leave room for speculation. It is evident that there have been and still are large areas of interpretation. However logical these interpretations, the fact still remains that finite evidence is lacking in many phases. The few available facts are interpreted in various ways. That these larvae induce nodules in various tissues and in successive stages of development in a susceptible species with no previous exposure to infection suggests the distinct possibility that these forms are in an evolutionary stage between multiple-host cycles and the present one-host cycle. Such an evolutionary stage is clearly seen with *Syngamus trachea*, which is capable of direct infection of the fowl but produces heavier infections via the optional intermediate host. However, much of our information on the life cycles of *Strongylus* is based on studies in which sensitization and immunity are not completely eliminated. Certainly comparative studies are needed on young animals in which even prenatal infection is prevented and mature animals with previous infections. It is altogether possible that prenatal infection is the common means of acquiring the primary infection.

The level of immunity to worm parasites is most commonly measured as the reduction in the number of worms in the usual habitat. A much less frequently recognized and rarely measured effect is the retarded or completely arrested development and the aberrant migration. Although *Nippostrongylus braziliensis* completes the pulmonary migration in less than 2 weeks after an initial infection, Yutuc in 1939 found apparently normal third-stage larvae in the lungs of a rat 6 months after the last of a series of repeated infections. Unusual or aberrant migrations of such larvae remain as a constant possibility. Although *A. caninum* does not migrate from the intestine of the dog following the initial oral infection (Foster and Cross, 1934), it was found (Foster, 1932, 1935) that in bitches immunized by previous oral infections 10 to 20% of the larvae administered orally during the latter part of pregnancy managed to penetrate the intestinal wall and migrate to the pups *in utero*. More recently, Yutuc (1949) demonstrated that larvae of both *Ancylostoma caninum* and *Toxocara canis* arrested in the tissues of a bitch before breeding resumed migration during pregnancy and produced prenatal infection in the pups.

Another, more dramatic, example of an injurious effect of the host response is seen in the fibrotic lymph nodes to wall off *Wuchereria bancrofti* and *Brugia malayi*. This and the resulting lymph blockage and elephantiasis is seen only after many years of repeated exposure to infection.

DEVELOPMENT IN ABNORMAL HOST

The effects of host pressures on the developing stages are also recognized in the so-called abnormal host, that is, the species of host in which infection is initiated but development is not completed. It will be recalled that neither *Ancylostoma caninum* nor *Haemonchus contortus* undergoes tissue migration following the ingestion of third-stage larvae by the usual hosts, the dog and sheep, respectively. Stoll (1943) has even found that the former are incapable of migration when injected parenterally in sheep. Nevertheless, Ransom and Foster (1920) report that the third-stage larvae of *H. contortus* when ingested by a guinea pig do migrate to the lungs. Likewise, *A. caninum* third-stage larvae migrate to the liver and lungs when fed to mice (Kerr, 1936). It is altogether possible that this represents the residual of a two-host cycle for *A. caninum* and perhaps even a phylogenetic or evolutionary residual for *H. contortus*. It is difficult, however, to visualize that *H. contortus* itself utilized a rodent intermediate host for effective transmission to sheep or cattle. Are these just two more examples of active migration to escape an unfavorable environment? What, if any, relation do these migrations bear to the hypodermal migrations of *Ancylostoma braziliense* in man that produce the well-known creeping eruption? I visualize that the latter is strictly an active migration to escape an unfavorable environment. Why they continue in the hypoderma with little or no migration to other tissues remains unexplained.

Burgia malayi and *B. pahangi* of man and civets, which mature in the lymphatics of the usual host, show recurrent evidence of aberrant development in other hosts. This includes the heart of hamsters and hares. In the former there was an occasional worm in the lymphatics (Zaini *et al.*, 1962). Buckley and Wharton (1961) have presented evidence that *B. pahangi* of the civet may remain undeveloped in human volunteers and even *B. malayi* after being passed through the cat may have the same tendency when returned to human volunteers.

A somewhat different situation is seen with the lungworm, *Angio-*

strongylus cantonensis, of the rat. In the rat the ingested third-stage larvae move to the brain, where they undergo two molts to the fifth (young adult) stage and then migrate to the vascular bed of the lungs (Mackerras and Sanders, 1955). However, in mice although the third-stage larvae reach the brain they die there quickly without further development or migration (Liat *et al.*, 1965), but in primates including man development is completed in the brain but it is retarded and apparently the worms remain there with no further migration, to the lungs or elsewhere (Weinstein *et al.*, 1963). Thus, the resulting pathology, host reaction, and clinical manifestations are much more severe than in the rat.

The Ascaroidea are of particular interest in this connection. The group is obviously in the transitional evolution between two-host and one-host cycles. The evidence, I think, supports Sprent's (1962) conclusion that it is evolution *from* the two-host cycle *to* the one-host cycle. Two species are known to be dependent upon a rodent intermediate host, *A. columnaris* of the skunk and *A. mustelarum* of the fisher. *Toxascaris leonina* is most effectively transmitted by a rodent intermediate host (Sprent, 1959) but as already noted can be transmitted directly. In both the canine or feline hosts and the rodent host, upon ingestion and hatching of eggs, the second-stage larvae penetrate the intestinal wall and remain there up to a week. Then in the rodent host the third-stage larvae migrate deeper into the tissues (including the lungs), where they may be encysted (Sprent, 1952). But, in the canine and feline hosts the third-stage larvae escape into the lumen of the intestine where they develop to maturity without further migration. *Ascaris lumbricoides, A. suum,* and *A. equorum* appear to have the same uniform cyclic migration through the usual definitive hosts and through the rodent hosts. A significant loss of larvae has been demonstrated during the migration in the pig following ingestion of eggs. A similar, but perhaps a somewhat smaller, loss appears to occur during the migration of *A. lumbricoides* in man. Nevertheless, all three of these forms evidently do not utilize an intermediate host in nature although experimentally the porcine host can be infected by feeding the larvae from mice. There is apparently no encystment or other retention in the mice.

Biologically *Toxocara canis* of dogs and *T. leonine* of cats are most interesting. In either the rodent host or the canine or feline host the second-stage larvae from ingested eggs penetrate the intestinal wall and migrate widely through the tissues including the liver and lungs. In the rodent host the larvae become encapsulated and appear to be the primary source of infection for mature dogs and cats (Sprent, 1955, 1958). In the canine or feline host a few larvae may complete the cyclic migration through the lungs back to the intestine, where they mature. It seems clear, however, that very few manage to so develop. Many are arrested in the tissues. Many of these may be destroyed by the host responses but some manage to renew, or continue, their migration in the bitch during pregnancy to produce prenatal infection in the pups. Douglas and Baker (1959) have shown that prenatal infection of the pups may occur as long as a year after the last ingestion of embryonated eggs by the bitch. Sprent has shown also that the bitch acquires intestinal infection in cleaning the pups. This would mean that embryonated eggs ingested by the bitch had hatched, and the larvae, after migrating to and remaining undeveloped in the tissues of the bitch, subsequently migrated *in utero* to the pups, were passed out in the feces of the pups *postpartum*, and were ingested by the same bitch in cleaning her pups. This extensive migration in both the canine and rodent host argues that the parasite is in a highly evolutionary state. This is further suggested by the fact that the larvae of *T. canis* will migrate and persist in the tissues of a wide variety of animals such as man, pig, sheep, chickens, and pigeons. In the chickens up to 50% of the eggs fed were recovered as larvae in the tissues and in pigeons up to 25%. In both cases over 90% were in the liver but the remainder were widely scattered in other tissues including the brain (Galvin, 1964). It is not surprising that this species should occur as a cause of visceral larval migrans in children (Beaver, 1962).

SUMMARY

Among the nematodes many species are pathologically and economically far more injurious during their larval stages than during the adult stage. This is true of some species which appear to have evolved a standard and uniform one-host life cycle. In general larval stages in intermediate hosts are encysted in tissues. Among the parasites evolving from the two-host cycle to the one-host cycle the biological equivalent of the intermediate host is seen in the larval migration in the tissues of the definitive host. Under such conditions many aberrant migrations may occur with unusual pathological effects. Such nematode larvae appear to have a greater capacity to initiate development in a wide variety of hosts. In many cases they have a tendency to be hyperactive and migrate longer and more widely than in the definitive host or the original intermediate host. As a result they may die and stimulate pathological host responses in a wide variety of sites and organs. The hyperactivity appears to me to be biological—similar to the hyperactivity demonstrated by free-living organisms to escape an unfavorable but not immediately lethal environment. A somewhat similar situation is seen both in the aberrant migration and host response in the so-called normal host immunized by repeated infections, but in which the level of immunity is not sufficient to be immediately lethal. Added to this may be the severe and debilitating foreign body cellular reaction with direct blockage or local organ destruction.

The aberrant migration of "accidental parasites" and "normal parasites" in the partially immune subject appears to be the cause of visceral larval migrans and tropical eosinophilia in man. These, as Beaver suggests, probably are manifestations of the same phenomenon. The same situation has been reported in domesticated animals and may become more widely recognized with improved diagnostic methods and the continuing control of the more massive parasitism. It emphasizes the greater need for prevention than for corrective therapy.

REFERENCES

Ackert, J. E. (1931). The morphology and life history of the fowl nematode *Ascaridia lineata* (*Schneider*). *Parasitology* **23**, 360-379.

Andrews, J. S. (1939). Life history of the nematode *Cooperia curticei* and development of resistance in sheep. *J. Agr. Res.* **58**, 771-786.

Baker, A. D. (1933). Some observations on the development of the caecal worm, *Heterakis gallinae* (Gmelin, 1790) Freeborn, 1923, in the domestic fowl. *Sci. Agri.* **13**, 356-363.

Beaver, P. C. (1962). Toxocarosis (visceral larva migrans) in relation to tropical eosinophilia. *Bull. Soc. Pathol. Exotique* **55**, 555-576.

Buckley, J. J. C., and Wharton, R. H. (1961). Anomalous results from an experimental infection of man with *Brugia malayi* (Brug, 1927). *J. Helminthol.* R. T. Leiper Suppl., pp. 17-24.

Chan, K. F. (1955). The distribution of larval stages of *Aspiculuris tetraptera* in the intestine of mice. *J. Parasitol.* **41**, 529-532.

Chandler, A. C., Alicata, J. E., and Chitwood, M. B. (1941). Life history (Zooparasitica) II. Parasites of vertebrates. *In* "An Introduction to Nematology" (J. R. Christie, ed.), Chapter 6, pp. 267-301. Babylon, New York.

Chapham, P. A. (1933). On the life-history of *Heterakis gallinae*. *J. Helminthol.* **11**, 67-86.

Danheim, B. L. (1925). Studies on the migratory habits of certain nematode larvae. *Trans. Am. Microscop. Soc.* **24**, 14-23.

Dikmans, G. (1931). An interesting tapeworm from the cat in Louisiana. *J. Parasitol.* **18**, 47.

Douglas, J. R., and Baker, N. F. (1959). The chronology of experimental intrauterine infections with *Toxocara canis* (Werner, 1782) in the dog. *J. Parasitol.* **45**, 43-44.

Enigk, K. (1950). Zur Entwicklung von *Strongylus vulgaris* (Nematodes) in Wirtstier. *Z. Tropenmed. Parasitol.* **2**, 287-306.

Foster, A. O. (1932). Prenatal infection with the dog hookworm, *Ancylostoma caninum*. *J. Parasitol.* **19**, 112-118.

Foster, A. O. (1935). Further observations on prenatal hookworm infection of dogs. *J. Parasitol.* **21**, 302-308.

Foster, A. O., and Cross, S. X. (1934). The direct development of hookworms after oral infection. *Am. J. Trop. Med.* **14**, 565-573.

Galvin, T. J. (1964). Experimental *Toxocara canis* infections in chickens and pigeons. *J. Parasitol.* **50**, 124-127.

Gordon, H. (1933). Appendical oxyuriasis and appendicitis bases on a study of 26,051 appendixes. *Arch. Pathol.* **16**, 177-194.

Kerr, K. B. (1936). Studies on acquired immunity to the dog hookworm, *Ancylostoma caninum. Am. J. Hyg.* **24**, 381-406.

Liat, L. B., Kong, O.-Y. C., and Joe, L. K. (1965). Natural infection of *Angiostrongylus cantonensis* in Malaysian rodents and intermediate hosts, and preliminary observations on acquired resistance. *Am. J. Trop. Med. Hyg.* **14**, 610-617.

Mackerras, M. J., and Sandars, D. F. (1955). The life history of the rat lung-worm *Angiostrongylus cantonensis* (Chen) (Nematoda: Metastrongylidae). *Australian J. Zool.* **3**, 1-25.

Ortlepp, R. J. (1937). Observations on the morphology and life-history of *Gaigeria pachyscelis* Raill. and Henry, 1910: A hookworm parasite of sheep and goats. *Onderstepoort J. Vet. Sci. Animal Ind.* **8**, 183-212.

Otto, G. F., and Schugam, N. J. (1940). The occurrence of adult hookworms, *Ancylostoma caninum,* in the lungs of an experimentally infected dog. *Am. J. Hyg.* **32**, 70-74.

Ransom, B. H., and Foster, W. D. (1920). Observations on the life history of *Ascaris lumbricoides. U.S. Dept. Agr., Tech. Bull.* **817**, 1-47.

Roberts, F. H. S. (1934). The large roundworm of pigs, *Ascaris lumbricoides* L., 1758. Its life history in Queensland, economic importance and control. *Queensland Dept. Agr. Stock, Animal Health Sta., Yeerongpilly, Bull.* **1**, 1-81.

Schwartz, B., and Alicata, J. E. (1934). The development of the trichostrongyle, *Nippostrongylus muris,* in rats following ingestion of larvae. *J. Wash. Acad. Sci.* **24**, 334-338.

Sprent, J. F. A. (1952). On the migratory behavior of the larvae of various *Ascaris* species in white mice. *J. Infect. Diseases* **90**, 165-176.

Sprent, J. F. A. (1955). On the invasion of the central nervous system by nematodes. *Parasitology* **45**, 41-55.

Sprent, J. F. A. (1958). Observations on the development of *Toxocara canis* (Werner, 1782) in the dog. *Parasitology* **48**, 184-209.

Sprent, J. F. A. (1959). The life history and development of *Toxascaris leonina* (von Linstow, 1902) in the dog and cat. *Parasitology* **49**, 330-370.

Sprent, J. F. A. (1962). The evolution of the Ascaridoidea. *J. Parasitol.* **48**, 818-824.

Stoll, N. R. (1943). The wandering of *Haemonchus* in the sheep host. *J. Parasitol.* **29**, 407-416.

Twohy, D. W. (1956). The early migration and growth of *Nippostrongylus muris* in the rat. *Am. J. Hyg.* **63**, 165-185.

Tyzzer, E. E. (1934). Studies on histomoniasis, or "blackhead" infection, in the chicken and the turkey. *Proc. Am. Acad. Arts Sci.* **69**, 190-264.

Weinstein, P. P., Rosen, L., Laqueur, G. L., and Sawyer, T. K. (1963). *Angiostrongylus cantonensis* infection in rats and Rhesus monkeys, and observations on the survival of the parasite *in vitro. Am. J. Trop. Med. Hyg.* **12**, 358-377.

Wetzel, R. (1930). On the biology of the fourth stage larva of *Oxyuris equi* (Schrank). *J. Parasitol.* **17**, 95-97.

Wetzel, R. (1931). On the biology of the fourth stage larva of *Dermatoxys veligera*

(Rudolphi 1819) Schneider, 1866, an oxyurid parasitic in the hare. *J. Parasitol.* **18**, 40-43.

Wetzel, R. (1940). Zur Entwicklung des grossen Palisadenwurmes (*Strongylus equinus*) in Pferd. *Arch. Wiss. Prakt. Tierheilk.* **76**, 81-118.

Wetzel, R., and Enigk, K. (1938). Wandern die Larven der Palisadenwurmer (Strongylus spec.) der Pferde durch die Lungen? *Arch. Wiss. Prakt. Tierheilk.* **73**, 83-93.

Winfield, G. F. (1933). Quantitative experimental studies on the rat nematode, *Heterakis spumosa*, Schneider, 1866. *Am. J. Hyg.* **27**, 168-228.

Wright, W. H. (1935). Observations on the life history of *Toxascaris leonina* (Nematoda: Ascaridae). *Proc. Helminthol. Soc. Wash., D.C.* **2**, 56.

Yutuc, L. M. (1949). Prenatal infection of dogs with ascarids, *Toxocara canis*, and hookworms, *Ancylostoma caninum. J. Parasitol.* **35**, 358-360.

Zaini, M. A., Ramachandran, C. P., and Edeson, J. F. B. (1962). *Brugia* species in the heart of hamsters. *Trans. Roy. Soc. Trop. Med. Hyg.* **56**, 6-7.

Discussion

Dr. Gaafar: Would you please comment on the so-called intermediate host in ascarids with relation to the stage of the larvae?

Dr. Otto: This is best illustrated with *Toxocara canis* where the second and third larval stages occur in the pregnant host.

However, in the case of *Ancylostoma caninum* too the puppies are obviously getting the infection prenatally, the mature female serving as an intermediate host. I think this is an evolutionary stage; the third-stage larvae are found in the tissues of the bitch and these escape to the puppy at pregnancy. The reason for the migration is not clear.

Dr. Gaafar: Where do larvae go after they have been encysted; do they have the power of migration to the gut?

Dr. Otto: This has not been clearly illustrated. I believe third-stage larvae of *T. canis* appear in the feces of the puppies and I suspect this is the source of infection in mature animals.

Dr. Gaafar: Essentially there are two migrations with *T. canis*; one with the second stage and one with the third and fourth stage.

Dr. Otto: I think most of the migration is up to the third stage only; puppies receive third stages from the bitch and the fourth is in the bowel of the puppy. I do not believe there is any marked migration by fourth-stage larvae of *T. canis*.

Dr. Gibbs: Relative to migration of *Syphacia* and *Aspircularis*—work done on this subject two years ago revealed that *Aspircularis* larvae migrated to the latter third of the large bowel following injection, with subsequent anterior migration to their final site in the anterior third. *Syphacia*, on the other hand, did not appear to migrate from the cecum.

Dr. Otto: Yes! There is very little migration of *Syphacia*.

Miss Rawes: I wonder if Dr. Otto would comment on the fact that we have found in British sheep that there is a nodular reaction to a primary infection of *Oesophagostomum columbianum*. This is in a country in which the parasite does not occur naturally so that the sheep could not possibly have experienced prior infection.

Dr. Otto: This is a difficult question. I would suggest either that the British strain of sheep is not always susceptible to the infection, and might be considered an abnormal host in a sense, or there may be some interspecific or nonspecific response to the worm.

Nutrition of Intestinal Helminths[1]

CLARK P. READ

Department of Biology, Rice University, Houston, Texas and Marine Biological Laboratory, Woods Hole, Massachusetts

Certain aspects of the eating habits of intestinal worms have been reviewed by Ackert and Whitlock (1940), Hobson (1948), Fairbairn (1960), Rogers (1961), Lee (1965), and Jennings (1966). In the preparation of the present paper, the author has reviewed the literature as completely as possible for his own benefit and selected for review certain aspects in which there has been continuing interest and some progress.

ABSORPTION OF ORGANIC COMPOUNDS

In considering absorption as an important phase in the nutrition of an organism, two aspects are of significance. One is the identification of the organs or cell layers which are involved in absorptive function and the other is the characterization of the absorptive function.

THE ABSORPTIVE SURFACES

Nematodes

On examination of the structure of nematodes, it is recognized that there are two major body areas through which absorption could occur, the external surface or the gut. In the case of *Ascaris*, there is good evidence that many small molecules of probable nutritional significance do not pass through the body wall. The cuticle is not significantly permeable to glucose or amino acids (Mueller, 1929; Cavier and Savel, 1952). Rogers and Lazarus (1949) found that ligated *Ascaris* absorbed negligible amounts of labeled inorganic orthophosphate from the suspending medium. It was shown by radioautography that the intestine of *Ascaris* is the main site of phosphate absorption. Zam *et al.* (1963) reported that ligated *Ascaris* does not take up Co^{60}-labeled vitamin B_{12} *in vitro*. It

[1] The work of the author and his colleagues described in this paper has been supported by grants from the National Institutes of Health, U.S. Public Health Service (AI 01384).

was also shown by these authors that unligated *Ascaris* did not take up the intrinsic factor–B_{12} complex, although the worm readily absorbed the unbound vitamin from the medium.

Several years ago, the present author carried out some experiments at the Molteno Institute, University of Cambridge, on the penetration of glycine-C^{14} into *Ascaris* from pigs. Female worms were ligated just behind the anterior end and just ahead of the anus and incubated for an hour in buffered Ringer's solution containing 1.0 mM labeled glycine. After incubation, the worms were removed and rapidly washed in several changes of Ringer's solution. Samples of perienteric fluid and of muscle tissue were examined for radioactivity: none was found. Control worms, incubated without ligation, had radioglycine in the perienteric fluid at an average chemical concentration of 2.5 mM.

On the other hand, there is evidence that certain anthelmintic hydrocarbons penetrate the *Ascaris* cuticle (Alexander and Trim, 1946; Trim, 1949). It was concluded by Trim that the outermost layer of the cuticle is probably the main barrier to penetration. It behaves as if it were a thin homogeneous layer of lipoid. Presumably, fat-soluble substances other than anthelmintics could pass through the cuticle, but it seems likely that this is not of nutritional significance. A possible exception would be the absorption of fat-soluble vitamins; this has not been examined in *Ascaris*.

It would be dangerous to generalize from studies on *Ascaris*, which, in many ways, is not a "typical" nematode. As a matter of fact, Weatherly *et al.* (1963) presented evidence that glucose and alanine enter the tissues of *Ascaridia galli* through the external surface. The apparent uptake of isotopically labeled compounds in 1- or 2-hour periods by worms, with mouth and anus sealed, was related to the exposed body surface. Vital dyes were not absorbed by sealed worms. From the data available on *Ascaris* and *Ascaridia*, it is plain that studies on other species would be highly desirable.

If the external surface of *Ascaris* is not permeable to amino acids and sugars, we are led to the simple idea that the gut must play an important role in absorption. The structure of *Ascaris* gut cells has been studied rather thoroughly by both light and electron microscopy and shows attributes suggesting both secretory and absorptive function. There are many points of similarity between gut cells of a number of intestinal nematodes. The luminal surfaces of such cells have microvilli, resembling those seen on the surfaces of other animal cells known to have absorptive functions. Such microvilli are present on gut cells of *Ascaris*, *Parascaris equorum*, *Rhabditis strongyloides*, *Capillaria hepatica*, *Trichinella spiralis*, *Setaria cervi*, and *Ancylostoma caninum* (Bretschneider, 1954; Peebles, 1957; Tokin, 1959; Browne and Chowdhury, 1959; Beckett and Boothroyd, 1961; Kagei, 1961; Kessel *et al.*, 1961; Joyon and Collin, 1962; Wright, 1963; Sheffield, 1964; Browne *et al.*, 1965). These microvilli constitute the so-called bacillary layer of the nematode gut epithelium seen by many workers using light microscopy. Further, Tanaka (1961) has shown that the microvilli (striated border) of *Ascaris* gut cells contain an adenosine triphosphatase.

Trematodes

Since Mansour (1959) showed that *Fasciola* removes glucose from the suspending medium at the same rate with or without the mouth ligated, it must be assumed that glucose may enter the worm through the external surface. Björkman and Thorsell (1964) demonstrated directly that ferritin particles are taken up through the tegument of *Fasciola*. Studies of the tegumentary ultrastructure have pointed up its essential similarity to the cestode tegument and furnished morphological evidence that it is a physiologically dynamic structure rather than a simple covering for the body (Threadgold, 1963; Björkman and Thorsell, 1964). The outer boundary of the tegument appears to be a plasma membrane, and the tegument contains numerous mitochondria and is connected by protoplasmic strands to subtegumentary cells. Contrary to Alvarado (1951) and Pantelouris and Gresson (1960), neither Threadgold nor Björkman and Thorsell found nuclei in the tegument. Except for the absence of prominent microvilli, the tegument of *Fasciola* is very much like that of cestodes (see below). It may be mentioned that Kurelec and Ehrlich (1963) showed that amino acids pass into the medium from *Fasciola*, with the mouth and excretory opening ligated, as rapidly as from unligated animals.

The description of the ultrastructure of *Schistosoma* tegument by Senft *et al.* (1961) is based on what appears to be inadequately fixed material. The tegumentary structure of this worm, as described by Hein (1904), whose drawing is reproduced in the paper of Senft *et al.*, is strikingly similar to the structure of *Fasciola* tegument as reconstructed by Threadgold (1963) and recent studies by Lumsden in our laboratory tend to support the interpretation of the trematode tegument offered by Threadgold and by Björkman and Thorsell (1964). On the basis of structure, it would be suspected that active transport of low molecular weight organic compounds occurs across the tegument of *Schistosoma*.

Fasciola hepatica has peculiar looped and branching projections on the gut epithelium. These peculiar structures were recognized and clearly figured by Sommer in 1880 and have been studied with the electron microscope by Gresson and Threadgold (1959) and Thorsell and Björkman (1965). The structures differ somewhat from the microvilli described on the surfaces of certain other animal cells which are regarded as showing specialization for absorption, and there seems to be some difference of opinion as to the functions of these cytoplasmic projections. Gresson and Threadgold (1959) and Thorsell and Björkman (1965) considered them to be processes concerned with absorption, whereas Dawes (1962) and Dawes and Hughes (1964) argued that they are mainly involved in an apocrine secretory cycle. Dawes and Hughes pointed out the similarities between these structures (and their function as they reconstructed it from histological study) and the secretory events in the vertebrate mammary gland. There seems to be agreement among some workers that the gut cells in *Fasciola* undergo secretory and absorptive cycles (Müller, 1923; Gresson and Threadgold, 1959; Pantelouris and Gresson, 1960; Dawes, 1962; Dawes and Hughes, 1964), but there are differences of opinion on the details of mechanism. Dawes and Hughes (1964) have commented with some acidity on these differences of opinion. Saito (1961) reported that ATPase activity is associated with these peripheral processes of *Fasciola* gut cells—this supports the concept that work is being done in this region, be it secretory or absorptive. Some thorough histochemical work, using freeze-substitution methods, might shed light on the function of the cytoplasmic processes.

Thorsell and Björkman (1965), in their study of the fine structure of the gut epithelium in *Fasciola*, described the cell projections as being delimited by a triple membrane and having a dense core. The latter workers showed that, after the intact fluke was incubated for 10 minutes in any one of several radioactive amino acids, the major site of labeling was the gut, strongly suggesting its role in the absorption of amino acids. It must be pointed out, however, that the autoradiographic localization of the isotope in these experiments only included material fixed into substances not extracted by Carnoy's fixative and may be presumed to be mainly an index of amino acid incorporated into protein. Free amino acids which might be absorbed and not incorporated in the 10-minute period would be extracted in fixation. The data of Thorsell and Björkman clearly showed that synthesis of Carnoy-insoluble material from amino acids occurs at a high rate in the cecal epithelium.

Pantelouris and Gresson (1960) injected labeled ferric chloride, labeled mouse blood, and labeled phenylalanine into the gut of *Fasciola*, then placed the worms in beakers of saline for periods up to 60 minutes or in the body cavity of mice for several days. The flukes were fixed at intervals and the tissues sectioned for radioautography. Unfortunately, the following assumptions seem to have been made in these experiments: (1) Substances injected into the gut do not leak out into the surrounding medium during incubation with subsequent uptake at other sites than the gut; (2) substances not extracted by fixatives are an index of absorption; (3) labeled substances leave the body only by "excretion." That the validity of these assumptions is unproven renders acceptance of the authors' conclusions difficult and it can only be said that *Fasciola* did absorb the labeled material in each case.

It may be remarked that the limited observations of Senft *et al.* (1961) on the ultrastructure of *Schistosoma* suggests that the gut of the blood fluke resembles that of *Fasciola*. Other trematodes have been reported to have villus-like extensions on cecal cells, but their morphology and function are not well understood (Byrd, 1935; Wotton and Sogandares-Bernal, 1963; Lacey, 1965; and others).

Cestodes

In the absence of a gut, it has long been thought that tapeworms absorb food through the external surface of the body. The external structure of the cestodes has traditionally been termed a cuticle. As Rothman (1959) suggested, it should more properly be termed a tegument since it is now recognized that it is hardly comparable with the cuticular body seen in many animal groups. Fine hairlike structures on the surface of cestodes were recognized many years ago (Schiefferdecker, 1874; Steudener, 1877; Moniez, 1884; and others). In some tapeworms these structures are readily seen with the optical microscope (among recent authors, see, for example, Rees, 1958; Lee and Tatchell, 1964). The use of the electron microscope has revealed their presence on the external surfaces of a number of species belonging to several orders of cestodes. These include *Hymenolepis diminuta, H. nana, Raillietina cesticillus, Hydatigera taeniaeformis, Dipylidium caninum, Calliobothrium verticillatum,* and *Lacistorhynchus tenuis* (Read, 1955; Kent, 1957; Threadgold, 1962; Waitz, 1962; Rosario, 1962; Rothman, 1963; Lumsden, 1965a). Cameron's (1964) statement that, "The processes shown in sections photographed by electron microscopes and which suggest villi, may in reality be artifacts . . ." is patently ridiculous. These structures (Figs. 1 and 2) are no more artifacts than such structures as flame cells. The surface microvilli of various cestodes have been observed by numerous workers using a variety of techniques. Artifacts in the preservation of fine structure of these processes are apparent in some work, but the presence of the processes is not an artifact. A recent study in our own laboratory by Lumsden (1965a) of the tegumentary fine structure of *Hymenolepis diminuta* has shown that the microvillus is bounded on its outer surface by a trilaminate membrane and has an inner core of supporting microtubular structures. Lumsden, comparing it with microvilli on various other absorptive cells, concluded that the cestode microvillus is, in its essentials, quite similar to that observed on, for example, the absorbing cells of the vertebrate intestine. Further, Lumsden concluded that the tegument is a coenocytic structure and presented biochemical evidence

FIG. 1. The tegument of *Hymenolepis diminuta* (×11,850). Osmic acid fixation; lead nitrate and uranium acetate stain. (Preparation and photograph by Dr. Richard D. Lumsden.)

(Lumsden, 1965b) that proteins of the tegument are elaborated in the subcuticular cells and rapidly exported to the tegument. At the present time, there is good reason to believe that the tegument itself is the major absorptive structure in the cestodes. Further evidences of its physiological activity are the presence of mitochondria (observed by Read,

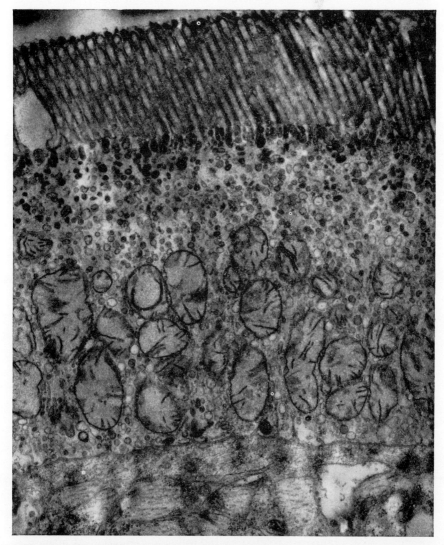

Fig. 2. The tegument of *Lacistorhynchus tenuis* (×11,850). Osmic acid fixation; lead nitrate and uranium acetate stain. (Preparation and photograph by Dr. Richard D. Lumsden.)

Kent, Threadgold, Waitz, Rosario, Rothman, and Lumsden, *loc. cit.*), phosphatases (Rogers, 1947; Yamao, 1952; Erasmus, 1957a,b; Kilejian *et al.*, 1961; Bogitsh, 1963; Waitz and Schardein, 1964; Lee and Tatchell, 1964), indophenol oxidase (Waitz and Schardein, 1964; referred to by these authors as cytochrome oxidase), succinic dehydrogenase (Hedrick, 1956; Lee and Rothman, 1964; Waitz and Schardein, 1964), and several other hydrolytic and oxidative enzymes (Rothman *et al.*, 1964); Lee and Tatchell, 1964; Lee and Rothman, 1964; Waitz and Schardein, 1964; Schardein and Waitz, 1965). These are not physiological indices to be expected in what has been termed a cuticle in other organisms. It may be mentioned that microvillus-like structures also occur on the surfaces of several larval taeniid cestodes (Siddiqui, 1963; Race *et al.*, 1965).

Acanthocephalans

Little work has been done on the fine structure of the body wall in this group of intestinal helminths which, like the cestodes, lacks a gut. Crompton (1964) and Crompton and Lee (1965) have made an outstanding contribution in their studies of the peripheral structures of *Polymorphus minutus*. They have shown that the organization of the tegument of this species is quite unique and differs sharply from the tegument of cestodes, trematodes, or nematodes.

ABSORPTIVE FUNCTION

Before discussing specific information on absorptive function, it may be desirable to review very briefly the kinds of processes which may be involved. The passage of ions and molecules through membranes can take place by at least five distinguishable types of processes: These are (1) mass flow through pores; (2) diffusion involving no specific structural relationship between the membrane and the diffusing material; (3) facilitated diffusion which involves a specific structural relationship between the membrane and the diffusing material; work is not done in the process although the kinetics resemble those seen in (4) active transport which involves both a structural relationship between the membrane and the permeating molecular species and a source of energy from metabolism. The kinetics of active transport and facilitated diffusion resemble those of classical enzyme or absorption phenomena and the substances transported are thought to form transient complexes with membrane components. The rate of absorption and concentration of the permeating substance are related by the following equation (Lineweaver and Burk, 1934):

$$v = V_{max} \, C/K_t + C$$

where v is rate of absorption, V_{max} is the maximal absorption rate, C is concentration of the substance, and K_t is the concentration yielding a half-maximal rate of absorption. In the presence of a competitive inhibitor, the rate of absorption and the concentrations of the competing components are related by

$$v = V_{max} \left/ \frac{K_t}{C} + 1 + \frac{(K_t I)}{(K^i C)} \right.$$

where $K^i =$ inhibition constant of the competitor, $I =$ concentration of the competitor, and other symbols as above; the additional process (5) is pinocytosis.

Recognizing that at least these five processes may be involved in absorption and recognizing that none of them are mutually exclusive, we may proceed to evaluate what we know of the processes in intestinal helminths.

Nematodes

The study of Weatherly et al. (1963) on the entry of glucose and alanine through the external surface of Ascaridia does not allow decision as to the process or processes involved. It was noted there was a decrease in cuticular absorption in fasted worms. Weatherly et al. indicated that this might be due to increased concentration of glucose in the perienteric fluid and, "Therefore, less glucose would penetrate through the cuticle as a result of diffusion." As a matter of fact, if Fick's law is operating in this system the apparent rate of diffusion of a *labeled* compound would not be thus affected. There would be less *net* movement of glucose or alanine into the worms, but the flux of the compounds would not be altered in this fashion. The data suggest that the entry of glucose and alanine occurs by processes other than diffusion, but do not allow a definite conclusion. It should be possible to carry out kinetic studies on the cuticular absorption of organic compounds by Ascaridia.

Very little is known of the absorption of nutrients in the gut of nematodes, although it may be pointed out to the general physiologist that the gut of a worm such as Ascaris has unusually good qualities for studying membrane transport phenomena. It is a monolayer of cells which in itself makes it a favorable material for transport studies. Fisher (1962) has described the use of a modified two-chambered ussing device for studying active transport of sugars and amino acids, with the opened and flattened Ascaris gut arranged as a diaphragm between the two chambers. Fisher (1966a) has also been able to demonstrate active transport of glucose by Ascaris gut but could not demonstrate transport of amino acids from one extracellular fluid phase to the other. Rather, the gut tissue accumulated the amino acids.

The present author studied the accumulation of C^{14}-labeled amino acids by strips of *Ascaris* gut. While these studies were not exhaustive, they showed that histidine, methionine, glycine, and valine were taken up at nonlinear rates with respect to concentration and that some amino acids competitively inhibited the uptake of others. The data do not allow a conclusion as to whether active transport was involved but do show that the entry of these amino acids into *Ascaris* gut tissue occurs by a mediated process having some specificity (either facilitated diffusion or active transport).

Fairbairn (1960) suggested that glucose absorption in nematodes might be favored by the rapid conversion of glucose to trehalose by intestinal and other tissues, since it had been shown that the trehalose content of nematodes is high (Fairbairn and Passey, 1957; Fairbairn, 1958). In a study of trehalose synthesis in *Ascaris* tissues, the gut was found to be the only tissue (except for cuticle and perienteric fluid) in which trehalose synthesis could not be demonstrated. While this does not strongly support Fairbairn's hypothesis, it does not alter the fact that glucose is rapidly converted to trehalose in *Ascaris* and that the nematode thus minimizes the work required to retain a low molecular weight energy source in the perienteric fluid which is separated from the gut lumen by a monolayer of cells. This may assume additional significance when it is recalled that, at least in *Ascaris*, the gut probably also functions as an excretory organ (Cavier and Savel, 1954; Weinstein, 1960; Fairbairn, 1960).

Although Zam *et al.* (1963) did not remark on this point, their data on the absorption of vitamin B_{12} by *Ascaris* indicate that the worm accumulates the vitamin to much higher internal concentrations than the concentration of the surrounding medium. It would be of interest to determine whether there is active transport of the vitamin in *Ascaris*. Mention may be made of the effects of the anthelmintic dithiazanine on the metabolism of the dog whipworm, *Trichuris vulpis*. Bueding *et al.* (1961) reported that this drug irreversibly inhibits the uptake of glucose from the surrounding medium and presented evidence that the effect was on uptake rather than on the subsequent metabolism of glucose. This suggests a specific mechanism for glucose transport in *Trichuris*. Fisher (1966b) tested the effects of dithiazanine on glucose transport in *Ascaris* gut and found that the drug blocks the transport mechanism.

Trematodes

There are few data available on absorption in trematodes. Thorsell and Björkman (1965) could not demonstrate pinocytosis of ferritin particles in the gut of *Fasciola*, although they had reported that the tegument of *Fasciola* took up ferritin (Björkman and Thorsell, 1964). Kureleć and Ehrlich (1963) referred to the movements of low molecular weight compounds into and out of the tissues of *Fasciola* as diffusion, although they presented no data that would allow a judgment as to whether this is indeed the mechanism.

Cestodes

At this time, more is known of the processes involved in absorption of low molecular weight organic compounds by tapeworms than is known of any group of invertebrate metazoans, parasitic or free-living. These organisms have certain advantages in the study of absorption in that substances enter the body solely through the external surface.

It has been clearly shown that urea enters the tissues of tetraphyllidean tapeworms by diffusion. Since these worms live in the spiral intestine of elasmobranch fishes in high concentrations of urea (200 to 500 mM) and this substance freely enters the parasite's tissues by diffusion, it is not surprising to find that urea comprises nearly 4 percent of the dry body weight in *Calliobothrium* (Read *et al.*, 1959). Evidence for diffusion as mechanism is as follows: The initial rate of entry is a linear function of the concentration of urea in the surrounding medium; urea in the tissue water comes to equilibrium on a mole-to-mole basis with that in the external fluid; Q_{10} for the entry process is 1.4–1.5 (Read *et al.*, 1959; Simmons *et al.*, 1960). It would be of considerable interest to determine the properties of the entry process for urea in the trypanorhynchid cestodes which live in the same intestinal environment as the tetraphyllideans. The trypanorhynchids metabolize urea at very high rates (Simmons, 1961) and attempts to obtain good measurements of absorption kinetics have been technically difficult.

At relatively high concentrations, purines and pyrimidines enter the tissues of *Hymenolepis diminuta* predominantly by diffusion. However, at low concentrations, a mediated process of absorption (active transport or facilitated diffusion) was readily detected. The use of a competitive inhibitor, such as hypoxanthine acting as an inhibitor of uracil absorption, allowed resolution of the two processes at intermediate concentrations (Fig. 3). Of considerable interest was the finding that, in some instances, the addition of a second pyrimidine, such as thymine, stimulated the absorption of another pyrimidine, such as uracil. The kinetics of the stimulation indicated that the effect was specifically on permeation rather than some more generalized effect on metabolism (MacInnis *et al.*, 1965).

The nucleosides, uridine, inosine, and adenosine, are absorbed by

112 CLARK P. READ

either facilitated diffusion or active transport in *Hymenolepis*. Pairs of ribosides compete for the uptake mechanism and the initial rate of riboside uptake was shown to be nonlinear with respect to concentration. Purines and pyrimidines had no significant effect on nucleoside absorption, except for hypoxanthine, which stimulated nucleoside uptake, an effect opposite to that produced by hypoxanthine on purine or pyrimidine uptake (MacInnis and Litchford, 1965, 1966; MacInnis *et al.*, 1965).

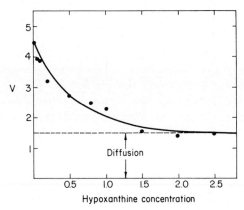

FIG. 3. The effect of increasing hypoxanthine concentration on the uptake of 0.02 mM uracil by *Hymenolepis*.

It has been shown that glucose is accumulated against a concentration difference by *Hymenolepis diminuta* (Phifer, 1960b; Fisher, 1965), *Hydatigera taeniaeformis* (von Brand *et al.*, 1964), and *Calliobothrium verticillatum* (Fisher, 1966). Phifer (1960a) found that the uptake of glucose by *Hymenolepis* was nonlinear with respect to concentration and the kinetics were typical of those seen in other mediated transport systems. Glucose transport was inhibited by iodoacetate, *p*-chloromercuribenzoate, taurocholate, and phlorizin; the inhibition by phlorizin was shown to be neither competitive nor noncompetitive, in the definitive sense of these terms. Phlorizin also inhibits the consumption of glucose by *Oochoristica, Phyllobothrium, Ophiotaenia,* and *Hydatigera* (Laurie, 1957, 1961; von Brand *et al.*, 1964). With *Hymenolepis*, Phifer (1960a) determined the K_t (concentration yielding half-maximal velocity) in short-interval experiments of 60-second duration, using labeled glucose, and obtained a value of 1.53 mM. Phifer also determined K_t by incubating for 30 minutes and analyzing the medium for glucose disappearance; in these experiments, K_t was 1.65 mM. From independent experiments, Read (1961) reported a K_t of 1.6 mM for glucose and 5.1 mM for galactose absorption.

Von Brand *et al.* (1964) concluded that adult *Hydatigera taeniaeformis* consumed glucose *in vitro* at rates which were independent of glucose concentration between 12.5 mg per 100 ml and 100 mg per 100 ml. In these experiments, the incubation volume was altered so that the total amount of glucose available to the worms was the same at all concentrations and the worms were incubated for a fixed interval of 2 hours. Glucose disappearance from the medium at the end of the 2-hour period was measured. However, there appear to be some contradictions in different experiments reported by von Brand *et al.* When adults of *Hydatigera* were incubated at concentrations of 50 and 100 mg per 100 ml in a total volume of 10 ml in each case, the mean glucose uptake was 230 and 304, respectively, under aerobic conditions and 250 and 476, respectively, under anaerobic conditions (Table I of von Brand *et al.*). On the other hand, when the volumes were altered so that worms incubated in 50 mg per 100 ml were in a 10-ml volume while those in a concentration of 100 mg per 100 ml were in a 5-ml volume, the respective uptakes at these two concentrations were 290 and 284 aerobically and 329 and 298 anaerobically (Table IV of von Brand *et al.*). This strongly suggests that the rates observed by von Brand *et al.* in different experiments represent the consumption in 2 hours under conditions such that change in concentration due to removal of glucose is sharply rate limiting before the end of 2 hours. It leaves open the question of whether the consumption, measured after 2 hours in these experiments, is proportional to the initial rate. It seems quite likely that in a 2-hour incubation, absorption by the worm will have reached some kind of steady state, that being defined as a condition in which influx rate equals efflux rate, with net uptake per unit time changing to a function of internal glucose utilization.

Von Brand *et al.* (1964) showed that in the absence of external glucose, there was a leakage of sugar from *Hydatigera* into the medium and that the addition of galactose increased the efflux of tissue sugar. The latter observation suggests that efflux is, at least in part, mediated and may be related to counterflow of sugars observed in some unicellular systems (Rosenberg and Wilbrandt, 1958; Cirillo, 1961).

Read (1961) found that galactose and several other monosaccharides competitively inhibit the uptake of glucose by *Hymenolepis*. The inhibitory activity, or lack thereof, of the sugars suggested that the transport system for glucose in this worm resembles the glucose transport system of vertebrate intestine (reviewed by Crane, 1960). On the other hand, similar studies by Fisher (in preparation) on *Hymenolepis* and *Calliobothrium* have shown that the transport system of the latter worm differs considerably from the vertebrate gut and from *Hymenolepis*. It would be of interest to compare the properties of the *Calliobothrium* system with that of its elasmobranch host, but data on the dogfish are not available.

Sodium ion is necessary for the uptake of glucose by *Hydatigera* (von Brand *et al.*, 1964), as in several vertebrate systems (Crane, 1960). Potassium ion does not appear to be essential for glucose transport in *Hymenolepis* (Phifer, 1960a).

Many authors (Erasmus, 1957a,b; Weatherly *et al.*, 1963; Nimmo-Smith and Standen, 1963; and others), both parasitologists and non-parasitologists, persist in accepting the notion that phosphatases are directly involved in the absorption of sugars. As a corollary, the phosphorylation of sugar during absorption is implied. This seems to be one of those hypotheses which attained widespread credence and respectability many years ago through its adoption by textbook writers. While there is some probability that adenosine triphosphatase is involved in the driving mechanism for active transport, there is virtually no evidence that phosphorylation of sugar is an event of active transport. Crane (1960) reviewed the evidence for and against such an event and concluded that there was considerable evidence against a phosphorylation mechanism but very little in support of such a hypothesis. A survey of the literature since Crane's review has not disclosed new evidence favoring it. Phifer (1960c) presented direct evidence that phosphatase is not involved in the absorption of glucose by the tapeworm *Hymenolepis*. Concentrations of phlorizin which inhibit glucose absorption have a negligible effect on phosphatase activity in the worm, although the inhibition of glucose absorption and of phosphatase by phlorizin has been used as an argument for a phosphorylation hypothesis. Jervis *et al.* (1956) also observed this discrepancy in the action of phlorizin on glucose transport and phosphatase activity in the vertebrate gut. The phlorizin inhibition of glucose utilization by the worm is a surface phenomenon as shown by the instantaneous reversal obtained by dipping the worms in Ringer's solution (Laurie, 1957; Phifer, 1960c) and by the fact that negligible quantities of tritiated phlorizin enter the tissues of the worm (Read, 1966). Phifer (1960c) also observed that phosphatase activity in *Hymenolepis* was readily inhibited by concentrations of molybdate ion that had no effect on glucose absorption. The common structural characteristics of the sugar analogs which competitively inhibit glucose absorption in *Hymenolepis* also argue against a phosphorylation hypothesis (Read, 1961; Crane, 1960). The most which can be said about a relationship between phosphatase activity and absorption is that there is a correlation between them in distribution, but it can be argued cogently that phosphatases in such cells serve to prevent the uptake of phosphorylated compounds which might upset the control of metabolism. Rothstein and Meier (1949) presented evidence that in yeast the surface phosphatases make available to the cell the organic residues of hydrolysis, the yeast cell being virtually impermeable to phosphorylated sugars.

The absorption of amino acids by cestodes was first studied by Daugherty (1957a,b), who examined the acquisition of labeled cystine and methionine by *Hymenolepis diminuta*. Subsequently, Daugherty and Foster (1958) compared the absorption of the same amino acids by *H. diminuta* and *Raillietina cesticillus*. In these studies it was shown that the rate of absorption was decreased by lowering the incubation temperature or by the addition of another amino acid to the external medium. Although their data did not demonstrate it, these authors concluded that active transport of cystine and methionine occurred in *Hymenolepis* and *Raillietina*. The first demonstration that tapeworms actively transport an amino acid was the observation that *Calliobothrium* accumulates valine against a concentration difference (Read *et al.*, 1960a). *Hymenolepis diminuta* and *H. citelli* accumulate methionine (Read *et al.*, 1963; Senturia, 1964) and subsequent studies in our laboratory by Kilejian, Simmons, and others have shown that a number of α-aminomonocarboxylic acids are accumulated by *H. diminuta* against a concentration difference.

The uptake of valine, leucine, serine, and lysine by *Calliobothrium* is nonlinear with respect to concentration and valine uptake is inhibited by several inhibitors of energy metabolism. Further, the uptake of valine by this worm was competitively inhibited by leucine, alanine, serine, and threonine, while the uptake of serine or leucine was reciprocally inhibited in a competitive manner by valine. Kinetic criteria were used to demonstrate that the inhibitions were competitive. Lysine did not inhibit the uptake of the monoamino acids nor was lysine uptake inhibited by the presence of monoamino acids (Read *et al.*, 1960a,b). Applying kinetic criteria, Read *et al.* (1963) examined the interactions in uptake by *Hymenolepis diminuta* of about 50 pairs of amino acids. In all cases in which one amino acid inhibited the uptake of another, the inhibitions were competitive in nature. The absorption of the basic amino acids, arginine and lysine, was not affected by the presence of monoamino acids, except for histidine; a survey of the effects of 26 amino acids on lysine uptake also revealed that absorption was inhibited by arginine, ornithine, and canavanine. Daugherty (1957b) reported that methionine uptake by *H. diminuta* was inhibited by lysine. We have never been able to confirm this. The absorption mechanism (locus) for arginine and lysine is qualitatively separate from the mechanisms involved in the uptake of monoamino acids. Histidine is exceptional; with its imidazole structure, histidine behaves both as a "neutral" and a "basic" amino acid (Read *et al.*, 1963). With a different experimental design, we have demonstrated this overlapping affinity of histidine for at least two separate loci. Arginine and phenylalanine do not interact with each other although either of them inhibits histidine uptake. When arginine and phenylalanine are both added, the inhibition of histidine uptake is the *arithmetic* sum of the inhibitions produced when either is added alone. Such an effect could only be produced if the two inhibitors (both of which are individually competitive) were acting independently at different sites for histidine uptake (Read and Kilejian, 1966).

Examination of the interactions of other amino acids in their absorption by *H. diminuta* revealed certain discrepancies in relative activity as competitive inhibitors. Further study supported the general conclusion that there is more than one qualitative type of absorption locus for monoamino acids but these loci have overlapping affinities for amino acids (Read *et al.*, 1963). Oxender and Christensen (1963) independently came to the same conclusion in examining the interactions of 256 combinations of amino acid pairs in their uptake by *H. diminuta* and the rat intestinal mucosa and of 128 combinations in the uptake by *Calliobothrium* and smooth dogfish mucosa. Using an appropriate program with the IBM 1620 computer, a correlation coefficient analysis of these data has been made, it supports the conclusion that in the absorption of monoamino acids by *H. diminuta*, there are at least three types of loci, reacting to differing extents with individual amino acids (MacInnis *et al.*, 1966). It may be emphasized that three is a minimum. Kilejian (1966) has shown that there are at least two membrane loci involved in proline uptake by *Hymenolepis*. The affinity of proline for the second locus only becomes apparent at relatively high concentrations. Kilejian also obtained evidence for the involvement of multiple loci in proline absorption by the use of competitive inhibitors.

Since tapeworms do not inhabit media containing pairs of amino acids but live in complex mixtures of these compounds, it is of considerable interest to examine the consequences of the competitive inhibition produced by an amino acid mixture on the absorption of a single amino acid component of the mixture. It was found that mixtures containing from 3 to 19 amino acids produce inhibitory effects resembling those seen with single competing amino acids, the mixture behaving as a competitive inhibitor with *Calliobothrium* and *Hymenolepis* (Read and Simmons, 1962; Read *et al.*, 1963). Since the general characteristics of amino acid absorption are those of enzyme reactions, it was reasoned that the enzyme inhibition treatment of Lineweaver and Burk (1934) could be extended to predict the effects of a mixture of competitive inhibitors. The following equation was derived:

$$v = V \left| \frac{(K_t)}{(S)} + 1 + \frac{(K_t)\,(S')}{(K_{t'})\,(S)} + \frac{(K_t)\,(S'')}{(K_{t''})\,(S)} + \cdots + \frac{(K_t)\,(S^n)}{(K_{t^n})\,(S)} \right.$$

where v is the rate of absorption of the single component under study; V is the maximal rate of absorption (estimated by experiment in the absence of inhibitors); K_t is the concentration of the single component giving half-maximal velocity (estimated by experiment in the absence of inhibitors); S is the concentration of the single component; S', S'', S^n are concentrations of each of other amino acids in the mixture; $K_{t'}$, $K_{t''}$, K_{t^n} are inhibition constants of each of the amino acids in the mixture (determined independently in experiments with pairs of amino acids).

The equation was tested with 12 amino acid mixtures acting as competitors of methionine uptake by *H. diminuta* and found to be predictive. Working in our laboratory, Senturia (1964) has shown that it is also predictive for the competitive effect of amino acid mixtures on the absorption of methionine by *H. citelli*.

It should be emphasized that the results just described have been obtained in short-term incubations and involve measurement of rates which are proportional to initial rates. From the standpoint of the ecology of these worms, net fluxes are of primary importance. Read *et al.* (1960a) showed that the efflux of valine previously accumulated by *Calliobothrium* was quite low in saline solutions but occurred quite rapidly if the external medium contained a monoamino acid of another molecular species. Read *et al.* (1963) studied the activity of 24 amino acids as inducers of methionine efflux in *Hymenolepis* and found a rough correlation of activity with their activity as individual inhibitors of amino acid uptake. Read and Rothman (1966) found that addition of mixtures of amino acids also resulted in a marked efflux of previously accumulated methionine, phenylalanine, proline, or serine, and Hopkins and Callow (1966) made similar observations on the effect of mixtures on methionine efflux from *Hymenolepis*. Kilejian (1966), studying the efflux of proline from *Hymenolepis*, concluded that there were two components: a small diffusion efflux was measured in a medium containing a mixture of amino acids other than proline. Further evidence for mediated efflux was the inhibition of proline efflux produced by a previously accumulated amino acid. Worms were incubated for 40 minutes in unlabeled methionine, then for two minutes in labeled proline, and finally in an efflux medium containing unlabeled methionine. Such worms showed a much lower efflux of proline than controls which had been incubated in saline during the first incubation period. On the other hand, the low diffusion efflux of proline which occurs in the absence of external amino acids was not affected by preloading the tissues with methionine. Kilejian's efflux studies provided evidence for compartmentalization of proline in the worm. When efflux of proline, accumulated in a previous 2-minute incubation, was allowed to proceed for an extended period, the rate of efflux became nonlinear. Further evidence for functional compartmentalization was obtained in a different type of experiment: Worms were brought to a steady state with respect to net flux of proline, by incubation for 60 minutes in 0.5 mM labeled proline, and efflux measured during a subsequent period in a mixture of unlabeled amino acids. From these data, a first-order rate constant was calculated. When the incubation was carried out in unlabeled proline and a trace quantity of proline-C^{14} added in the last 5 minutes of the incubation, there was a marked alteration in the kinetics during the efflux incubation. The rate constant was doubled, indicating that the label was not uniformly distributed in the internal proline pool of the worm. Glucose has interesting effects on the accumulation of amino acids by tapeworms. These are not well understood at the present time. The presence of glucose in the medium decreases the amount of valine accumulated by *Calliobothrium* at the steady state (Read *et al.*, 1966) and the amount of methionine accumulated by *Hymenolepis* in a 50-minute incubation (Colthart and Read, 1966). Further, Kilejian (1966) showed that, if *Hymenolepis* is previously incubated for 40 minutes in 4 mM glucose, the subsequent uptake of labeled proline in a 2-minute incubation is markedly inhibited. Kilejian revealed that this is a general effect, since the uptake of "basic" amino acids was affected, as well as that of various "neutral" amino acids. Ammonium ion enhances accumulation of at least some amino acids by *Hymenolepis* and, when glucose is present, tends to cancel the inhibitory effect of glucose on amino acid uptake.

The level of accumulation of proline at the steady state is a function of the external concentration in *Hymenolepis* and is decreased by the presence of other amino acids in the external medium (Kilejian, 1966). The steady state level of accumulation of valine by *Calliobothrium* is also decreased by the presence of a mixture of amino acids in the medium (Read *et al.*, 1966).

Preloading the worm's tissues with hydroxyproline inhibited the subsequent uptake of those amino acids which react with the membrane loci through which proline is absorbed and similarly affected the uptake of other amino acids which enter the tissues through the same loci as proline. Uptake of the basic amino acids, known to enter through completely separate loci, was not affected by preloading the worm with hydroxyproline. Preloading the tissues of *Hymenolepis* by incubation in various other amino acids had no effect on subsequent proline uptake (Kilejian, 1966).

Hopkins and Callow, working in the author's laboratory, verified that in the presence of an amino acid mixture methionine shows a rapid efflux from the tissues of *Hymenolepis*. When *Hymenolepis* was incubated for 10 minutes in methionine-C^{14} and subsequently placed in the intestine of a rat, the loss of methionine from the tissues of the worm closely approximated that observed *in vitro*. In 30 minutes 95 percent of the free radiomethionine was lost from the worms. Control studies showed that more than 90 percent of the label remained in methionine after 120 minutes. Although measurements were not made of rates of incorporation of radiomethionine into protein, it is clear that the *Hymenolepis*-host relationship is very dynamic in character and that flow of compounds from parasite to host occurs at high rates (Hopkins and Callow, 1966).

Acanthocephala

Rothman and Fisher (1964) showed that the acanthocephalans *Moniliformis* and *Macracanthorhynchus* accumulate methionine against a concentration difference. The rate of uptake was nonlinear, with respect to concentration, and it was shown that methionine uptake was competitively inhibited by other amino acids. The inhibition of methionine absorption produced by addition of a mixture of other amino acids conformed to the inhibition predicted by the multiple inhibitor equation formulated by Read *et al.* (1963) for the inhibition of amino acid uptake in a cestode.

Edmonds (1965) reported that the uptake of leucine-C^{14} by *Moniliformis* was inhibited by DL-valine, DL-serine, and DL-methionine and that measurable amounts of radioactivity appeared in the worms when the hosts were given leucine-C^{14} intraperitoneally. Edmonds' experiments were preliminary in nature but point up the desirability of further work on the absorption of nutrients by acanthocephalans in the host.

GENERAL REMARKS

It has become increasingly apparent that understanding of the nutritional relationships of parasites and hosts will require a body of knowledge not yet available to us. Although information on the physiology of vertebrate gut has accumulated at a high rate during the past 15 years, very few data have been gathered with a viewpoint relating to parasitism. A much greater effort to understand the workings of the gut in relation to specific parasitisms is needed.

As a matter of fact, we might visualize a two-pronged, and mutually essential, approach to these problems. The first of these involves the cultivation of host and parasite apart. This will allow definition of "absolute" nutritional requirements (the term absolute is used in a highly qualified sense), but may not allow definition of many features of the integrated host-parasite system. As a crude example, cultivation *in vitro* may not allow realistic definition of the combination of features which allows a parasite to attach to the gut in one host but not in another. *In vitro* the parasite is not parasitic and, in one sense, is a captive. Studying a worm *in vitro* has the same limitations as studying behavior and physiology of caged vertebrate animals. These remarks are not intended to detract from the value of *in vitro* studies since they are indeed essential to understanding the potentialities of the members of a parasitism.

The second avenue of approach involves the investigation of the integrated system. I should like to carefully differentiate this approach from the methodology of traditional physiology and natural history. It will eventually involve the programming of variables in the integrated system. Data from *in vitro* studies will be needed but it is now clear that other types of data are also required. A program for the data-gathering process is required in this approach. We may anticipate that such will develop during the next 10 years.

REFERENCES

Ackert, J. E., and Whitlock, J. H. (1940). Feeding habits of nematode parasites of vertebrates. *In* "An Introduction to Nematology" (J. R. Christie, ed.), Section II, Part II. Babylon, New York.

Alexander, A. E., and Trim, A. R. (1946). The biological activity of phenolic compounds. The effect of surface active substances upon the penetration of hexyl resorcinol into *Ascaris lumbricoides* var. *suis*. *Proc. Roy. Soc.* **B 133**, 220.

Alvarado, R. (1951). El tegumento, la musculature y el parénquima de *Fasciola hepatica*. *Trab. Inst. Cienc. Nat. Acosta* **3**, 1-90.

Beckett, E. B., and Boothroyd, B. (1961). Some observations on the fine structure of the mature larva of the nematode *Trichinella spiralis*. *Ann. Trop. Med. Parasitol.* **55**, 116-124.

Björkman, N., and Thorsell, W. (1964). On the fine structure and resorptive function of the cuticle of the liver fluke, *Fasciola hepatica* L. *Exptl. Cell Res.* **33**, 319-329.

Bogitsh, B. J. (1963). Histochemical studies on *Hymenolepis microstoma* (Cestoda: Hymenolepididae). *J. Parasitol.* **49**, 989-997.

Bretschneider, L. H. (1954). Die submikroskopische Structur der Darmgellen von *Ascaris suilla*: Eine elektromoptische Analyse. *Koninkl. Ned. Akad. Wetenschap., Proc.* **C57**, 524-539.

Browne, H. G., and Chowdhury, A. B. (1959). The ultrastructure of the intestinal wall of *Ancylostoma caninum*. *J. Parasitol.* **45**, 241-247.

Browne, H. G., Chowdhury, A. B., and Lipscomb, L. (1965). Further studies on the ultrastructure and histochemistry of the intestinal wall of *Ancylostoma caninum*. *J. Parasitol.* **51**, 385-391.

Bueding, E., Kmetec, E., Swartzwelder, C., Abadie, S., and Saz, H. J. (1961). Biochemical effects of dithiazanine on the canine whipworm, *Trichuris vulpis. Biochem. Pharmacol.* **5**, 311-322.

Byrd, E. E. (1935). Life history studies of Reniferinae (Trematoda: Digenea) parasitic in Reptilia of the New Orleans area. *Trans. Am. Microscop. Soc.* **54**, 196-225.

Cameron, T. W. M. (1964). Host specificity and evolution of helminthic parasites. *Advan. Parasitol.* **2**, 1-34.

Cavier, R., and Savel, J. (1952). La synthese du glycogene, a partir de quelques glucides et de certains de leurs dérivés par l'*Ascaris* du porc, *Ascaris lumbricoides* Linné, 1758. *Compt. Rend.* **234**, 2562-2564.

Cavier, R., and Savel, J. (1954). Le métabolisme protéique de l'*Ascaris* du porc, *Ascaris lumbricoides* Linné, 1758, est-il ammoniotélique ow uréotelique? *Compt. Rend.* **238**, 2448-2450.

Cirillo, V. P. (1961). The transport of non-fermentable sugars across the yeast cell membrane. *In* "Membrane Transport and Metabolism" (A. Kleinzeller and A. Kotyk, eds.), Academic Press, New York.

Colthart, J. D., and Read, C. P. (1966). In press.

Crane, R. (1960). Intestinal absorption of sugars. *Physiol. Rev.* **40**, 789-825.

Crompton, D. W. T., and Lee, D. L. (1965). The fine structure of the body wall of *Polymorphus minutus* (Goeze, 1782) (Acanthocephala). *Parasitology* **55**, 357-364.

Daugherty, J. W. (1957a). Intermediary protein metabolism in helminths. IV. The active absorption of methionine by the cestode, *H. diminuta. Exptl. Parasitol.* **6**, 60-67.

Daugherty, J. (1957b). The active absorption of certain metabolites by helminths. *Am. J. Trop. Med. Hyg.* **6**, 464-470.

Daugherty, J. W., and Foster, W. B. (1958). Comparative studies on amino acid absorption by cestodes. *Exptl. Parasitol.* **7**, 99-107.

Dawes, B. (1962). A histological study of the caecal epithelium of *Fasciola hepatica* L. *Parasitology* **52**, 483-493.

Dawes, B., and Hughes, D. L. (1964). Fascioliasis: The invasive stages of *Fasciola hepatica* in mammalian hosts. *Advan. Parasitol.* **2**, 97-168.

Edmonds, S. J. (1965). Some experiments on the nutrition of *Moniliformis dubius* Meyer (Acanthocephala). *Parasitology* **55**, 337-344.

Erasmus, D. A. (1957a). Studies on phosphatase systems of cestodes. I. Studies on *Taenia pisiformis* (Cysticercus and adult). *Parasitology* **47**, 70-80.

Erasmus, D. A. (1957b). Studies on phosphatase systems of cestodes. II. Studies on *Cysticercus tenuicollis* and *Moniezia expansa* (adult). *Parasitology* **47**, 81-91.

Fairbairn, D. (1958). Trehalose and glucose in helminths and other invertebrates. *Can. J. Zool.* **36**, 787-795.

Fairbairn, D. (1960). The physiology and biochemistry of nematodes. *In* "Nematology. Fundamentals and Recent Advances with Emphasis on Plant Parasitic and Soil Forms" (J. N. Sasser and W. R. Jenkins, eds.), pp. 267–296. Univ. of North Carolina Press, Chapel Hill, North Carolina.

Fairbairn, D. and Passey, R. F. (1957). The occurrence and distribution of trehalose and glycogen in the eggs and tissues of *Ascaris lumbricoides. Exptl. Parasitol.* **6**, 566-574.

Feist, C. F., Read, C. P., and Fisher, F. M., Jr. (1965). Trehalose synthesis and hydrolysis in *Ascaris suum. J. Parasitol.* **51**, 76-78.

Fisher, F. M., Jr. (1962). Methods for the study of transport mechanisms in the isolated intestine of *Ascaris lumbricoides. J. Parasitol.* **48**, 26-27.

Fisher, F. M., Jr. (1965). Studies on the accumulation of hexoses by cestodes. *J. Parasitol.* **51**, 40.

Fisher, F. M., Jr. (1966a). Personal communication.

Fisher, F. M., Jr. (1966b). Manuscript in preparation.

Gresson, R. A. R., and Threadgold, L. T. (1959). A light and electron microscope study of the epithelial cells of the gut of *Fasciola hepatica* L. *J. Biophys. Biochem. Cytol.* **6**, 157-162.

Hedrick, R. M. (1956). The distribution of succinic dehydrogenase activity in *Hymenolepis diminuta* and *Raillietina cesticillus. J. Parasitol.* **42**, Suppl., 34.

Hobson, A. D. (1948). The physiology and cultivation in artificial media of nematodes parasitic in the alimentary tract of animals. *Parasitology* **38**, 183-227.

Hopkins, C. A., and Callow, L. L. (1966). Methionine flux between a tapeworm (*Hymenolepis diminuta*) and its environment. *Parasitology* (in press).

Jennings, J. B. (1966). Nutrition and digestion in flatworms. *In* "Chemical Zoology" (M. Florkin and B. Scheer, eds.), Vol. I. Academic Press, New York (in press).

Jervis, E. L., Johnson, F., Sheff, M. F., and Smyth, D. H. (1956). The effect of phlorizin on intestinal absorption and intestinal phosphatase. *J. Physiol.* (*London*) **134**, 675-689.

Joyon, L., and Collin, J. P. (1962). Ultrastructure de la membrane cellulaire de l'intestin d'Ascaris du cheval (*Parascaris equorum* Goetze). *Compt. Rend. Soc. Biol.* **156**, 651-654.

Kagei, N. (1961). *Acta Med. Univ. Kagoshima.* **3**, 237 (quoted by Wright, 1963).

Kent, H. N. (1957). Aspect biochimique de la spécificité chez les cestodes. *1st Symp. Specificite Parasitaire Parasites Vertebres, Neuchatel, 1957* pp. 293–308. Univ. of Neuchatel, Neuchatel, Switzerland.

Kessel, R. G., Prestage, J. J., Sekhon, S. S., Smalley, R. L., and Beames, H. W. (1961). Cytological studies on the intestinal epithelial cells of *Ascaris lumbricoides suum. Trans. Am. Microscop. Soc.* **80**, 103-118.

Kilejian, A. (1966). Formation and maintenance of the proline pool in the cestode *Hymenolepis diminuta.* Manuscript in preparation.

Kilejian, A., and Read, C. P. (1966). Migratory behavior of *Hymenolepis diminuta. J. Parasitol.* (in press).

Kilejian, A., Schinazi, L. A., and Schwabe, C. W. (1961). Host-parasite relationships in echinococcosis. V. Histochemical observations on *Echinococcus granulosus. J. Parasitol.* **47**, 181-188.

Kureleć, B., and Ehrlich, I. (1963). Über die Natur der von *Fasciola hepatica* (L.) in vitro ausgeschiedenen Amino- und Ketosäuren. *Exptl. Parasitol.* **13**, 113-117.

Lacey, R. J. (1965). The histological structure of *Crepidostomum isostomum* Hopkins, 1931. *J. Parasitol.* **51**, 24.

Laurie, J. S. (1957). The *in vitro* fermentation of carbohydrates by two species of cestodes and one species of Acanthocephala. *Exptl. Parasitol.* **6**, 245-260.

Laurie, J. S. (1961). Carbohydrate absorption in cestodes from elasmobranch fishes. *Comp. Biochem. Physiol.* **4**, 63-71.

Lee, D. L. (1965). "The Physiology of Nematodes." Oliver & Boyd, Edinburgh and London.

Lee, D. L., and Tatchell, R. J. (1964). Studies on the tapeworm *Anoplocephala perfoliata* (Goeze, 1782). *Parasitology* **54**, 467-479.

Lee, D. L., Rothman, A. H., and Senturia, J. B. (1963). Esterases in *Hymenolepis* and in *Hydatigera*. *Exptl. Parasitol.* **14**, 285-295.

Lineweaver, H., and Burk, D. (1934). The determination of enzyme dissociation constants. *J. Am. Chem. Soc.* **56**, 658-666.

Lumsden, R. D. (1965a). Cytological studies on the absorptive surfaces of cestodes. Ph.D. Dissertation, Rice University.

Lumsden, R. D. (1965b). Autoradiographic and electron microscope studies on the synthesis and intracellular transport of macromolecules in the cestode integument. *J. Parasitol.* **51**, 41-42.

MacInnis, A. J., and Litchford, C. H. (1965). Nucleoside preferring transport locus in the rat tapeworm, *Hymenolepis diminuta*. *J. Parasitol.* **51**, 41.

MacInnis, A. J., and Litchford, C. H. (1966). Manuscript in preparation.

MacInnis, A. J., Fisher, F. M., Jr., and Read, C. P. (1965). Membrane transport of purines and pyrimidines in a cestode. *J. Parasitol.* **51**, 260-267.

Mansour, T. E. (1959). Studies on carbohydrate metabolism of the liver fluke, *Fasciola hepatica*. *Biochim. Biophys. Acta* **34**, 456-464.

Moniez, R. (1884). Mémoires sur les Cestodes. *Trav. Inst Zool. Lille Sta. Maratime Wimereux* **3**, Part 2.

Mueller, J. F. (1929). Studies on the microscopal anatomy and physiology of *Ascaris lumbricoides* and *Ascaris megalocephala*. *Z. Zellforsch. Mikroskop. Anat.* **8**, 361-403.

Müller, W. (1923). Die Nahrung von *Fasciola hepatica* und ihre Verdaung. *Zool. Anz.* **57**, 273-281.

Nimmo-Smith, R. H., and Standen, O. D. (1963). Phosphomonoesterases of *Schistosoma mansoni*. *Exptl. Parasitol.* **13**, 305-322.

Oxender, D. L., and Christensen, H. N. (1963). Distinct mediating systems for the transport of neutral amino acids by the Ehrlich cell. *J. Biol. Chem.* **238**, 3686-3699.

Pantelouris, E. M., and Gresson, R. A. R. (1960). Autoradiographic studies on *Fasciola hepatica* L. *Parasitology* **50**, 165-169.

Peebles, C. R. (1957). Ultra-structure of *Rhabditis strongyloides*. *J. Parasitol.* **43**, Suppl., 45.

Phifer, K. O. (1960a). Permeation and membrane transport in animal parasites: The absorption of glucose by *Hymenolepis diminuta*. *J. Parasitol.* **46**, 51-62.

Phifer, K. O. (1960b). Permeation and membrane transport in animal parasites: Further observations on the uptake of glucose by *Hymenolepis diminuta*. *J. Parasitol.* **46**, 137-144.

Phifer, K. O. (1960c). Permeation and membrane transport in animal parasites: On the mechanism of glucose uptake by *Hymenolepis diminuta*. *J. Parasitol.* **46**, 145-153.

Race, G. J., Larsh, J. E., Jr., Esch, G. W., and Martin, J. H. (1965). A study of the larval stage of *Multiceps serialis* by electron microscopy. *J. Parasitol.* **51**, 364-369.

Read, C. P. (1955). Intestinal physiology and the host-parasite relationship. *In* "Some Physiological Aspects and Consequences of Parasitism" (W. H. Cole, ed.), pp. 27-43. Rutgers Univ. Press, New Brunswick, New Jersey.

Read, C. P. (1961). Competitions between sugars in their absorption by tapeworms. *J. Parasitol.* **47**, 1015-1016.

124 CLARK P. READ

Read, C. P. (1966). Unpublished data.

Read, C. P., and Kilejian, A. (1966). In press.

Read, C. P., and Rothman, A. H. (1966). Unpublished data.

Read, C. P., and Simmons, J. E., Jr. (1962). Competitive effects of amino acid mixtures on the uptake of single amino acids by *Calliobothrium. J. Parasitol.* **48**, 494.

Read, C. P., Douglas, L. T., and Simmons, J. E., Jr. (1959). Urea and osmotic properties of tapeworms from elasmobranchs. *Exptl. Parasitol.* **8**, 58-75.

Read, C. P., Simmons, J. E., Jr., Campbell, J. W., and Rothman, A. H. (1960a). Permeation and membrane transport in parasitism: Studies on a tapeworm-elasmobranch symbiosis. *Biol. Bull.* **119**, 120-133.

Read, C. P., Simmons, J. E., Jr., and Rothman, A. H. (1960b). Permeation and membrane transport in animal parasites: Amino acid permeation into cestodes from elasmobranchs. *J. Parasitol.* **46**, 33-41.

Read, C. P., Rothman, A. H., and Simmons, J. E., Jr. (1963). Studies on membrane transport, with special reference to parasite-host integration. *Ann. N.Y. Acad. Sci.* **113**, 154-205.

Read, C. P., Fisher, F. M., Jr., and Simmons, J. E., Jr. (1966). Unpublished data.

Rees, G. (1958). A comparison of the structure of the scolex of *Bothriocephalus scorpii* (Muller, 1776) and *Clestobothrium crassiceps* (Rud, 1819) and the mode of attachment of the scolex to the intestine of the host. *Parasitology* **48**, 468-492.

Rogers, W. P. (1947). Histological distribution of alkaline phosphatase in helminth parasites. *Nature* **159**, 374-375.

Rogers, W. P. (1961). "The Nature of Parasitism: The Relationship of Some Metazoan Parasites to their Hosts," 287 pp. Academic Press, New York.

Rogers, W. P., and Lazarus, M. (1949). The uptake of radioactive phosphorus from host tissues and fluids by nematode parasites. *Parasitology* **39**, 245-250.

Rosario, B. (1962). The ultrastructure of the cuticle in the cestodes *Hymenolepis nana* and *H. diminuta. Proc 5th Intern. Conf. Electron. Microscopy, Philadelphia, 1962* Vol. II, Art. LL18. Academic Press, New York.

Rosenberg, T., and Wilbrandt, W. (1958). Uphill transport induced by counterflow. *J. Gen. Physiol.* **41**, 289-296.

Rothman, A. H. (1959). The physiology of tapeworms, correlated to structures seen with the electron microscope. *J. Parasitol.* **45**, Suppl. 2, 28.

Rothman, A. H. (1963). Electron microscopic studies of tapeworms: The surface structures of *Hymenolepis diminuta* (Rudolphi, 1819) Blanchard, 1891. *Trans. Am. Microscop. Soc.* **82**, 22-30.

Rothman, A. H., and Fisher, F. M., Jr. (1964). Permeation of amino acids in *Moniliformis* and *Macracanthorhynchus. J. Parasitol.* **50**, 410-414.

Rothman, A. H., and Lee, D. L. (1963). Histochemical demonstration of dehydrogenase activity in the cuticle of cestodes. *Exptl. Parasitol.* **14**, 333-336.

Rothstein, A., and Meier, R. (1949). The relationship of the cell surface to metabolism. IV. The role of cell surface phosphatases of yeast. *J. Cellular Comp. Physiol.* **34**, 97-114.

Saito, A. (1961). Histochemical study on the digestive tract of *Fasciola hepatica. J. Tokyo Med. Coll.* **19**, 1487-1797 (in Japanese with English summary).

Schardein, J. L., and Waitz, J. A. (1965). Histochemical studies of esterases in the cuticle and nerve cords of four cyclophyllidean cestodes. *J. Parasitol.* **51**, 356-363.

Schiefferdecker, P. (1874). Beiträge zur Kenntnis des feineren Baues der Taenien. *Z. Naturwiss.* **8**, 459-487.

Senft, A. W., Philpott, D. E., and Pelofsky, A. H. (1961). Electron microscope observations of the integument, flame cells, and gut of *Schistosoma mansoni*. *J. Parasitol.* **47**, 217-229.

Senturia, J. B. (1964). Studies on the absorption of methionine by the cestode, *Hymenolepis citelli*. *Comp. Biochem. Physiol.* **12**, 259-272.

Sheffield, H. G. (1964). Electron microscope studies on the intestinal epithelium of *Ascaris suum*. *J. Parasitol.* **50**, 365-379.

Siddiqui, E. H. (1963). The cuticle of cysticerci of *Taenia saginata*, *T. hydatigena* and *T. pisiformis*. *Quart. J. Microscop. Sci.* **104**, 141-144.

Simmons, J. E., Jr. (1961). Urease activity in trypanorhynch cestodes. *Biol. Bull.* **121**, 535-546.

Simmons, J. E., Jr., Read, C. P., and Rothman, A. H. (1960). Permeation and membrane transport in animal parasites: Permeation of urea into cestodes from elasmobranchs. *J. Parasitol.* **46**, 43-50.

Steudener, F. (1877). Untersuchungen über den feineren Bau der Cestoden. *Abhandl. Naturforsch. Ges. Halle* **13**, pp. 277-316.

Tanaka, Y. (1961). Histochemical study on tissues of *Ascaris lumbricoides*, with special reference to the digestive organ. *J. Tokyo Med. Coll.* **19**, 1499-1510 (in Japanese with English summary).

Thorsell, W., and Björkman, N. (1965). Morphological and biochemical studies on absorption and secretion in the alimentary tract of *Fasciola hepatica* L. *J. Parasitol.* **51**, 217-223.

Threadgold, L. T. (1962). An electron microscope study of the tegument and associated structures of *Dipylidium caninum*. *Quart. J. Microscop. Sci.* **103**, 135-140.

Threadgold, L. T. (1963). The tegument and associated structures of *Fasciola hepatica*. *Quart. J. Microscop. Sci.* **104**, 505-512.

Tokin, I. B. (1959). Ulrastructure of the brush border of the intestinal cell of *Parascaris equorum*. *Dokl. Akad. Nauk SSSR* **125**, 902-904.

Trim, A. R. (1949). The kinetics of the penetration of some representative anthelmintics and related compounds into *Ascaris lumbricoides* var. *suis*. *Parasitology* **39**, 281-290.

Waitz, J. A. (1962). Studies on the structure and physiology of the cestode *Hydatigera taeniaeformis* Batsch, 1786. *Dissertation Abstr.* **23**, 1840.

Waitz, J. A., and Schardein, J. L. (1964). Histochemical studies of four cyclophyllidean cestodes. *J. Parasitol.* **50**, 271-277.

Weatherly, N. F., Hansen, M. F., and Moser, H. C. (1963). *In vitro* uptake of C^{14} labeled alanine and glucose by *Ascaridia galli* (*Nematoda*) of chickens. *Exptl. Parasitol.* **14**, 37-48.

Weinstein, P. P. (1960). Excretory mechanisms and excretory products of nematodes: An appraisal. *In* "Host Influence on Parasite Physiology" (L. A. Stauber, ed.), p. 898. Rutgers Univ. Press, New Brunswick, New Jersey.

Wotton, R. M., and Sogandares-Bernal, F. (1963). A report on the occurrence of microvillus-like structures in the caeca of certain trematodes (Paramphistomatidae). *Parasitology* **53**, 157-161.

Wright, K. A. (1963). The cytology of the intestine of the parasitic nematode *Capillaria hepatica* (Bancroft, 1893). *J. Ultrastruct. Res.* **9**, 143-155.

Yamao, Y. (1952). Histochemical studies on endoparasites. VII Distribution of the glycero-monophosphatases in the tissues of the cestodes *Anoplocephala perfoliata, A. magna, Moniezia benedeni, Moniezia expansa,* and *Taenia taeniaeformis. Dobutsugaku Zasshi* **61**, 254-260.

Zam, S. G., Martin, W. E., and Thomas, L. J., Jr. (1963). *In vitro* uptake of Co⁶⁰-vitamin B_{12} by *Ascaris suum. J. Parasitol.* **49**, 190-196.

Discussion

L. S. Roberts: With regard to Weatherly's observations on glucose absorption across the tegument of Ascaridia, the amounts involved were so small that we have questioned whether they are physiologically significant. Do you have a comment on this?

Dr. Read: Yes, this is difficult to interpret because they incubated worms in labeled glucose for an interval of time, which was such that one would expect metabolism to have occurred, and they reported no attempt to identify labeled metabolites in the experimental media. Thus after incubation for a period there is a rather small amount of radioactivity which may or may not be of nutritional significance. I think the data are difficult to evaluate since it is difficult to know how much metabolism occurs—how much might have come out.

The Vertebrate Developmental Cycle
of *Babesia* and *Theileria*[1]

MIODRAG RISTIC

*College of Veterinary Medicine and Illinois Center for Zoonoses Research,
University of Illinois, Urbana, Illinois*

Babesia and *Theileria* species are protozoan parasites that invade the blood stream of the vertebrate host. In nature both parasites are transmitted through arthropod vectors and both cause important diseases of livestock in the tropics and subtropics. The development in the respective vertebrate hosts is somewhat different; *Babesia* invades only erythrocytes while lymphocytes, histiocytes, and erythrocytes may be the host cells for *Theileria*.

According to Neitz (1956), *Babesia* and *Theileria* are members of the suborder Piroplasmidea. This suborder includes certain erythrocytic parasites of mammals which do not produce hemozoin and is represented by the families Babesidae and Theileridae. The members of the former family multiply within erythrocytes while the members of the family Theileridae multiply chiefly in the cells of the lymphatic system.

Babesia is the most important genus in the family Babesidae. *Babesia bigemina*, the causative agent of Texas fever, was the first protozoon parasite shown to be transmitted by an arthropod (Smith and Kilbourne, 1893). Systematic control of the tick, *Boophilus annulatus,* resulted in elimination of the clinical infection from the United States.

For many years it was thought that sporadically occurring infections of dogs with *B. canis* were the only babesiosis in the United States. Nevertheless an outbreak of equine babesiosis was described in Florida recently (Sippel *et al.,* 1962) and blood examination using the Giemsa method demonstrated 97 infected horses in Florida and, at least, 6 additional horses in Georgia.

During the course of routine hematological examination of a sple-

[1] Some investigations reported in this paper were supported by research grants Al-03315-06 and HE-05871-05 from the National Institutes of Health, United States Public Health Service.

nectomized deer, we observed large numbers of erythrocytic parasites identified as a *Theileria* species (Kreier *et al.*, 1962). This was the first report of theileriosis in deer in the United States. The only other communication reporting *Theileria* in this country was that of Splitter (1950), who identified *Theileria mutans* in an ox.

This communication describes the results of studies on the causative agents of equine, canine, and murine babesiosis and cervine theileriosis conducted by the author and his associates during the past 4 years. Other recent research developments, particularly in bovine theileriosis, are also discussed. For a more comprehensive review of the *Babesia* and *Theileria* species, the reader is referred to Ershov (1956), Neitz (1956, 1957), Levine (1961), Barnett (1963), and Riek (1963).

BABESIA SPECIES

STUDIES OF A FLORIDA ISOLANT OF EQUINE *Babesia*

The procedure used was the fluorescent antibody (FA) method, which is a serological staining technique. The staining of a parasite by this technique is based upon its serological reaction with a dye-conjugated antibody. If specifically reactive, all major erythrocytic growth and developmental stages of *Babesia* capable of stimulating production of antibody in infected animals should be revealed by the FA technique. The procedures used for extraction of anti-*Babesia* globulin and performance of the FA test have been reported (Ristic *et al.*, 1964).

On the basis of size, mode of multiplication, and number of parasites per infected erythrocyte, it appeared that there were two species of *Babesia* present in equine blood from Florida. Parasites resembling *Babesia caballi* represented a majority of the parasitic population. These parasites were larger than half the diameter of an erythrocyte, multiplied by binary fission, and occurred in erythrocytes singly or in pairs (Fig. 1, a and b). A second form of parasite was typical of *Babesia equi*. These parasites were smaller than half the diameter of an erythrocyte, multiplied by fission into four, a stage of development known as Maltese cross, and occurred in erythrocytes singly or in groups of two to four irregularly arranged forms (Fig. 1, c and d).

Phase-contrast microscopic examinations were performed on the parasites in the blood of horses infected with the presumed Florida isolant which had been freed from erythrocytes by sonic oscillation according to described methods (Ristic, 1962). Some forms of the parasites appeared to be provided at one end with a flagellum-like structure which had rotary movement. To prevent disruption of this structure, infected erythrocytes were subjected to only 30 seconds of sonic exposure. Thin films were made from this material and stained by the FA technique. The forms of the parasite that were observed by FA microscopy are shown (Fig. 2, a–d). Of interest are small cytoplasmic extrusions to the surface of the parasites (Fig. 2, b and c, arrows).

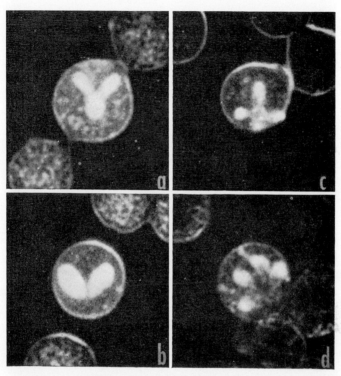

Fig. 1. Stages of development of equine *Babesia* parasites stained with fluorescein-labeled antibody; *B. caballi* (a, b) and *B. equi* (c, d). Magnification: ×1200.

Ultrathin sections of infected horse blood were prepared for electron microscopic study in accordance with described procedures (Ristic, 1960). Electron micrographs revealed two parasites in sectioned erythrocytes (Fig. 3, A and B). A "cigar-shaped" *Babesia* with a centrally located, double-membraned nucleus and endoplasmic reticulum-like structures in the cytoplasm is evident in Fig. 3A. The cytoplasm of the parasite (Fig. 3B) has a peripherally located food vacuole-like structure. On no occasion have we observed the presence of hemozoin in the cytoplasm of *Babesia*. Each parasite was bounded by a single cytoplasmic membrane.

SEROLOGICAL FEATURES OF BABESIOSIS

Diagnosis of the acute phase of babesiosis has usually been made by examination of stained blood films. Animals that recover from acute infection become latent carriers and cannot be differentiated clinically from noninfected animals. In such animals *Babesia* can seldom be found in blood stained films. Demonstration of antibodies rather than the parasites themselves has been found to be useful for detecting *Babesia* car-

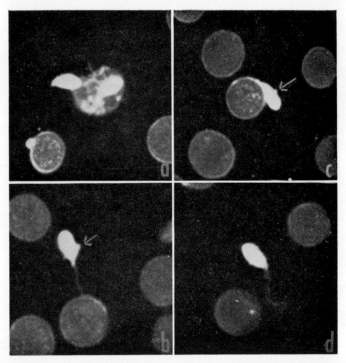

FIG. 2. Tailed forms of equine *Babesia* parasites stained with fluorescein-labeled antibody. The tail of the intraerythrocytic parasite is twisted into a loop (a). The bodies of the parasites (b, c) show a protuberance (arrows). Magnification: ×800.

riers. A complement fixation test was used for diagnosis of equine babesiosis (Hirato, 1945); subsequently the test was used for detection of bovine babesiosis (Mahoney, 1962) and for differentiating between strains of *Babesia canis* (Schindler, 1965). In our laboratory, a method has been devised for preparation of soluble antigen by protamine sulfate precipitation of lysed erythrocytes from *Babesia*-infected horses (Ristic and Sibinovic, 1964). This antigen, termed "PS," was used for gel-diffusion tests to detect serum antibodies in horses convalescing, or recovered, from babesiosis. The specificity of the test was shown by absence of reactions with sera of horses with various other infections including viral infectious anemia. Biochemical studies of the PS antigen revealed that it was mucoprotein in nature (Sibinovic, 1965). More recent studies indicated that a serologically active component of this antigen could with-

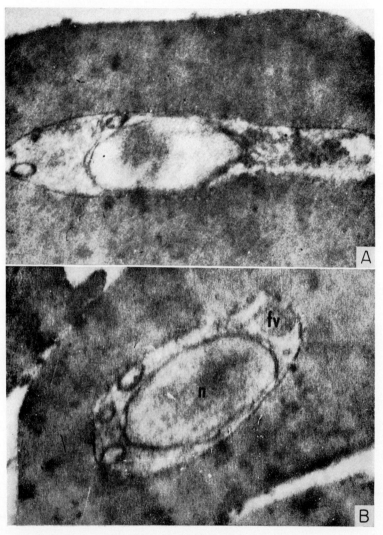

FIG. 3. Electron micrographs of ultrathin sections of erythrocytes infected with equine *Babesia* parasites. A parasite with a centrally located nucleus and a cytoplasmic membrane which tapers into a pointed end, giving the parasite a cigar-shaped appearance (A). An apparently less developed form of *Babesia* whose nucleus (n) occupies most of the organism contains a food vacuole-like structure (fv) in its cytoplasm (B). Magnification: × 30,000.

stand boiling water (approximately 98° C) for 30 minutes, had bio-chemical characteristics of polysaccharide, and could be adsorbed on the surface of sheep erythrocytes. Such adsorbed erythrocytes were used in a passive hemagglutination (HA) test for detection of antibodies in horses with latent babesiosis. There was good correlation between re-sults of the gel diffusion and the HA test. The latter test was also suit-able for titration of serum antibodies (Sibinovic and Ristic, 1966).

On the basis of the observation of D'Alesandro (1963) that soluble antigens were present in sera of rats acutely infected with *Trypanosoma lewisi*, it was thought that similar antigens might be present in sera of animals with acute babesiosis and preliminary experiments have demon-strated this to be so. It was found that the serum from acutely infected animals would react with sera from recovered animals in a gel-diffusion test. Antibodies to antigens in serum of acutely infected animals become demonstrable 3 months after infection and persisted for at least 7 more months. Of 32 fractions obtained by continuous-flow electrophoresis from the serum of an acutely infected horse, seven contained an antigen not found in preinfection serum. Two of these seven fractions reacted in gel precipitation reactions with serum from a carrier horse (Sibinovic *et al.*, 1965).

Analytical ultracentrifugation of serum from acutely infected horses and dogs indicated that there were two antigens with sedimentation co-efficients (S) of 7 to 8 and 20 to 23 in both sera. The validity of the data was confirmed by electrophoretic study and by zonal density gradient centrifugation. The results of the gel-precipitation tests indicated that each of the 20 to 23 S components constituted single cross-reacting an-tigens. The S component 7 to 8 had one cross-reacting antigen in both the horse and dog materials. An additional S 7 to 8 antigen was present in dogs which reacted with sera of recovered dogs only. These antigens were destroyed when heated at 65° C for 30 minutes. They were ad-sorbed to bentonite particles and to tanned erythrocytes and used in separate agglutination tests for detection of anti-*Babesia* antibodies (Sibinovic *et al.*, 1966).

AUTOIMMUNIZATION AND ANEMIA IN BABESIOSIS

Our experiments with *Bebesia rodhaini* infections of rats revealed that the associated anemia was not correlated with the degree of parasitemia. Microscopic examination of the spleen and bone marrow of infected animals showed that both uninfected and infected erythrocytes were en-gulfed by macrophages. Autoagglutinins for trypsin-treated autologous or homologous erythrocytes were detected in sera of a number of infected rats. The appearance of the agglutinins was correlated with maximal anemia and with appearance of marked erythrophagocytosis (Schroeder *et al.*, 1966). In view of the analogy of these findings with those from studies of *Anaplasma marginale* of cattle (Ristic, 1961; Mann and Ristic, 1963; Kreier *et al.*, 1964; Schroeder and Ristic, 1965) and *Plasmodium berghei* of rats (Zuckerman, 1960; Cox *et al.*, 1965) it is suggested that the anemia associated with *B. rodhaini* infections of rats may be the result of autoimmunization.

DISCUSSION

Our observations indicated that two species of parasites probably have been involved in equine babesiosis in Florida. However, confirmation must await isolation of at least one of the two Babesia species. Cross-serological absorption, followed by application of FA-antibody, precipitation, and agglutination techniques with absorbed serum should help ascertain whether there are different as well as common antigens for each species. On the basis of the FA studies, we have seen no serological cross reaction between *B. caballi*, *B. canis*, and *B. rodhaini*. Thus, the FA test may prove useful as a means of determining speciation of blood protozoan parasites.

The tailed forms of *Babesia* that were demonstrated by phase and FA microscopy have been observed early in infection. They may be confined to certain growth and developmental stages of the parasite. The tails or fibrils have a resemblance to those observed by Huff and his associates (1960) in the merozoites of *Plasmodium gallinaceum* by means of time-lapse photomicrography. However, the cytoplasmic extrusions demonstrated on some of the tailed forms also resemble the undulating membranes of some protozoa.

It was indicated that intracellular phagotrophy, similar to that observed in malaria parasites (Rudzinska and Trager, 1957, 1959) may take place in equine *Babesia*. There was, however, no residual hemozoin present in the cytoplasm of the parasite. This observation confirms the suggestion made by Rudzinska and Trager (1962) that the digestion of hemoglobin by *B. rodhaini*, unlike that of *Plasmodium* spp., is a complete process which leaves no hemozoin in the parasite's cytoplasm.

Equine babesiosis had been considered to be exotic to the United States until recently (Maurer, 1962). The relatively rapid spread of the infection in various localities of Florida and Georgia, after its apparent introduction from the Caribbean area, indicated that common and geographically well-distributed arthropod vectors existed in this country. At least one species of tick, *Dermacentor nitens*, has been incriminated as a vector (Roby and Anthony, 1963). Development of serological tests for detection of carrier or subclinical forms of babesiosis should contribute greatly to control of the disease.

The study of the soluble serum antigens of *Babesia* appears to offer great possibilities toward understanding of the mechanism of acquired immunity. It appears that these antigens develop during the acute phase of the infection when maximal numbers of erythrocytes are parasitized by rapidly growing and dividing *Babesia*. Antibodies to the soluble antigens became demonstrable first at 3 months after infection. The demonstrability of antibody coincides with the beginning of the carrier stage when premunition against reinfection is usually found. It is possible that these antigens possess the ability to stimulate production of immune antibody in infected horses or dogs. Preliminary observations in this direction have been very encouraging.

It appears that the anemia associated with *B. rodhaini* infections of rats was better correlated to erythrophagocytosis and the presence of serum autohemagglutinins than it was to parasitemia. Inasmuch as phagocytosis was limited chiefly to uninfected erythrocytes and hemagglutinins which reacted with erythrocytes of uninfected rats were exhibited, it is suggested that this anemia may be a result of autoimmunization. It is further suggested that since infected erythrocytes were also removed from the peripheral circulation by phagocytes, the mechanism may also function in acquired resistance to *B. rodhaini* (Cox, 1964; Schroeder *et al.*, 1966). Investigations directed toward defining the role of autohemagglutinins in the pathogenesis of anemia associated with babesiosis and other blood parasitic infections are now in progress in our laboratory. Preliminary results indicate that autohemagglutinins may function as opsonins.

Theileria SPECIES

DEFINITION AND NOMENCLATURE

The classification of the *Theileria* is still a subject of disagreement among taxonomists. A recent and conservative, but not entirely satisfactory method of classification was proposed by Neitz and Jansen (1956) and Neitz (1957). On the basis of differences between the cycle of development of *Theileria parva*, which multiplies by schizogony within the lymphocytes only, and the remaining *Theileria* species, which reproduce within lymphocytes and in the erythrocytes, they proposed that *T. parva* be retained in the family Theileridae and that the remaining species be included in the family Gonderiidae. Evidence that there is a strong cross immunity between *Gonderia lawrencei*, *Gonderia bovis*, and *Theileria parva* (Barnett and Brocklesby, 1958) has led other workers to the opinion that the morphological characteristics of blood protozoan parasites are insufficient and unacceptable as the sole means for their identification and classification. Thus, Barnett (1963) explained that, "It would also be in accord with the views of the related disciplines of bacteriology and virology where the immunological or antigenic status is the basis of the taxonomic grouping of morphologically or biologically similar parasites."

PATHOGENESIS OF CERVINE THEILERIOSIS

The identification of *Theileria* parasites in a splenectomized deer was based on morphological features of the organism in Giemsa-stained blood films. The time from splenectomy until the parasites first appeared in the erythrocytes was 4 weeks. The animal developed microcytic and hypochromic anemia and a maximum of 50% of the erythrocytes contained one or more parasites. The mean corpuscular volume (MCV) before clinical infection was 36.0 μ^3 and the mean corpuscular hemoglobin was 12.6 $\mu\mu$g; at the point of maximal infection, the mean corpuscular hemoglobin content was 9.3 $\mu\mu$g. During the subsequent 4 weeks, the MCV continued to decrease to a minimal value of 18.0 cμ shortly before the animal died (Kreier *et al.*, 1962). Schizonts (Koch bodies) were seen in impression smears of the bone marrow of one of six artificially infected deer. They were seen in what seemed to be primitive cells of the erythrocytic system, in undifferentiated mesenchymal cells, or extracellularly. The essential pathological changes were nonspecific inflammatory reaction or a hemorrhagic septicemia (Schaeffler, 1962).

MORPHOLOGY OF CERVINE *Theileria*

In Giemsa-stained preparations, the parasite appeared to be pleomorphic. Both nuclear and cytoplasmic components were clearly visible in most of the parasites. The cytoplasm stained light blue, and the nuclear region a deep, purple-red. The parasites were comma-shaped, bipolar, tailed, or resembled safety pins and dumbbells in form. Electron microscopic studies of ultrathin sections of infected erythrocytes revealed that the parasites had complex structural organization (Fig. 4). They had a distinct double plasma membrane and a large nucleus delineated by a double membrane occupying one end of the body. A number of membranous structures were present in the cytoplasm, some of which morphologically resembled elements of endoplasmic reticulum. An electron-lucid polar body, located at the end opposite the nucleus, and a centrally placed double-membraned vacuole could also be observed (Kreier *et al.*, 1962).

The chromatin bodies of *Theileria* gave a pink reaction in the Feulgen

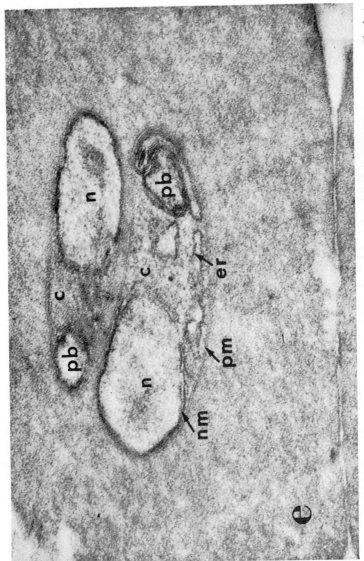

FIG. 4. An electron micrograph of an ultrathin section of erythrocyte infected with two cervine *Theileria* parasites: e, erythrocyte; n, nucleus; nm, nuclear membrane; er, endoplasmic reticulum; c, cytoplasm; pm, plasma membrane; and pb, polar body. Magnification ×82,000.

test for DNA, a dark blue one with toluidine blue, and yellow with acridine orange. A reaction was also obtained with acridine orange and toluidine blue stains for RNA. The parasites were stained blue in the mercuric–bromphenol blue test for basic protein, but tests for arginine and tyrosine were negative. No polysaccharides could be demonstrated in the parasites by the periodic acid–Schiff technique. The Prussian blue test revealed iron in the form of minute dark blue granules in the cytoplasm and lipids were detected in both the nucleus and cytoplasm of the organism by Sudan Black B stain in 70% alcohol. The test for calcium was negative (Schaeffler, 1962).

Staining of the *Theileria* by the FA method gave no serological cross reaction with *A. marginale* or *Eperythrozoon ovis* (Kreier *et al.*, 1962).

PROPAGATION OF *Theileria* IN TISSUE CULTURES

Great progress has been made in devising tissue culture systems for *in vitro* propagation of *Theileria*. The most successful efforts have been with *Theileria annulata*. Working independently, Tsur and Adler (1965) and Hulliger *et al.* (1965) propagated *T. annulata* through several serial passages in monocytic tissue cells. The most intriguing observation was that only those monocytes of the bovine host that were infected *in vivo* continue to multiply and support *in vitro* propagation of the parasites. In contrast noninfected monocytes, although they originated from infected animals, had less or no tendency for *in vitro* growth. On the basis of studies of the effect of sera and cellular extracts from immune animals on the *in vitro* multiplication of *Theileria*, Hulliger *et al.* (1965) concluded that immunity to *Theileria* is cell-bound rather than humoral.

ANTIGENS AND ANTIBODIES IN *Theileria*

Several antigen-antibody systems have been used in attempts to develop a means for the serological diagnosis of theileriosis or to provide better criteria for differentiation among *Theileria* species. Bailey and Cowan (1961) were able to demonstrate a reaction in the agar gel diffusion system between an extract obtained from lymph nodes of *Theileria*-infected cattle and the serum of cattle recovered from clinical theileriosis. Schaeffler (1963) prepared an agglutinogen from *Theileria* species of deer based upon the technique used for preparation of agglutinating antigen from *A. marginale* (Ristic, 1962).

MECHANISM OF IMMUNITY IN *Theileria*

There are two clinical phases of theileriosis (*Theileria parva*) according to Barnett (1963), who investigated the pathogenesis of the disease. The first phase is characterized by schizogony in the lymphatic tissue during which time the animal has rise of body temperature and general depression. In the second, clinical recovery takes place, schizonts disappear very rapidly, and the body temperature returns to normal; however, the erythrocytic parasites persist and even increase in number. This and other observations prompted Barnett (1963) to postulate that different immune mechanisms are involved in each phase, and that if any antibody production does take place, the antibodies of the two phases are serologically different. However, Schindler and Wokatsch (1965) showed with the indirect Coons FA test that fluorescence was not confined to the intraerythrocytic parasites but that lymphocytic stages (Koch's bodies) gave even more intense fluorescence. The latter finding is not inconsistent with Barnett's hypothesis of the existence of "two antigen-antibody systems," since it is possible that sera used by Schindler and Wokatsch (1965) contained both types of antibody. It should be added that by introducing this hypothesis Barnett questioned the existence of protective serum antibody in animals with *Theileria* infection. Barnett's (1963) doubt is further substantiated by recent findings of Hulliger *et al.* (1965) that *in vitro* immunity to *Theileria* in tissue cultures is cell bound rather than humoral.

Discussion and Conclusion

The theileriosis of deer has not yet been assigned to any particular species. It can be said, however, that it is not *T. mutans*, because it occurred in deer and could not be transmitted to the ox or sheep, whereas the *T. mutans* found in a calf by Splitter (1950) could be maintained only in the ox.

The wealth of forms and their apparent irregularity are probably reason for the confusion which exists on classification of the Theileridae and Babesidae. As with most other protozoa, their classification has been based predominantly on morphological and not biological characteristics. Only during recent years has the application of immunology, serology, and immunochemistry become popular in characterizing the blood parasites.

We have learned from the study of biology of other microbes, that is, the viruses and bacteria, that the specificity of proteins that is the basis of immunoserology has been intimately associated with the development of these parasites and has played an important role in their interaction with their vertebrate hosts. It is also known that the specificity of the group and species antigens has been a useful aid for definition of the agents. While we should not expect that emerging interest in biology and particularly immunology of blood parasites will provide all the answers as to their true nature, we may hope that results of these studies may serve as a realistic base for better understanding of the facts and principles by which these parasites can be differentiated.

REFERENCES

Bailey, K. P., and Cowan, K. (1961). Personal communication as cited in S. F. Barnett. (1963). The biological races of the bovine *Theileria* and their host-parasite relationship. *In* "Immunity to Protozoa" (P. C. C. Garnham, A. E. Pierce, and I. Roitt, eds.), p. 193. Blackwell, Oxford.

Barnett, S. F. (1963). The biological races of the bovine *Theileria* and their host-parasite relationship. *In* "Immunity to Protozoa (P. C. C. Garnham, A. E. Pierce, and I. Roitt, eds.), pp. 180-195. Blackwell, Oxford.

Barnett, S. F., and Brocklesby, D. W. (1958). Immunization against E.C.F. with Aurofac. *E. African Vet. Res. Organ., Ann. Rept., 1956-1957.* p. 47. Government Printer, Nairobi.

Cox, H. W. (1964). Comments on autoimmunity in malaria. *Am. J. Trop. Med. Hyg.* **13**, 225-227.

Cox, H. W., Schroeder, W. F., and Ristic, M. (1965). Erythrophagocytosis associated with anemia in rats infected with *Plasmodium berghei. J. Parasitol.* **51**, Suppl., 35-36.

D'Alesandro, D. A. (1963). Soluble parasite antigens in the serums of rats infected with *Trypanosoma lewisi. J. Protozool.* **10**, 22.

Ershov, V. S. (1956). "Parasitology and Parasite Diseases of Livestock" (translated by A. Birron, H. G. Hechler, and J. I. Lengy). State Publ. House Agr. Lit., Moscow. (Jerusalem, Israel, Program for Scientific Translations 1960, available from Office of Technical Services, U.S. Dept. Commerce, Washington, D.C.)

Hirato, K., Ninomiya, Y., Uwano, T., and Kutii, T. (1945). Studies on the complement-fixation reaction for equine piroplasmosis. *Japan. J. Vet. Sci.* **7**, 197-205.

Huff, C. G., Pipkin, A. C., Weathersby, A. B., and Jensen, D. V. (1960). The morphology and behavior of living erythrocytic stages of *Plasmodium gallinaceum* and *P. fallax* in their host cells. *J. Biophys. Biochem. Cytol.* **7**, 93-102.

Hulliger, L., Brown, C. G. D., and Wilde, J. K. H. (1965). Theileriosis (*T. parva*) immune mechanism investigated *in vitro*. Progress in Protozoology. *Proc. 2nd Intern. Congr. Protozool. London, 1965*, Intern. Conf. Ser. No. 91, p. 37. Excerpta Med. Found., Amsterdam.

Kreier, J. P., Ristic, M., and Watrach, A. M. (1962). *Theileria sp.* in a deer in the United States. *Am. J. Vet. Res.* **23**, 657-662.

Kreier, J. P., Ristic, M., and Schroeder, W. F. (1964). Anaplasmosis. XVI. The pathogenesis of anemia produced by infection with *Anaplasma. Am. J. Vet. Res.* **25**, 343-352.

Levine, N. D. (1961). "Protozoan Parasites of Domestic Animals and Man." Burgess, Minneapolis, Minnesota.

Mahoney, D. F. (1962). Bovine Babesiosis: Diagnosis of infection by a complement fixation test. *Australian Vet. J.* **38**, 48-52.

Mann, D. K., and Ristic, M. (1963). Anaplasmosis. XIII. Studies concerning the nature of autoimmunity. *Am. J. Vet. Res.* **24**, 703-708.

Maurer, F. D. (1962). Equine piroplasmosis—another emerging disease. *J. Am. Vet. Med. Assoc.* **141**, 699-702.

Neitz, W. O. (1956). Classification, transmission and biology of piroplasms of domestic animals. *Ann. N.Y. Acad. Sci.* **64**, 56-111.

Neitz, W. O. (1957). Theileriosis, gonderioses and cytauxzoonoses. A review. *Onderstepoort J. Vet. Res.* **27**, 275-430.

Neitz, W. O., and Jansen, B. C. (1956). A discussion on the classification of the theilerioses. *Onderstepoort J. Vet. Res.* **27**, 7-18.

Riek, R. F. (1963). Immunity to babesiosis. In "Immunity to Protozoa" (P. C. C. Garnham, A. E. Pierce, and I. Roitt, eds.), pp. 160-179. Blackwell, Oxford.

Ristic, M. (1960). Anaplasmosis. *Advan. Vet. Sci.* **6**, 111-192.

Ristic, M. (1961). Studies in anaplasmosis. III. An autoantibody and symptomatic macrocytic anemia. *Am. J. Vet. Res.* **22**, 871-876.

Ristic, M. (1962). A capillary tube-agglutination test for anaplasmosis—a preliminary report. *J. Am. Vet. Med. Assoc.* **141**, 588-594.

Ristic, M., and Sibinovic, S. (1964). Equine babesiosis: diagnosis by a precipitation in gel and by a one-step fluorescent antibody inhibition test. *Am. J. Vet. Res.* **25**, 1519-1526.

Ristic, M., Oppermann, J., Sibinovic, S., and Phillips, T. N. (1964). Equine piroplasmosis—a mixed strain of *Piroplasma caballi* and *Piroplasma equi* isolated in Florida and studied by the fluorescent-antibody technique. *Am. J. Vet. Res.* **25**, 15-23.

Roby, J. O., and Anthony, D. W. (1963). Transmission of equine piroplasmosis by *Dermacentor nitens* Neumann. *J. Am. Vet. Med. Assoc.* **142**, 768-769.

Rudzinska, M. A., and Trager, W. (1957). Intracellular phagotrophy by malaria parasites: An electron microscope study of *Plasmodium lophurae*. *J. Protozool.* **4**, 190-199.

Rudzinska, M. A., and Trager, W. (1959). Phagotrophy and two new structures in the malaria parasite *Plasmodium berghei*. *J. Biophys. Biochem. Cytol.* **6**, 103-112.

Rudzinska, M. A., and Trager, W. (1962). Intracellular phagotrophy and *Babesia rodhaini* as revealed by electron microscopy. *J. Protozool.* **9**, 279-288.

Schaeffler, W. F. (1962). *Theileria cervi* infection in white-tailed deer (*Dama virginiana*) in the United States. Ph.D. Thesis, University of Illinois, Urbana, Illinois.

Schaeffler, W. F. (1963). Serologic tests for *Theileria cervi* in white-tailed deer and other species of *Theileria* in cattle and sheep. *Am. J. Vet. Res.* **24**, 784-791.

Schindler, R. (1965). Serological and immunological investigations in babesiosis. Progress in Protozoology. *Proc. 2nd Intern. Congr. Protozool. London, 1965* Intern. Conf. Ser. No. 91, p. 34. Excerpta Med. Found., Amsterdam.

Schindler, R., and Wokatsch, R. (1965). Versuche zur Differenzierung der Theilerienspezies des Rindes durch serologische Untersuchungen. *Z. Tropenmed. Parasitol.* **16**, 17-23.

Schroeder, W. F., and Ristic, M. (1965). Anaplasmosis. XVII. The relation of autoimmune processes to anemia. *Am. J. Vet. Res.* **26**, 239-245.

Schroeder, W. F., Cox, H. W., and Ristic, M. (1966). Anemia, parasitemia, erythrophagocytosis and hemagglutinins in *Babesia rodhaini* infection. *J. Exptl. Parasitol.* (in press).

Sibinovic, S. (1965). Serologic activity and biologic properties of a soluble antigen of *babesia caballi*. Master's Thesis, Veterinary Science, University of Illinois, Urbana, Illinois.

Sibinovic, S., and Ristic, M. (1966). A passive hemagglutination test for diagnosis of equine babesiosis. Ph.D. Thesis, University of Illinois, Urbana, Illinois.

Sibinovic, K. H., Ristic, M., Sibinovic, S., and Phillips, T. N. (1965). Equine babesiosis: Isolation and serologic characterization of a blood serum antigen from acutely infected horses. *Am. J. Vet. Res.* **110**, 147-153.

Sibinovic, K. H., MacLeod, R. Sibinovic, S., Ristic, M., and Cox, H. W. (1966). Biophysical and serologic properties of purified soluble *Babesia* antigen from infected horses and dogs. *J. Immunol.* (in press).

Sippel, W. L., Cooperrider, D. E., Gainer, J. H., Allen, R. W., Mouw, J. E. B., and Teigland, M. B. (1962). Equine piroplasmosis in the United States. *J. Am. Vet. Med. Assoc.* **141**, 694-698.

Smith, T., and Kilbourne, F. L. (1893). Investigations into the nature, causation and prevention of southern cattle fever. *U.S. Dept. Agr., Bur. Animal Ind. Bull.* **1**, 177.

Splitter, E. J. (1950). *Theileria mutans* associated with bovine anaplasmosis in the United States. *J. Am. Vet. Med. Assoc.* **117**, 134.

Tsur, I., and Adler, S. (1965). Growth of lymphoid cells and *Theileria annulata* schizonts from bovine blood during the reaction period. Progress in Protozoology. *Proc. 2nd Intern. Congr. Protozool. London, 1965* Intern. Conf. Ser. No. 91, pp. 37-38. Excerpta Med. Found., Amsterdam.

Zuckerman, A. (1960). Autoantibody in rats with *Plasmodium berghei. Nature* **185**, 189-190.

Discussion

Dr. Holbrook: At Beltsville we have seen no indication of division by binary fission. In studies by staining and time lapse photography the only division we have seen has been by budding.

Dr. Ristic: I would argue the question that what we see is binary fission rather than budding.

Dr. Damian: Since true autoimmunity is considered to be due to a central failure in the immune response rather than to exogenous antigen, I wonder if the erythrocytic phagocytosis which you mentioned might be due to the adsorption to the red cell membrane of the soluble antigens which you describe, than to be sensitized by antibody followed by phagocytosis.

Dr. Ristic: We are considering that possibility, particularly because we have observed development of a brief period of anemia following injection of soluble antigens into dogs.

Dr. Riek: Budding seems to be the only method of division in the erythrocytic forms of *Babesia bigemina* as far as I can detect. Binary fission may occur rarely or be more frequent in other species. Have you seen evidence in equine babesias of this so-called double "nucleus" observed in *B. bigemina?* The second "nucleus" in *B. bigemina* does not appear to be a food vacuole as histochemical staining does not indicate the presence of glycogen or glycogen-like substances.

The anaplasmoid form you have shown in the electron micrographs—from where does it arise and what is its relationship in the life cycle? Have you evidence of a cycle other than that in the erythrocytes?

Dr. Ristic: No evidence has been observed of the so-called double "nucleus" in equine babesias. We believe that these anaplasmoid forms represent an early stage of development of the parasite; however, we do not exclude the possibility that some of them are Heinz bodies frequently observed in a typical equine anemia.

We have only indirect evidence that the parasite may have a developmental cycle other than erythrocytic. This is based upon the observation of a great temperature fluctuation during a single day followed by the appearance or disappearance of the parasite from the peripheral circulation.

The *in Vitro* Cultivation of Helminths with Reference to Morphogenesis

PAUL P. WEINSTEIN

U. S. Department of Health, Education and Welfare, Public Health Service, National Institutes of Health, National Institute of Allergy and Infectious Diseases, Laboratory of Parasitic Diseases, Bethesda, Maryland

CULTIVATION AS A TOOL FOR MORPHOLOGICAL STUDIES

Until fairly recently, morphological studies on parasitic helminths were conducted primarily on specimens obtained from host animals. Although such material is suitable for diverse types of observations, it is also restrictive in many ways. Growth and differentiation are dynamic processes which are difficult to follow under the cryptic conditions of an *in vivo* situation. The flow of morphological events has usually been interpreted and reconstructed from populations of organisms recovered from a series of hosts infected for particular periods of time. Although a vast amount of important information has been derived from such studies, they have not been uniformly successful. To begin with, the most easily recovered stages of a parasite, usually the mature adults, are the ones that have received the greatest amount of attention. Early larval stages are often difficult to recover, particularly when they migrate extensively, and the discontinuity that may be present between the forms obtained during the course of a study may make the interpretation of morphological changes subjective and hypothetical. Particular periods in the development of a parasitic helminth, as for example during the premolt and molt of a nematode, may be characterized by a profound quiescence. Such stages may be extremely difficult to recover from tissues as when using a Baermann apparatus, since they do not migrate actively.

Most important perhaps is the fact that growth and differentiation, which are ultimately expressed in morphological change, may be dependent upon particular physicochemical triggering mechanisms of the

143

hosts' internal environment, or in the supply of specific nutrients or ratios thereof. Such factors, which have a most important bearing on structural change at a gross as well as cellular level, are extremely difficult to study under controlled conditions *in vivo*. Hopefully, with the development of cultivation methods, they will be more readily subject to analysis under appropriate *in vitro* conditions.

A further problem is posed by helminth parasites, particularly those that are found exclusively in man, such as *Wuchereria bancrofti,* for which no experimental hosts have yet been discovered. In these instances virtually nothing is known of the growth and morphological changes that occur from the time of infection to the development of the adult worm. It is conceivable that cultivation may ultimately be an important tool for the study of such organisms. As a further extension of this concept, it seems probable that cultivation procedures may eventually also play an important role in the study of helminths that are presently virtually impossible to investigate using experimental infections, for example, vast numbers of parasites of marine animals which undergo complex life cycles involving several different hosts. Among marine parasites only adult or larval stages may be known, with no clue as to the further development of either. Or, based on morphological and taxonomic considerations, a hypothetical life history may be postulated connecting various already recognized larval and adult forms which may range through fish, mammal, arthropod, annelid, molluscan, and other hosts in a variety of patterns. Such life history studies have been difficult to conduct and complete *in vivo* for many obvious reasons. Often the experimental hosts are large animals, wide-ranging in habitat, which are virtually impossible to maintain under laboratory conditions for the relatively long periods of time necessary for the development of the parasite. In addition, it is extremely difficult to obtain such experimental hosts which are not already infected, or to maintain them free from further infection. Certainly, cultivation experiments with limited objectives in regard to development are now feasible. Ultimately, with sufficient experience and information, it should be possible to obtain in culture complete life histories of parasites whose natural *in vivo* counterparts are still unknown.

Finally, attention should be directed to the advantages of the examination of living rather than dead specimens. Morphological studies of parasites have all too often in the past been conducted on killed and fixed gross specimens or on tissue sections. Usually this has arisen from the fact that many parasitic helminths rapidly show degenerative changes upon removal from the host, and to prevent such distortions from occurring they are immediately killed and fixed for future examination. Such drastic treatments often destroy and distort many delicate morphological structures and relations of parts. With the development of appropriate conditions for maintenance and growth, living helminths can now be examined, while preserving the morphological integrity of gross as well as cytological features. The useful tools of phase contrast, polarization, interference, and ultraviolet microscopy, microspectrophotometry, and the staining of living organisms with vital and fluorescent dyes, all become more amenable for use with cultivation procedures.

Although few studies on the cultivation of helminths have been deliberately conceived as morphological experiments, many observations have been recorded of structural features and morphological changes of organisms in culture. As a by-product, such observations have made it apparent that a reevaluation and more detailed study of the structure of parasites and the morphological differentiation they undergo during development *in vivo* were frequently necessary in order to establish the validity of the changes noted in culture, particularly when no prior pertinent *in vivo* observations existed. Only a few examples are referred to in the brief account that follows.

CHANGES IN GROSS MORPHOLOGY AND ORGAN STRUCTURE

Table I lists a number of studies that have utilized morphological observations as a basis of assessing differentiation and growth in culture. The cestode studies have relied to a great extent on morphological criteria of strobilar segmentation and organogenesis, especially with regard to the reproductive system and its products. In addition, morphological changes occurring during the cultivation of plerocercoid fragments have been described. Cultivation studies have contributed fundamentally new information on cestode morphology primarily in studies on *Echinococcus*. Early vesicle formation and the development of calcareous corpuscles and scolices were observed in cultures of undifferentiated germinal tissue of *E. multilocularis* (Rausch and Jentoft, 1957). Similar study of *E. granulosus* has revealed that protoscolices can develop into cysts by two different methods (Smyth, 1962). The nature and origin of the outer laminated cyst membrane has been a controversial subject for a long period, some viewing it as of host origin. Smyth's observations on cultured material, however, have clearly demonstrated that the great bulk, if not all of it, is formed by the parasite, and he suggests that the presence of this outer limiting membrane may be the basis for the formation of the unilocular cyst. Inasmuch as this membrane does not seem to be formed by *E. multilocularis,* he believes that its lack may account for the appearance of multilocular cysts, and may provide a structural basis for the differences in cyst formation between the two species.

The various factors that affect the molting of nematodes are poorly understood. Molting in *Trichinella spiralis* has been a controversial sub-

TABLE I

SOME CULTIVATION STUDIES PRESENTING DATA ON
MORPHOGENESIS OF PARASITIC HELMINTHS

Organism	Initial stage	Reference
Cestodes		
Schistocephalus solidus	Plerocercoid	Smyth, 1959 (review)
Ligula intestinalis	Plerocercoid	Smyth, 1959 (review)
Diphyllobothrium dendriticum	Plerocercoid	Smyth, 1959 (review)
Spirometra mansonoides	Procercoid	Berntzen and Mueller, 1964
Echinococcus multilocularis	Larval	Rausch and Jentoft, 1957
E. granulosus	Larval	Smyth, 1962
Hymenolepis diminuta	Early larval and cysticercoid	Taylor, 1961
H. nana	Early larval and cysticercoid	Berntzen, 1962; Taylor, 1961
Trematodes		
Posthodiplostomum minimum	Metacercaria	Ferguson, 1940
Diplostomum phoxini	Metacercaria	Bell and Smyth, 1958; Smyth, 1959
Schistosoma mansoni	Schistosomulae	Senft and Weller, 1956
S. mansoni	Schistosomulae	Cheever and Weller, 1958
S. mansoni	Schistosomulae	Clegg, 1959
Paragonimus westermani	Metacercaria	Yokogawa *et al.*, 1955, 1958
Nematodes		
Eustrongylides ignotus	Larva	von Brand and Simpson, 1944
Ancylostoma caninum, A. duodenale	Egg	Weinstein, 1953
Nippostrongylus brasiliensis	Filariform larva	Weinstein and Jones, 1956, 1959
Hyostrongylus rubidus, Oesophogostomum quadrispinulatum	Filariform larva	Diamond and Douvres, 1962
Various ruminant nematodes	Filariform larva	Douvres, 1962; Leland, 1963
Trichinella spiralis	Infective muscle larva	Weller, 1943; Kim, 1961, 1962; Meerovitch, 1964; Berntzen, 1965
Loa loa	Microfilaria	Taylor, 1960
Dirofilaria immitis	Microfilaria	Sawyer and Weinstein, 1963a,b
D. immitis	Infective third stage	Taylor, 1960; Sawyer, 1963; Yoeli *et al.*, 1964

ject for many years. Larvae digested from muscle and placed in culture have been described as undergoing several successive molts without exsheathment (references, Table I). Meerovitch (1964) believes that the infective muscle form is a third-stage larva which must go through two further molts to become an adult. Berntzen (1965), however, has presented evidence indicating that the muscle form is a fourth stage which can mature to an adult in culture by undergoing only one further molt.

The third molt of *Dirofilaria immitis* was stated to occur *in vivo* between the 9th and 12th day after infection of the dog host (Orihel, 1961). Data obtained from culture (Taylor, 1960; Sawyer, 1963; Yoeli *et al.*, 1964), however, indicated that a molt occurred *in vitro* after approximately 2 to 4 days' cultivation. Subsequent comparative study by Sawyer and Weinstein (1965) to determine whether the *in vitro* observations might represent an artifact demonstrated that the third molt in the dog and suckling rat was initiated *in vivo* about 24 hours after infection, and was completed by approximately 48 hours in the dog and shortly thereafter in the rat. In culture by comparison, molting and exsheathment occurred between the 45th and 65th hours.

EFFECTS OF SPECIFIC PHYSICOCHEMICAL CONDITIONS ON MORPHOLOGICAL DEVELOPMENT

TEMPERATURE

Smyth (1946) established that raising the temperature to 40°C was the main factor in stimulating differentiation of progenetic plerocercoids to the sexually mature adult form. Similarly, a rise in temperature to 37° was needed to initiate the early differentiation of third-stage *Nippostrongylus brasiliensis* larvae *in vitro* (Weinstein and Jones, 1956).

GAS PHASE

Third-stage filariform larvae of *Haemonchus contortus* when exposed to high concentrations of CO_2 *in vitro* were stimulated to form an enlarged buccal capsule and molt to the fourth stage (Sommerville, 1964, 1966). In *Trichinella* cultures, sheath formation could be induced by the simple expedient of change in gas phases, even for short periods (Berntzen, 1965).

CELLULAR AND SUBCELLULAR CHANGES

SPERM MORPHOLOGY

In *Nematospiroides dubius* cultures, sperm in the impregnated females changed from the elongate to the globular form and accumulated in the seminal receptacle, as in worms reared in mice (Sommerville and Weinstein, 1965).

PIGMENTS

Cobamide pigment which concentrates in coelomocytes of nematodes (Weinstein, 1961, 1965) serves as a "vital dye" by which location, migration, and growth of these obscure cells can be more readily followed. The original formation of brown pigment inclusions in the intestinal cells of many species of nematodes will be discussed below.

ABNORMAL MORPHOLOGICAL ASPECTS

The stunted nature of organisms grown in culture, particularly of the adult forms, has generally been noted. It has also been observed frequently that total body development lags when compared with the time in which growth occurs *in vivo* (Weinstein and Jones, 1956; Douvres, 1962). In addition there may be a differential lag in organogenesis, the genital structures sometimes being partially retarded in comparison with the other body structures (Douvres, 1962). Among the nematodes, the separation of the molt may be irregular, resulting in malformed cuticles. In some instances, exsheathment is abnormal and the split cuticle is retained as a bag hanging at the posterior end, or it may not disengage at the oral aperture because the esophageal lining has apparently failed to separate properly. It is apparent that although cultivation procedures already offer an important tool for morphological studies, results must be interpreted with caution and carefully checked whenever possible against material derived from *in vivo* development in a normal host.

LYSOSOMES IN THE INTESTINAL CELLS OF NEMATODES

As an example of a morphological problem at the cellular level which was particularly appropriate for study using cultivation procedures, I would like to summarize some observations made on intestinal cell inclusions in several species of nematodes. The nematode intestine is a tube, the cells of which are arranged in a single layer. Comparative general morphology and cytological features among the various free-living and parasitic nematode groups have been summarized in the valuable review by Chitwood and Chitwood (1950). They have attempted to sort out a rather bewildering array of intracellular inclusions on the basis of color, solubility, and optical characteristics in transmitted, reflected, and polarized light, recognizing that little information existed on chemical reactions. Of particular interest is the widespread distribution among parasitic nematodes of reddish-brown inclusions classified as inorganic sphaerocrystals and olivaceous spheroids, as well as the presence, particularly among free-living nematodes, of "rhabditin," a birefringent sphaerocrystal. It had been reported previously that when third-stage larvae of *Nippostrongylus brasiliensis* began to grow in culture golden-brown spheroidal particles soon became prominent in the intestinal cells, and that this pigmentation could be induced *in vitro* by feeding hemolyzed red blood cells (Weinstein and Jones, 1956, 1959). Examination of filariform larvae prior to inoculation into culture revealed that the intestinal cells contained large numbers of small, colorless, irregularly spheroidal inclusions. Closely timed observations of larvae following their inoculation into culture demonstrated that these inclusions were the sites of pigmentation, and that as cultivation progressed they increased in size to become the previously recognized golden-brown particles. Study of living larvae recovered from rat lungs soon after their arrival at that site following infection demonstrated that the same phenomenon occurred *in vivo*. All stages from the third to the fifth reared in cultures containing hemoglobin, as well as those which developed *in vivo*, contained large numbers of these pigmented spheroids in all the gut cells.

Examination in polarized light of filariform larvae derived from charcoal culture revealed that the intestinal cell inclusions were intensely birefringent and exhibited a Maltese cross, comparable with the rhabditin granules described by Maupas (1900) and Cobb (1914). These birefringent granules were not detected in the egg of *N. brasiliensis* examined by polarized light during the early stages of embryogenesis. However, a few became visible in the primordial intestinal cells of the early C-shaped embryo, and thereafter the birefringent inclusions rapidly increased in quantity as the embryo differentiated. No other cells of the larva but those of the gut contained these birefringent structures. As the hatched larvae developed through the two rhabditiform stages to the filariform, these intestinal inclusions considerably increased in numbers and at no time showed evidence of pigmentation. It was noted that, as the gut cell inclusions became pigmented in third-stage larvae cultivated at 37°C in a defined medium supplemented with hemoglobin, birefringence was lost. A similar loss in optical activity was seen in larvae recovered from the lungs of rats about 18 hours after infection, during which time they had fed on blood. This loss of birefringence was determined to be independent of the pigmentation process, since larvae cultivated at 37°C in a chemically defined medium alone in which pigmentation did not occur showed a similar loss of optical activity in many of the gut cell inclusions within approximately 24 hours. In both *in vitro* and *in vivo* conditions, the loss of birefringence occurred in general in the anterior gut cells first, and proceeded posteriorly.

The intestinal cell inclusions stained intensely in living larvae cultivated in media containing a low concentration of neutral red, the cytoplasm remaining colorless. In similar cultures containing acridine orange, the granules fluoresced yellow-green to deep brick red. Of particular signifi-cance was the strongly positive reaction of the gut cell granules of filariform larvae for acid phosphatase with the Gomori procedure.

In collaboration with Dr. Harley Sheffield, electron micrographs of the intestine of adult worms have demonstrated the pigmented inclusion to be a dense spheroidal particle showing a fine granular structure, enclosed in a single membrane.

Cultivation studies with hatched larvae and the examination of adults of *Ascaris lumbricoides* (pig), *Toxocara canis*, and *T. cati* have given results generally comparable with those described for *N. brasiliensis*. In the newly hatched second-stage larvae of all three species, birefringent gut inclusions are interposed between the lipid globules, which are iso-tropic. The birefringent granules become pigmented a golden-brown color when hemoglobin is fed to the larvae at 37°C, and they also soon lose their birefringence. Both the colorless birefringent and the pigmented inclusions stain intensely with neutral red. Within the gut cells of the adults of these three species, large numbers of yellow to golden brown spheroids are present, comparable with those seen in the cultivated larvae except for their great increase in size; they also stain rapidly and intensely with neutral red. These cytoplasmic particles are compa-rable in size and position in the intestinal cells to the "B-granules" of Hirsch and Bretschneider (1937) and Bretschneider (1954).

In preliminary studies conducted with *Caenorhabditis briggsae* and *Panagrellus redivivus* it was found that both isotropic and birefringent rhabditin particles also stained deeply with neutral red.

On the basis of the results obtained with the intestinal cell inclusions of *N. brasiliensis* with regard to acid phosphatase reaction, vital staining with neutral red and acridine orange, and ultrastructure, it is concluded that these cytoplasmic particles should be classified as lysosomes corre-sponding to the "primary lysosome" of de Duve (1963), as similarly recognized by Novikoff (1963), Allison and Young (1964), and Ogawa *et al.* (1961); a summary of the morphology and cytochemical and bio-chemical characteristics of lysosomes can be found in these publications. Biochemical studies are now needed to confirm this concept. It appears possible, on the basis of the additional data obtained with the ascarids and the free-living species, that lysosomes may be universally present in the intestinal cells of nematodes.

Pigmentation of lysosomes in many varieties of cells is known to occur owing to their accumulating end products of hemoglobin degradation, lipofuscin, and other products of metabolism (review by Novikoff, 1963). Of interest in this regard is the distribution of a lipofuscin-ceroid-like iron-containing pigment found in the gut cells of adult *A. lumbricoides* by Carbonell and Apitz (1959). Iron is also present in the intestinal brown pigment in *N. brasiliensis* as demonstrated by Perl's reaction after pretreatment with peroxide. Particles with similar properties and apparently of the same nature as those in *N. brasiliensis* occur in the intestinal cells of *Ancylostoma caninum* (Browne *et al.*, 1965).

Pharmacological implications are of interest also, owing to the known effect of many drugs on the integrity of the lysosomal membrane, either stabilizing or disrupting it. Membrane injury or dissolution resulting in the release of contained hydrolases may play an important role in cell injury and death (de Duve, 1963). Allison and Weinstein (1965) have found that carbon tetrachloride and tetrachloroethylene will rapidly degranulate neutral red-stained gut cell inclusions of cultured *N. brasiliensis* third-stage larvae and release the dye, in association with the death of the organisms. The significance of this correlation requires further investigation.

A detailed report of the various findings described above will be published elsewhere.

SUMMARY

1. Cultivation procedures will undoubtedly play an increasingly important role in the study of helminth morphogenesis, and has already made important contributions to this field at both the gross and cellular level.

2. Cultivation has proved to be a useful tool with which to study the intracellular developmental history of discrete cytoplasmic particles in the intestinal cells of free-living and parasitic nematodes. The data obtained support the view that these structures are lysosomes. Implications of these findings are discussed.

REFERENCES

Allison, A. C., and Weinstein, P. P. (1965). Unpublished data.
Allison, A. C., and Young, M. R. (1964). Uptake of dyes and drugs by living cells in culture. *Life Sci.* 3, 1407-1414.
Bell, E. J., and Smyth, J. D. (1958). Cytological and histochemical criteria for evaluating development of trematodes and pseudophyllidean cestodes *in vivo* and *in vitro*. *Parasitology* 48, 131-148.
Berntzen, A. K. (1962). *In vitro* cultivation of tapeworms. II. Growth and maintenance of *Hymenolepis nana* (Cestoda: Cyclophyllidea). *J. Parasitol.* 48, 785-797.
Berntzen, A. K. (1965). Comparative growth and development of *Trichinella spiralis in vitro* and *in vivo* with a redescription of the life cycle. *Exptl. Parasitol.* 16, 74-106.
Berntzen, A. K., and Mueller, J. F. (1964). *In vitro* cultivation of *Spirometra mansonoides* (Cestoda) from the procercoid to the adult. *J. Parasitol.* 50, 705-711.

Bretschneider, L. H. (1954). Die submikroskopische Struktur der Darmzelle von *Ascaris suilla*. Eine elektronenoptische Analyse. I and II. *Koninkl. Ned. Akad. Wetenschap., Proc.* C**57**, 524-539.

Browne, H. G., Chowdhury, A. B., and Lipscomb, L. (1965). Further studies on the ultrastructure and histochemistry of the intestinal wall of *Ancylostoma caninum*. *J. Parasitol.* **51**, 385-391.

Carbonell, L. M., and Apitz, R. J. (1959). Histochemical study of a pigment in the digestive tube of *Ascaris lumbricoides*. *Exptl. Parasitol.* **8**, 591-595.

Cheever, A. W., and Weller, T. H. (1958). Observations on the growth and nutritional requirements of *Schistosoma mansoni in vitro*. *Am. J. Hyg.* **68**, 322-339.

Chitwood, B. G., and Chitwood, M. B. (1950). "An Introduction to Nematology," Chapter 7. Monumental Printing Co., Baltimore, Maryland.

Clegg, J. A. (1959). Development of sperm by *Schistosoma mansoni* cultured *in vitro*. *Bull. Res. Council Israel* E**8**, 1-6.

Cobb, N. A. (1914). Rhabditin. Contribution to a science of nematology. *J. Parasitol.* **1**, 40-41.

de Duve, C. (1963). The lysosome concept. *In* "Lysosomes" (A. V. S. de Rueck and M. P. Cameron, eds.), p. 1-31. Little, Brown, Boston, Massachusetts.

Diamond, L. S., and Douvres, F. W. (1962). Bacteria-free cultivation of some parasitic stages of the swine nematodes *Hyostrongylus rubidus* and *Oesophagostomum quadrispinulatum* (*O. longicaudum*). *J. Parasitol.* **48**, 39-42.

Douvres, F. W. (1962). The *in vitro* cultivation of *Oesophagostomum radiatum*, the nodular worm of cattle. I. Development in vitamin-supplemented and non-supplemented media. *J. Parasitol.* **48**, 314-320.

Ferguson, M. S. (1940). Excystment and sterilization of metacercariae of the avian strigeid trematode, *Posthodiplostomum minimum*, and their development into adult worms in sterile culture. *J. Parasitol.* **26**, 359-372.

Hirsch, G. C., and Bretschneider, L. H. (1937). Die Arbeitsräume in dem Darmzellen von *Ascaris;* die Einwirkung des Hungerns; die Sekretbildung. *Cytologia* (*Tokyo*) Fujii Jubilee Volume, Part 1, pp. 424-436.

Kim, C. W. (1961). The cultivation of *Trichinella spiralis in vitro*. *Am. J. Trop. Med. Hyg.* **10**, 742-747.

Kim, C. W. (1962). Further study on the *in vitro* cultivation of *Trichinella spiralis*. *Am. J. Trop. Med. Hyg.* **11**, 491-496.

Leland, S. E., Jr. (1963). Studies on the *in vitro* growth of parasitic nematodes. I. Complete or partial parasitic development of some gastrointestinal nematodes of sheep and cattle. *J. Parasitol.* **49**, 600-611.

Maupas, E. (1900). Modes et formes de reproduction des nematodes. *Arch. Zool. Exptl. Gen.* **8**, 461-624.

Meerovitch, E. (1964). Studies on the *in vitro* axenic development of *Trichinella spiralis* 1. Basic culture techniques, pattern of development, and the effects of the gaseous phase. *Can. J. Zool.* **43**, 69-79.

Novikoff, A. B. (1963). Lysosomes in the physiology and pathology of cells: Contributions of staining methods. *In* "Lysosomes" (A. V. S. de Rueck and M. P. Cameron, eds.), p. 36-73. Little, Brown, Boston, Massachusetts.

Ogawa, K., Mizuno, N., and Okamoto, M. (1961). Lysosomes in cultured cells. *J. Histochem. Cytochem.* **9**, 202.

Orihel, T. C. (1961). Morphology of the larval stages of *Dirofilaria immitis* in the dog. *J. Parasitol.* **47**, 251-262.

Rausch, R., and Jentoft, V. L. (1957). Studies on the helminth fauna of Alaska.

XXXI. Observations on the propagation of the larval *Echinococcus multilocularis* Leuckart, 1863, *in vitro*. *J. Parasitol.* **43**, 1-8.

Sawyer, T. K. (1963). *In vitro* culture of third-stage larvae of *Dirofilaria immitis*. *J. Parasitol.* **49**, 59.

Sawyer, T. K., and Weinstein, P. P. (1963a). The *in vitro* development of microfilariae of the dog heartworm *Dirofilaria immitis* to the "sausage-form." *J. Parasitol.* **49**, 218-224.

Sawyer, T. K., and Weinstein, P. P. (1963b). Morphologic changes occurring in canine microfilariae maintained in whole blood cultures. *Am. J. Vet. Res.* **24**, 402-407.

Sawyer, T. K., and Weinstein, P. P. (1965). Third molt of *Dirofilaria immitis in vitro* and *in vivo*. *J. Parasitol.* **51**, 48.

Senft, A. W., and Weller, T. H. (1956). Growth and regeneration of *Schistosoma mansoni in vitro*. *Proc. Soc. Exptl. Biol. Med.* **93**, 16-19.

Smyth, J. D. (1946). Studies on tapeworm physiology. I. The cultivation of *Schistocephalus solidus in vitro*. *J. Exptl. Biol.* **23**, 47-70.

Smyth, J. D. (1959). Maturation of larval pseudophyllidean cestodes and strigeid trematodes under axenic conditions; the significance of nutritional levels in platyhelminth development. *Ann. N. Y. Acad. Sci.* **77**, 102-125.

Smyth, J. D. (1962). Studies on tapeworm physiology X. Axenic cultivation of hydatid organism, *Echinococcus granulosus;* establishment of a basic technique. *Parasitology* **52**, 441-457.

Sommerville, R. I. (1964). Effect of carbon dioxide on the development of third stage larvae of *Haemonchus contortus in vitro*. *Nature* **202**, 316-317.

Sommerville, R. I. (1966). The development of *Haemonchus contortus* to the fourth stage *in vitro*. *J. Parasitol.* **52**, 127-136.

Sommerville, R. I., and Weinstein, P. P. (1965). Reproductive behavior of *Nematospiroides dubius in vivo* and *in vitro*. *J. Parasitol.* **50**, 401-409.

Taylor, A. E. R. (1960). Maintenance of filarial worms *in vitro*. *Exptl. Parasitol.* **9**, 113-120.

Taylor, A. E. R. (1961). Axenic culture of the rodent tapeworms *Hymenolepis diminuta* and *H. nana*. *Exptl. Parasitol.* **11**, 176-187.

von Brand, T., and Simpson, W. F. (1944). Physiological observations upon a larval *Eustrongylides*. VII. Studies upon survival and metabolism in sterile surroundings. *J. Parasitol.* **30**, 121-129.

Weinstein, P. P. (1953). The cultivation of the free-living stages of hookworms in the absence of living bacteria. *Am. J. Hyg.* **58**, 352-376.

Weinstein, P. P. (1961). El estado actual del cultivo axenico de helmintos. *Acta Cient. Venezolano* **12**, 115-119.

Weinstein, P. P. (1965). Some relations of B_{12}-synthesizing bacteria to nematodes. *J. Parasitol.* **51**, 55.

Weinstein, P. P., and Jones, M. F. (1956). The *in vitro* cultivation of *Nippostrongylus muris* to the adult stage. *J. Parasitol.* **42**, 215-236.

Weinstein, P. P., and Jones, M. F. (1959). Development *in vitro* of some parasitic nematodes of vertebrates. *Ann. N. Y. Acad. Sci.* **77**, 137-162.

Weller, T. H. (1943). The development of the larvae of *Trichinella spiralis* in roller tube tissue cultures. *Am. J. Pathol.* **19**, 503-515.

Yoeli, M., Upmanis, R. S., and Most, H. (1964). Studies on filariasis. III. Partial growth of the mammalian stages of *Dirofilaria immitis in vitro*. *Exptl. Parasitol.* **15**, 325-334.

Yokogawa, M., Oshima, T., and Kihata, M. (1955). Studies to maintain excysted metacercariae of *Paragonimus westermani in vitro*. I. Survival period of excysted metacercariae *in vitro*. *Japan. J. Parasitol.* **4**, 388-393.

Yokogawa, M., Oshima, T., and Kihata, M. (1958). Studies to maintain excysted metacercariae of *Paragonimus westermani in vitro*. II. Growth of excysted metacercariae *in vitro*. *Japan. J. Parasitol.* **7**, 51-55.

Discussion

Dr. Stirewalt: We see similar golden brown globules in the gut ceca of schistosomules grown *in vitro* in Rose chambers under dialysis membranes. Under these conditions the parasites are separated from serum by the dialysis membrane. Presumably there are relatively few red blood cells in the serum. Would you comment on a possible substitute for the red blood cells as a source of this material?

Dr. Weinstein: Of course it would be necessary to confirm that hemoglobin is not passing through the membrane. I think that the pigment need not necessarily be hemoglobin, in nematodes, in fact the golden brown pigment is composed of a multiple number of pigments. It would be interesting to examine cell inclusions in many types of parasites. We know little about the way by which high molecular weight substances enter cells, but pinocytosis is probably one method.

Dr. Harpur: Have you tried tetrazolium salts?

Dr. Weinstein: Not yet; this work is just under way.

Blood Alterations in Helminth Infection[1]

NORMAN F. BAKER AND JAMES R. DOUGLAS

*Department of Veterinary Microbiology, School of Veterinary Medicine,
University of California, Davis, California*

Owing to the physiological functions of blood and its intimate relationships with all body tissues, it is to be expected that in many, if not all, helminth infections slight to extensive alterations may occur in either the formed or unformed elements of this tissue.

Blood changes per se encompass an extremely wide array of subject matter and thus the authors have elected to confine their remarks to alterations which occur in the erythron and which are manifested as an anemia. Further, they will first restrict their discussion to specific examples of helminths which have been shown to produce a specific change in the erythron and in which the mechanism of this change has been elucidated. Subsequent to this, they will present experimental data relative to the blood changes occurring in ruminants infected with members of the family Trichostrongylidae.

No attempt has been made to compile a complete reference list, but rather those publications that will lead interested persons to important references are cited.

The word "anemia" as utilized in this presentation connotes the condition characterized by a reduced amount of hemoglobin per unit volume of circulating blood. The term "erythron" is taken to include all circulating components of the blood, the bone marrow from which these cells arise, and the vascular and extravascular components of the body which contribute to the maintenance of a normal level of functional hemoglobin in the vascular system. This concept of the erythron is illustrated in Fig. 1.

It is apparent from a functional viewpoint that any nutritional, biochemical, or pathological condition that alters the normal dynamics of the erythron will ultimately manifest itself in changes which may be detected in the peripheral blood. These manifestations are most often

[1] Experimental work was supported in part by Western Regional Project W-35 and by USDA, ARS line projects ADP b1-18 and b1-25.

expressed in the development of anemia. Owing to the fact that samples of the peripheral blood are readily obtainable and laboratory methods relatively simple, numerous studies of alterations in erythrocyte morphology of the peripheral blood as the result of disease have been

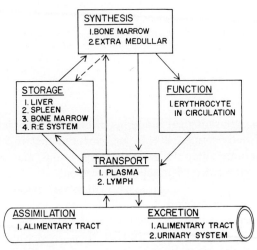

Fig. 1.   An illustrative representation of flow patterns in the erythron.

conducted. These studies have led to a morphological classification (Wintrobe, 1961) of anemias (Table I) which, although not entirely satisfactory from a dynamic view, is nevertheless extremely valuable, and in many instances is quite useful as an aid to the elucidation of the fundamental alteration in the erythron.

In view of the fact that the morphological type of anemia found, as

TABLE I

Morphological Classification of Anemia and Associated Alterations
in the Erythron[a]

Type of anemia	Insult to erythron
I. Macrocytic	A. Deficiency of vitamin B_{12} or folic acid
	B. Increased hemopoiesis
II. Normocytic	A. Acute hemorrhage
	B. Hemolysis
	C. Bone marrow hypoplasia
III. Simple microcytic	A. Malformed erythrocytes
IV. Hypochromic microcytic	A. Iron deficiency
	B. Copper deficiency

[a] Adapted from Wintrobe (1961).

well as the fundamental cause, is often associated with characteristic alterations in iron metabolism it will be well at this time to consider iron metabolism in the light of the erythron (Fig. 2).

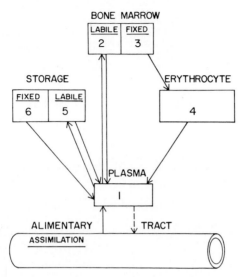

Fig. 2. An illustrative representation of flow patterns in iron metabolism (adapted from Pollycove and Mortimer, 1961).

As noted in Figure 2, essentially all mobilization and transfer of iron from one pool to another occurs through the plasma. In the plasma the iron does not occur as free iron, but rather as iron bound to the β-1-metal-combining protein, transferrin. Transferrin *in vitro* may bind up to 1.25 μg of iron per milligram; however, *in vivo* it is usually found to be only 30 to 50 percent saturated. For this reason the iron-binding capacity of plasma has been divided into two fractions, the manifest iron-binding capacity (MIBC) and the latent iron-binding capacity (LIBC). The sum of these two fractions has been designated the total iron-binding capacity (TIBC) while the ratio (expressed as a percentage) of the MIBC to the TIBC is referred to as percent saturation (Baker and Douglas, 1957a). Studies of these fractions in various disease conditions have revealed more or less characteristic changes, and therefore have resulted in an additional aid to the elucidation of underlying causes of anemia (Table II).

The advent of the radioactive isotopes of iron, carbon, cobalt, and chromium, as well as others, has offered tools for either direct or indirect quantitative studies of iron metabolism and other diagnostic aspects of the anemias. Without presenting detailed methods of study with such isotopes, we will now begin to examine the types of anemias found in helminth diseases.

TABLE II

THE PLASMA IRON COMPONENTS IN ANEMIAS OF VARIOUS ETIOLOGICAL ORIGINS[a]

Anemia	Manifest iron-binding capacity	Latent iron-binding capacity	Total iron-binding capacity	Percent saturation
Pernicious	+	−	−	+
Iron deficiency	−	+	+	−
Copper deficiency	−	+	+	−
Hemolytic	+	$\underline{0}$	$\underline{0}$	+
Hypoproteinemia	−	−	−	+
Infection	−	−	−	−

[a] Symbols: +, increased; −, decreased; $\underline{0}$, normal or slight decrease.

MACROCYTIC ANEMIAS

As indicated in Table I, macrocytic anemia may result from vitamin B_{12} or folic acid deficiency, the best known instance being that of pernicious anemia in man. While true pernicious anemia, that is, that resulting from a deficiency of intrinsic factor, does not occur as the result of helminth infection, the tapeworm *Diphyllobothrium latum* in some instances is capable of producing, in man, an anemic condition which is clinically identical to that of pernicious anemia.

The anemia which results may be quite severe with erythrocyte counts as low as 0.5 to 1.0 million per cubic millimeter and hemoglobin levels as low as 3.0 gm per 100 ml of blood. Prior to the work of von Bonsdorff (1956) the pathogenesis of *D. latum* was generally attributed to toxic or allergotoxic properties; however, it is now accepted that there is a true competition between the parasite and its host for dietary "extrinsic factor," namely, vitamin B_{12}. This, incidentally, is the only established instance of such a competition between host and parasite resulting in disease. That the disease does not occur in a higher number of infected persons appears to be attributable to first, the location of the parasite— those higher in the intestine being in a more competitive position—and second, the quantity of vitamin B_{12} in the diet (von Bonsdorff, 1956).

As indicated, the anemia is macrocytic with an increased mean corpuscular volume, a proportional increase in the mean corpuscular hemoglobin, and little or no change in the mean corpuscular hemoglobin concentration (Wintrobe, 1961).

As in true pernicious anemia the primary change in the erythron is expressed in the maturation of the erythrocyte and synthesis of hemoglobin. There is also a significant decrease in erythrocyte survival time, the rate of removal being increased approximately threefold (Singer et al., 1948). The bone marrow is hypertrophic and megaloblastic.

While the exact role of vitamin B_{12} in the synthesis of hemoglobin is not established, it is suspected from the known functions of vitamin B_{12} that its erythropoietic action is related to its role as a cofactor in the biosynthesis of nucleic acids (Cantarow and Shepartz, 1962), which are essential to the maturation of the erythrocyte and synthesis of hemo- globin. This inhibition occurs in spite of adequate metabolic iron supplies and thus appropriate examination of the blood (serum) will reveal an increased serum iron, decreased total iron-binding capacity, and increased saturation of transferrin. Such a condition if of significant dura- tion would lead to decreased assimilation (absorption) of iron and in- creased tissue iron storage.

It is apparent that the reduction of erythrocyte survival time in per- nicious anemia also insults the erythron and constitutes a hemolytic process. Causes of the reduced erythrocyte survival are not fully under- stood; however, present evidence indicates that they may result from an altered cell membrane and (or) stroma and from an alteration in the environment of the circulating erythrocyte. While the permeability of the erythrocyte is increased to glucose, thiourea, and malonamid, it is unchanged insofar as glycerin is concerned. Further, while there is no change in resistance to hypotonic saline solutions, resistance to hemolysis with saponin is greatly reduced, all of which suggest intrinsic changes in the cell structure (Wintrobe, 1961). Indications that plasma factors may be involved are found in the work of Hamilton et al. (1954) wherein it was demonstrated that red blood cells from normal donors transfused into recipients with pernicious anemia were removed at a rate similar to that of the recipient's own erythrocytes. In addition, when red blood cells of patients with pernicious anemia were transfused into normal recipients, their survival time was essentially the same as normal cells transfused into persons with pernicious anemia.

Treatment of "pernicious anemia" caused by Diphyllobothrium latum can usually be confined to the use of a suitable anthelmintic. In the usual patient marked reticulocytosis will occur in 4 to 5 days after treat- ment and is followed shortly by dramatic increases in both hemoglobin levels and erythrocyte counts with normal values being attained in 30 to 40 days. In instances where the patient is either a "latent" pernicious anemia victim or is on a diet deficient in vitamin B_{12}, it may sometimes be necessary to supplement anthelmintic therapy with parenteral and (or) dietary extrinsic factor.

While Taenia saginata and Ascaris lumbricoides have been associated with "true" macrocytic anemia, there is no evidence to indicate that they or other helminths should be considered as etiological agents of the condition (Wintrobe, 1961; von Bonsdorff, 1956).

The macrocytic anemias that occur as the result of increased hemopoiesis (Table I) are the result of increased demands on the erythropoietic system due to hemorrhage or hemolysis and are usually preceded by a normocytic anemia. For this reason they may best be considered under the normocytic anemias.

NORMOCYTIC ANEMIAS

The normocytic anemias result primarily from acute blood loss, blood destruction, and marrow hypoplasia (Table I). Of all the anemias that occur in helminth diseases, normocytic anemias, at least in the early stages of the disease, are by far the most common. In most instances the mechanism by which the anemias are produced is quite clear-cut, being due to the blood sucking propensities of the parasite. Clinically, however, the course of the disease often progresses to the point that the condition becomes one of chronic blood loss with the ensuing development of a microcytic or microcytic hypochromic anemia.

From Fig. 2 it is apparent that where blood loss through hemorrhage occurs the primary loss of iron occurs from the circulating erythrocytes, pool 4. As a result of this, the avoidance of anemia would require an equally great increase in the amount of iron supplied to the bone marrow from the storage pools, 5 and 6, and (or) that from absorption with subsequent effective erythropoiesis compensating for the loss. In general, such rapid compensation cannot occur and as a result a normocytic anemia results. During the very early stages of blood loss, there may be an equally great loss of plasma and routine peripheral blood studies may not indicate the anemic change. As extravascular fluids enter the vascular system, however, the deficiency of red blood cells will be expressed in reduced erythrocyte count, hemoglobin, and packed cell volume. Since the total amount of iron that can be absorbed is limited, a continued loss of red blood cells (chronic hemorrhage) of sufficient amount will ultimately result in depletion of storage iron and the anemia will become hypochromic microcytic in type. The response to acute blood loss will usually be accompanied by the release of reticulocytes and, in some instances, other immature erythrocytes which have a greater mean corpuscular volume and may thus result in a transitory macrocytic anemia.

Further deductions as to the type of anemia occurring in animals infected with bloodsucking helminths may be made from Fig. 2. For example, if the animal is quite young, a milk diet, coupled with iron requirements for an expanding erythrocyte pool, will have resulted in small amounts of iron in labile and fixed stores. As a consequence, the resulting anemia may be manifested in its earliest detectable state as microcytic or microcytic hypochromic in type.

Of the helminths which cause anemia as the result of bloodsucking activities, the best known are the hookworms and *Haemonchus* spp. Other parasitic diseases, such as schistosomiasis accompanied by capillary rupture and fascioliasis with extensive liver destruction, may result in significant blood loss. Such infections will not, however, be considered in this report.

Hookworm anemia has been known for at least two centuries, the clinical manifestations having been described in the West Indies as early as 1742 (Faust, 1955). The anemia produced is typically described as being microcytic and hypochromic. The amount of blood lost is to a large extent determined by the number of worms present (Clark *et al.*, 1961; Roche, 1962), although the degree of anemia is determined by factors influencing the iron available for erythropoiesis. For example, it would be expected that a given number of worms would produce a much more profound anemia in young puppies which had been infected *in utero* (kennel anemia) than in more mature animals which had acquired the infection by either the cutaneous or oral route. Further, the rate at which the parasitic population is acquired and (or) matures would greatly influence the severity of the initial insult to the erythron and the erythron's subsequent ability to compensate for the blood loss through increased effective erythropoiesis.

Considering the above discussion and the time at which the blood sample is taken in relation to the stage of the disease, one would expect to find a normocytic, macrocytic, or a microcytic hypochromic anemia. As the anemia progressed, the plasma iron (MIBC) would decrease as would the percent saturation of transferrin, and if severe hypoproteinemia was not superimposed, an increase in the TIBC would be found. The use of radioactive isotopes of iron would in most cases reveal a markedly increased turnover rate of plasma iron, although the actual amount of plasma iron transfer would progress from an increased amount to a markedly reduced amount as a function of available iron. The rate of incorporation of isotopic iron in hemoglobin would be greater than normal; however, the total amount of isotope incorporated in hemoglobin and its persistence in the circulating red blood cells would be reduced as a function of the amount lost through intestinal hemorrhage. (See following data relative to haemonchosis.)

In most instances hookworm anemia responds quite rapidly to anthelmintic treatment and supportive iron therapy. Indeed, in many instances iron therapy alone will suffice to return peripheral hemoglobin values to normal. This, however, does not alleviate the excessive demands on the erythron and cannot be considered as adequate therapy. In some instances iron therapy will not alleviate the anemic condition as the bone marrow may become aplastic.

In addition to iron deficiency, reduced levels of vitamin B_{12} in serum, impairment of folic acid absorption, and reduced nitrogen absorption, as well as lack of other nutritional substances (Layrisse *et al.*, 1961) have been observed in human patients with severe hookworm infections. The importance of these observations cannot adequately be evaluated at this time; however, they do suggest the importance of a well-balanced and highly nutritious diet in supportive therapy of hookworm infection.

Whitlock (1950) has presented the thesis that among the Trichostrongylidae, *Haemonchus* spp. are the only members which are capable of producing primary disease in young sheep, although judgment is withheld insofar as cattle and goats are concerned. That this interpretation may be open to question is well exemplified by Wintrobe (1961), who points out that anemia is a symptom of disease and is always secondary. To a large extent Whitlock's conclusion is based on the fact that mineral deficiencies are probably important factors in the pathogenesis of other trichostrongyle infections. While the latter point is undoubtedly true, it is the present authors' contention that classification of *Haemonchus* as an agent of primary disease on this basis is invalid since we have seen such nutritional factors also play a significant role in hookworm disease, and for that matter, in haemonchosis. The authors do find themselves in complete agreement with Whitlock's (1950) statement, "The fundamental questions to be solved in the study of the anemias in the trichostrongylidoses are the identification of the species of trichostrongylids that can cause anemia and the pathogenic mechanism by which they operate." It is with these two questions that the remainder of this paper is concerned.

THE ERYTHRON IN HAEMONCHOSIS

Haemonchus contortus has been shown to produce disease primarily by extraction of the host's blood (Fourie, 1931; Boughton and Hardy, 1935; Andrews, 1942; Baker *et al.*, 1959, Clark *et al.*, 1962). Early in the disease there is a reduced erythrocyte count, a decreased hemoglobin level, and a reduced packed cell volume. The volume and color indices of the red cells are increased and, on examination of stained blood smears, anisocytosis, polychromasia, and an increased number of reticulocytes are found. Examination of bone marrow indicates that active erythropoiesis and a myeloid hyperplasia occur, all of the above being indicative of acute blood loss prior to the development of iron deficiency. Andrews (1942) found that in two fatal cases of haemonchosis 1.57 and 2.5 times the total blood volume were lost in the feces during the course of infection. Further, Martin and Clunies-Ross (1934) calculated that 2000 females would require a minimum of 29 ml of blood per day for egg production alone. Such figures are in good agreement with those reported by Baker et al. (1959) and by Clark et al. (1962). As the infection progresses the peripheral hemogram changes to one of poikilocytosis, hypochromia, and decreased MCV. Such changes were interpreted by Fourie (1931) as indicating exhaustion of the hemopoietic tissues, an interpretation that has been confirmed insofar as iron reserves are concerned (Baker et al., 1959).

Baker et al. (1959) presented data on lambs with naturally occurring haemonchosis which indicated the relationship of this disease to the previous discussions of iron deficiency (blood loss) and of the erythron. In that study, lamb 550A exhibited a macrocytic hypochromic anemia, a type of anemia that might well be expected in the early stages of blood loss with effective erythropoiesis and reticulocytosis. Lamb 549 demonstrated a microcytic normochromic anemia. Lamb 453 showed a macrocytic normochromic to hypochromic anemia which, over the next 9 days, progressed to a microcytic anemia; and lamb 476 exhibited a microcytic hypochromic anemia.

The red blood cell survival and blood loss in lamb 453 were studied by the use of Cr^{51}-labeled erythrocytes. The relative half-life of the labeled red blood cells was found to be 2.8 days as compared with a mean of 13.5 days in two control animals. Analysis of radioactivity appearing in the feces indicated that a total of 250 ml and 175 ml of blood was lost in the parasitized animal via intestinal hemorrhage on the 4th and 10th days, respectively. During that period the average hemoglobin level was 3.25 gm/100 ml. Since hemoglobin consists of 0.34 percent iron, the average daily iron loss would have been 23.5 mg, a very significant amount. Whether or not all of this iron would have been lost from the body is open to question. Roche and Perez-Gimenez (1959) demonstrated that a significant part (average of 44.1 percent) of the iron from intestinal hemorrhage due to hookworms in man was reabsorbed. Georgi (1964), however, has indicated that no intestinal reabsorption of hemoglobin iron occurs in sheep. His work, however, involved normal sheep and did not account for the possible alteration of the hemoglobin molecule as it passed through the intestinal tract of the parasite. The data of Clark et al. (1962) obtained from Haemonchus-infected lambs indicated that significant amounts were reabsorbed.

To further indicate the relationship of haemonchosis to the anemic changes involved, five worm-free lambs, approximately 6 months in age, were artificially infected with 20,700 third-stage *Haemonchus* larvae *per os*. The data obtained (Fig. 3) clearly indicate the early development of a macrocytic (response to acute hemorrhage) anemia. In these animals the MCH did not increase proportionately to the MCV and thus the anemia tended to be hypochromic from the earliest onset. As a result of the sudden demands on the erythron, these changes were at first ac-

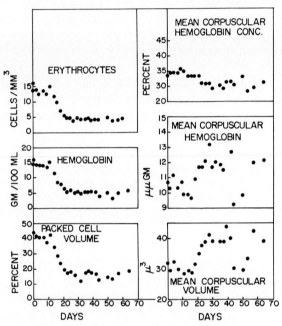

FIG. 3.   Mean erythrocyte count, hemoglobin level, packed cell volume, and Wintrobe indices of five lambs with experimental haemonchosis.

companied by an increased MIBC and percent saturation of transferrin (Fig. 4) but as the demands continued there was a decrease in the MIBC and percent saturation, with a lesser decrease in the TIBC. Had the study been continued, it is probable that an increase in TIBC would have ensued, presupposing that the influence of hypoproteinemia would not have prevented such an event.

In the present study one lamb (2402) was subjected to an iron kinetic study utilizing Fe^{59} on the 31st day following infection. At this time the hemoglobin level was 5.9 gm/100 ml and was decreasing, the PCV was 12 percent, and the erythrocyte count was 5.15×10^6 cells/mm^3. The MIBC was 97 µgm per 100 ml serum. Figure 5 illustrates that as compared

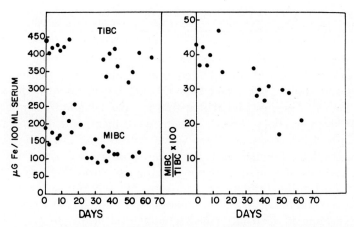

FIG. 4. Mean plasma iron components of five lambs with experimental haemonchosis.

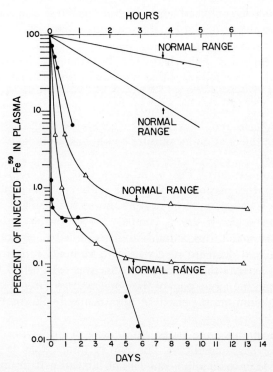

FIG. 5. Plasma clearance of Fe59 in a lamb (2402) with experimental haemonchosis.

with normal the plasma clearance of iron-59 was extremely rapid during the first 4 hours, the half-time being 0.2 hour. Such a turnover rate in this animal would result in a total daily plasma iron transfer of 97.2 mg of iron, that is, 4 mg per kilogram body weight per day, a value approximately four times that of normal 3-month-old lambs and seven times that of 1-year-old lambs (Baker and Douglas, 1957b). Further, in the same normal lambs, it was estimated that 0.83 mg per kilogram body weight and 0.44 mg per kilogram body weight were incorporated into hemoglobin daily. If one compares these values with that of the present lamb and assumes that all of the iron in the diseased animal was used for hemoglobin synthesis, it is indicated that the rate of hemoglobin formation was increased in this instance by approximately five to nine times. If we now take a theoretical lamb of the same weight (24.2 kg) and assign him a blood volume of 1500 ml, a hemoglobin level of 15 gm per 100 ml blood, and a red blood cell survival time of 100 days, we find that he would require 21 mg (0.86 mg/kg) of iron per day to maintain his normal hemoglobin level. This being the case we can then deduce that since approximately 4.6 times as much hemoglobin was being formed by the present *Haemonchus*-infected lamb, the rate of blood removal must have exceeded 175 ml per day since this amount would have resulted in a "steady state" insofar as his hemoglobin level at the start of the trial (5.9 gm/100 ml) was concerned. The fact that his hemoglobin level continued to decrease indicates that more than this amount of blood was removed. This figure of 175 ml of blood loss per day is in good agreement with that of the previous study (Baker *et al.*, 1959) in which the use of Cr^{51}-labeled red blood cells revealed the daily blood loss in a similar animal, infected under pasture conditions, to be between 175 and 250 ml per day.

Further examination of Fig. 5 indicates that the isotopic iron being removed from the plasma equilibrated with another labile iron pool after 24 hours and remained in equilibrium as the result of feedback for a period of 48 hours. If this is compared with the erythrocyte uptake (Fig. 6), it is noted that equilibration terminated approximately 24 hours prior to the decrease in erythrocyte content. It is thus the conclusion of the authors that this equilibrium was established between the plasma pool and the labile pool of the bone marrow (Fig. 2), and further that a hemoglobinization period of approximately 24 hours existed in this lamb.

Figure 6 illustrates a red blood cell uptake of Fe^{59} typical of a severe external hemorrhagic condition. The rate of iron uptake is greater than normal, but owing to simultaneous loss of labeled cells from the peripheral blood the maximal amount incorporated is reduced. If a hemolytic process was present, or if the hemorrhage was internal, it would be expected that a significant amount of the labeled iron would recycle and thus remain in the circulating erythrocytes. That the isotope disappeared from the body indicates that a hemolytic process or internal hemorrhage did not occur or that neither was of much significance in relation to the loss produced by external hemorrhage.

With regard to the etiology of the anemia of haemonchosis, the plasma and tissue levels of copper should be examined at this time since the anemias of copper and iron deficiency are identical in morphological type. In our studies (Baker *et al.*, 1959; Baker, 1960) we have at no time found serum copper levels to be depressed in haemonchosis. Further-

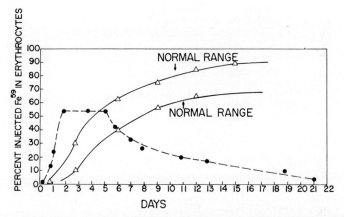

Fig. 6.   Erythrocyte uptake of Fe[59] in a lamb (2402) with experimental haemonchosis.

more, in copper deficiency the utilization of iron would be expected to decrease, a finding not in agreement with the results of the foregoing experiment. It is therefore concluded that the anemia of haemonchosis is due to the bloodsucking habits of the worm and, consequently, to iron deficiency which results. Whether or not there is also a decrease in the absorption of iron has not been established, although such an event has been suggested where concurrent infections with other gastrointestinal nematodes occur (Baker *et al.*, 1959). In addition, depletion of available protein may occur and contribute to eventual bone marrow exhaustion.

From a therapeutic standpoint, it would appear that suitable anthelmintic treatment followed by supportive therapy would be adequate in haemonchosis. The observation of Baker *et al.* (1959), however, that tissue iron stores were still quite deficient, even 60 days following anthelmintic therapy and iron supplement, would indicate that parenteral iron or blood transfusion would be indicated in extreme cases. In this regard, we would like first to discuss a clinical case of haemonchosis, treated by blood transfusion following anthelmintic therapy, and then briefly indicate a problem associated with blood transfusion in sheep.

In the first instance a mature, although young, ram was admitted to the University of California Veterinary Clinic with an advanced case of haemonchosis. In addition to anthelmintic treatment, he was given blood transfusions. The course of the disease and hematological observations are presented in Fig. 7. It is noted first that even though rather large amounts of blood, 750 ml on day 0 and 500 ml on day 5, were admin-

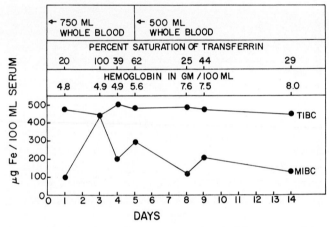

Fig. 7.   Hematological observations in a ram that had been treated for advanced haemonchosis.

istered by transfusion, there was not a proportional increase in the circulating hemoglobin. Further, it was noted that 72 hours following the first transfusion 100 percent saturation of transferrin occurred. In a much shorter time, a similar but not so dramatic rise in saturation of transferrin occurred following the second transfusion. These observations suggested the presence of isoimmune antibodies and an immunological removal of the transfused erythrocytes. A similar condition has also been observed in cattle (Baker *et al.*, 1961). In view of this, cross-transfusion studies were conducted in sheep. Six sheep, including one pair of homozygous twins, were utilized as principals in the study. In three sheep, donor blood, labeled with Fe[59] from normal sheep, in amounts of 1000 ml, was transfused into the jugular vein immediately after the removal of an equal amount of blood. In the case of the homozygous twins, one of whose red blood cells were labeled, 1055 ml of blood was removed from each and immediately transfused into the other. In two additional sheep this same procedure was followed. In one additional animal, 1400 ml of labeled blood was removed and then transfused into the same animal. The survival of transfused cells was followed for a 3-week period.

In the three animals receiving labeled blood from random donors the transfused cells were entirely removed between 120 and 200 hours following transfusion; in all other animals the cells appeared to have a normal survival time. It is, therefore, apparent that in a fairly high percentage of random transfusions in sheep one can expect isoimmune antibodies to result in removal of the functional erythrocytes transfused. From a therapeutic standpoint in haemonchosis, however, it was noted that by 400 hours after the transfusion approximately 60 percent of the iron-59 from hemoylzed red blood cells reappeared in the circulating hemoglobin. Thus even though the transfused cells may be short-lived, the transfusion constitutes parenteral iron therapy.

THE ERYTHRON IN OTHER TRICHOSTRONGYLE INFECTIONS

Herlich (1959) and Mahrt et al. (1964) did not find anemic changes in cattle infected with Ostertagia ostertagi while Threlkeld (1948) reported significant reductions in hemoglobin levels of calves infected with this nematode and Todd et al. (1951) reported a hyperchromic macrocytic anemia in lambs infected with O. circumcincta. Leland et al. (1960) reported an early polycythemic hypovolemia which, if animals survived, became an oligocythemic hypovolemia in both calves and lambs infected with Trichostrongylus axei. Kates and Turner (1960) also found a moderate anemia in lambs infected with this parasite, but Doran (1955) and Herlich (1959) were unable to detect an anemia in experimental infections of calves. While certain workers (Andrews, 1939; Shumard et al., 1957) did not observe anemia in lambs infected with T. colubriformis and T. colubriformis in combination with Nematodirus spathiger, Gallagher (1963) observed reduced erythrocyte numbers and moderate anemia in experimental T. colubriformis infections of lambs. Kates and Turner (1953) reported that they found no significant hematological changes in lambs infected with N. spathiger. Studies with Cooperia spp. (Bailey, 1949; Herlich as cited by Mahrt et al., 1964) have in general indicated no anemic changes.

More recently, Herlich (1962) has been interested in the consequences of parasitism in domestic ruminants as it occurs in the natural environment, namely, as a result of infection with several species of nematodes. With this in mind he studied mixed experimental infections of O. ostertagi, T. axei, T. colubriformis, and C. punctata in calves. Although he produced marked clinical signs and reductions in serum phosphorus, glucose, and protein, at no time did he observe anemia. In actuality, the only change in the erythron he observed was an elevation in the hemoglobin levels and packed cell volumes within one week of the onset of diarrhea. In calves that recovered, these values returned to normal with cessation of diarrhea. These results are of considerable interest to the present authors since the experimental infections resulted in parasite burdens similar to those that are encountered in California where the environment is not normally conducive to the development of *Haemonchus* spp. In dealing with clinical outbreaks, the authors have, in the same herd, observed cattle with hemoglobin levels as low as 5 gm/100 ml, and animals exhibiting identical signs with normal hemoglobin values. It should be pointed out that in contrast to the animals studied by Herlich (1962), in the majority of the animals studied by the present authors diarrhea and other clinical signs often persisted until either death or therapy intervened.

During the past several years the authors have had the opportunity to acquire animals from ranches where outbreaks of gastrointestinal parasitism have occurred and move them to the University of California where studies related to the erythron could be conducted. For the most part the animals have been yearling feeder steers and heifers and have acquired infection on irrigated pasture. When acquired, all animals were showing "typical" advanced parasitism as seen in California in mixed infections of *O. ostertagi*, *T. axei*, and *Cooperia* spp. Clinically the signs are colliquative diarrhea, dehydration, emaciation, and in some instances intermandibular edema. There is often slight pallor of mucous membranes, but only rarely are signs of severe anemia present.

Though the animals were acquired from eight different ranches over several years, the clinical signs and parasitological status of the animals have been quite uniform. Thus, in the present report they will be considered as having originated from a single ranch at a given time.

Studies in these animals have included (1) erythrocyte count, packed cell volume, and hemoglobin level, (2) plasma and blood volume, (3) serum iron components, (4) serum copper level, (5) serum protein and protein fractions, (6) liver copper and iron stores, (7) serum albumin compartmentalization and turnover, (8) iron kinetics, (9) erythrocyte life span as measured by Cr^{51} labeling, and (10) total body water and body water turnover.

The methods utilized in these studies may be found in the following references: Wintrobe, 1961; Baker and Douglas, 1957a,b; Baker *et al.*, 1959, 1961, 1966; Schalm, 1961; Cornelius *et al.*, 1962; Black *et al.*, 1964.

In Table III are found the erythrocyte counts, hemoglobin levels,

TABLE III
HEMATOLOGICAL DATA AND WINTROBE INDICES IN PARASITIZED CATTLE

Animal number	Hemoglobin (gm/100 ml)	Packed cell volume (%)	Erythrocyte count (cells × 10⁶/ mm³)	Mean corpuscular volume (μ³)	Mean corpuscular hemoglobin (μμg)	Mean corpuscular hemoglobin concentration (%)
226	11.5	39	7.71	50.6	14.9	29.4
227	9.4	31	5.86	52.9	16	30.3
228	12.8	46	9.11	50.5	14.1	27.8
230	10.3	36	8.11	44.4	12.7	28.6
231	10.2	34	6.56	51.8	15.5	30.0
232	12.6	40	8.03	49.8	15.7	31.5
233	8.8	28.5	6.10	46.7	15.4	30.9
234	11.4	36	7.88	45.7	14.5	31.6
235	13.5	42	8.80	47.7	15.3	32.1
236	10.4	32	5.27	60.7	19.7	32.5
II-1	5.8	19.0	4.47	42.5	13.0	30.5
II-2	7.2	23.0	4.18	55.0	17.2	31.3
II-3	8.3	26.0	5.26	49.4	15.8	31.9
III-1	5.2	16	4.00	40.0	13.0	32.5
III-2	10.2	32	7.46	58.5	18.7	31.8
36	6.1	19.3	4.2	46.0	14.8	32.2
58	6.6	20.0	4.2	47.5	15.7	32.9
67	7.3	23.5	5.0	47.0	14.6	31.0
86	9.5	26.6	6.1	42.6	15.5	35.7
1579	8.0	25.0	6.35	39.4	12.6	32.0
1580	8.1	28.0	6.60	42.4	12.3	28.9
1581	9.8	28.0	5.75	48.5	17.0	35.0
1582	9.5	29.0	6.8	42.5	14.0	32.8
1583	10.3	32.0	6.9	46.4	14.9	32.2
1584	9.5	29.0	6.7	43.3	14.2	32.8
1585	8.8	28.0	5.5	51.0	16.0	31.4
1586	8.1	25.0	5.15	48.5	15.7	32.4
1587	9.5	30.0	6.45	46.5	14.7	31.6
1588	10.6	33.0	7.75	42.5	13.7	32.2
1589	6.5	22.0	4.70	46.8	13.8	29.54
1188	9.5	28	7.1	39.4	13.4	33.9
1064	9.5	29	7.7	37.7	12.3	32.7
1357	10.5	33	9.75	33.8	10.8	31.8
1189	12.9	38	7.8	48.7	16.5	33.9
1069	10.6	32	8.3	38.6	12.8	33.1
1539	6.9	21.5	—	—	—	32.0
1540	7.8	23	—	—	—	33.9

packed cell volumes, and Wintrobe indices, while Table IV presents the plasma iron components and plasma copper levels of representative animals at or near the time of their arrival at the University of California. It is noted that insofar as the Wintrobe indices are concerned, they are within the normal ranges and thus where anemia has occurred, it is of

TABLE IV

Serum Iron and Copper Levels in Parasitized Cattle[a]

Animal number	MIBC (μg/100 ml)	LIBC (μg/100 ml)	TIBC (μg/100 ml)	$\frac{MIBC}{TIBC} \times 100$ (%)	Cooper (μg/100 ml)
227	173	56	229	76	—
230	180	91	271	63	—
231	145	120	262	54	151
233	165	168	232	50	139
234	200	116	316	63	142
II-1	168	232	400	42	29
II-3	230	218	448	51	21
III-1	94	—	—	—	30
III-2	224	—	—	—	66
36	74	—	—	—	—
58	158	—	—	—	—
67	132	—	—	—	—
86	151	—	—	—	—
1188	108	213	321	33.6	94
1064	81	123	204	39.7	—
1357	126	226	352	35.8	94
1189	118	—	—	—	—
1069	124	—	—	—	—
1539	89	—	—	—	140
1540	93	—	—	—	110

[a] Abbreviations: MIBC, manifest iron-binding capacity; LIBC, latent iron-binding capacity; TIBC, MIBC + LIBC; (MIBC/TIBC) × 100, percent saturation of transferrin.

a normocytic normochromic type. This would indicate (Table II) that the anemia was most likely due to hemorrhage, hemolysis, and (or) reduced erythropoiesis. It should be recalled in this instance, however, that the small size of the erythrocytes of sheep and cattle limits the value of the Wintrobe indices (Whitlock, 1950). Further examination of Table IV, however, indicates that (1) the iron components are within the normal range, (2) the MIBC is raised while the LIBC is normal or reduced, resulting in a normal to increased saturation percentage, or (3) both the MIBC and TIBC are reduced resulting in a normal percentage saturation. This would tend to eliminate chronic blood loss and iron deficiency as a factor in the anemia.

In some individuals (II-1, II-3, and III-2) the plasma copper values are quite low and, as will be indicated later (Table V), liver storage of this element was also low in these animals. Since copper deficiency anemia cannot be differentiated from iron deficiency anemia through routine peripheral blood studies, the finding of such low copper values

TABLE V

TISSUE IRON AND COPPER STORES IN PARASITIZED CATTLE

Animal number	Tissue Fe (mg/100 gm)[a]	Tissue Cu (mg/100 gm)
II-1[b]	1.91	8.7
II-2	44.6	0.6
II-3[b]	1.80	4.4
III-1	19.5	—
III-2	8.22	—
1540	16.8	—
1539	23.1	—
1188	10.8	—

[a] Determinations on wet weight basis.
[b] Determined at autopsy 132 days after anthelmintic therapy.

in these animals was of interest even though other animals (1539 and 1540) with similar degrees of anemia revealed normal serum copper levels. In view of this, it may be well to examine further data obtained from animals II-1, II-2, and II-3 (Fig. 8). Animal number II-2 is not included in Fig. 8 since it succumbed on the 14th day of study. On the first day of the study this animal's hemoglobin level was 7.2 gm per 100 ml and had declined to 5.5 gm per 100 ml at the time of death. At autopsy, liver analysis revealed tissue stores of copper to be 0.6 mg/100 gm (wet wt.) and iron stores to be 44.5 mg/100 gm (wet wt.).

In Fig. 8 it is noted that the hemoglobin levels of both animals (II-1 and II-3) continued to decrease for a period of at least 12 days following successful anthelmintic therapy which was administered on the second day of study. Following this, these levels began to increase gradually and reached nearly normal levels between the 68th and 89th days after treatment. During this period the plasma iron levels had decreased accordingly, indicating that iron was being utilized more readily in hemoglobin synthesis. However, at no time during this period did plasma iron levels decrease to a point where iron deficiency would be indicated. On the 94th day of the study 180 mg of copper (copper glutamate solution) was injected into the brisket of animal II-1. Although no apparent influence was exerted on the hemoglobin level, a marked decrease in plasma iron and an increase in plasma copper occurred. It is probable that the decrease in iron was not due to increased hemopoiesis but rather to the severe inflammatory reaction which followed the injection (Cartwright *et al.*, 1946).

Both animals were autopsied on the 135th day of the trial, at which time liver analyses for copper and iron stores were conducted. The results were as follows: Animal II-1, liver copper and liver iron, respectively, 8.7 mg/100 gm and 1.91 mg/100 gm; Animal II-3, liver copper

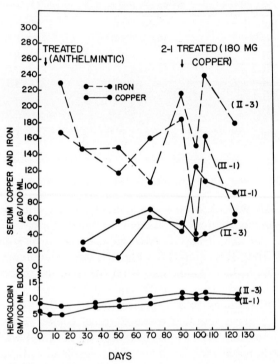

Fig. 8. Hemoglobin levels, plasma iron levels, and plasma copper levels in animals II-1 and II-3 following therapy for gastrointestinal parasitism.

and liver iron, respectively, 4.4 mg/100 gm and 1.8 mg/100 gm. From these results it is apparent that although the parenteral copper therapy did not influence the body iron stores, it definitely was of value in replenishing the body copper reserves. The importance of this is yet to be elucidated. While discussing these particular animals, we should indicate that in both animals the relative erythrocyte survival time as determined with Cr[51] was normal (Baker *et al.*, 1961), although that of animal II-1, initiated on the 13th day of the trial, was in the lower limits of normality (10.6 days). Studies of animal II-3, initiated on the 35th day of the trial, revealed a half-time survival of 14.2 days. Thus in these animals it appears safe to conclude that the anemia was primarily due to decreased effective erythropoiesis, although prior to anthelmintic treatment ineffective erythropoiesis and (or) hemolysis may have contributed to the anemia (Baker and Douglas, 1957b).

In addition, while iron deficiency did not occur during the anemic stage, following treatment, iron demands did deplete excess storage (Table V). These sources were not adequate to meet the demands of hemoglobin synthesis and the maintenance of normal storage values.

Additional evidence in these animals that increased erythropoiesis following therapy and inadequate absorption of iron resulted in depletion of iron reserves was found in the Wintrobe indices during the period of recovery. It was noted between the 14th and 51st days that a decrease in both the MCH and MCHC occurred with a slight decrease in the MCV on the 14th day. These changes indicate the development during this period of a hypochromic, and possibly a microcytic hypochromic, anemia suggestive of a mild metabolic iron deficiency.

In general, we can dispense with the tissue storage of iron by stating that in animals autopsied during the anemic stage of the disease, decreased iron storage would not be expected (Table V). Our studies with copper, however, are too limited to draw definite conclusions regarding tissue storage of this element.

In attempts to better elucidate the kinetics of iron in the erythron of these parasitized animals, studies utilizing Fe^{59} were conducted in both anemic and nonanemic individuals. Results of these studies are presented in Tables VI and VII and Fig. 9, 10, and 11.

In Table VII it is noted that in general the transfer rate, mg per 100 ml plasma, is lower in the more anemic animals (36, 58, 67), although animal 233 is a notable exception to this generalization. Baker and Douglas (1957b), Kaneko et al. (1961), and Kaneko (1963) found normal plasma iron transfer to be 1.9 mg/100 ml, 1.3 mg/100 ml, and 0.93 mg/100 ml for 3-month-old, 6-month-old, and yearling animals, respectively. The normal value in yearling steers should therefore, be somewhere between 0.9 and 1.3 mg/100 ml, indicating a normal or slightly excessive transfer of iron was occurring in all but the three previously mentioned anemic animals and in animal 234, which had a normal hemoglobin level.

Examination of the plasma clearance curves, Figs. 9 and 10, reveals that during the first 4 days the Fe^{59} was removed from the plasma at a rate equal to or greater than the turnover rate of a normal yearling steer (Kaneko, 1963). Following this, the majority of animals, and particularly those having normal hemoglobin levels, revealed a feedback of iron suggestive of a hemolytic syndrome (Kaneko, 1963). If this is the case it is then axiomatic that erythropoiesis must be accelerated or anemia would be present. That hemolysis did occur is indicated in Fig. 11, where it is noted that these same animals generally showed a more rapid uptake of Fe^{59} in circulating erythrocytes, as well as shorter hemoglobinization time (Pollycove and Mortimer, 1961). External scintillation monitoring of the liver, spleen, sacral marrow (Fig. 11), and iliac marrow

TABLE VI

HEMATOLOGICAL DATA IN PARASITIZED CATTLE AT THE TIME OF IRON KINETIC STUDIES

Animal number	Body wt. (kg)	Plasma volume (ml/kg)	Blood volume (ml/kg)	Hemo-globin (gm/ 100 ml)	Plasma iron (µg/ 100 ml)	Plasma volume (ml)	Blood volume (ml)
36	178[a]	—	—	6.2	73	6000	7340
58	178[a]	—	—	6.55	150	6280	7750
67	178[a]	—	—	7.3	132	5670	7412
86	178[a]	—	—	9.5	151	8200	11,200
231	168	54.2	75.0	8.7	141	9100	12,550
233	164	56.2	73.1	7.4	165	9900	11,980
234	174	40.0	59.0	10.3	200	7000	10,300
1188	128	38.0	49.5	9.9	111	4850	6325
1064	166	37.2	51.0	10.3	81	6160	8470
1357	162	35.2	58.9	13.9	131	5700	9520
1189	196	37.2	56.0	15.4	120	7284	10,950

[a] Mean of groups.

TABLE VII

IRON KINETIC CALCULATIONS FROM IRON-59 TRIALS

Animal number	Pool size (mg/ 100 ml)	Half time (hr)	Fractional transfer rate (day 1)	Transfer rate (day 1) mg/ day	Transfer rate (day 1) mg/ 100 ml	Transfer rate (day 1) mg/ kg	Maximal Fe^{59} uptake by RBC (%)
36	0.073	1.9	8.8	38.4	0.64	0.38[a]	60
58	0.150	5.0	3.3	30.8	0.49	0.38[a]	73
67	0.132	4.5	3.7	27.8	0.49	0.38[a]	—[b]
86	0.151	3.8	4.3	54.0	0.66	0.38[a]	70
231	0.141	2.5	6.6	84.6	0.94	0.50	78
233	0.165	2.03	8.2	124.0	1.35	0.81	100
234	0.200	5.0	3.3	46.2	0.66	0.26	62
1188	0.111	1.78	9.3	50.5	1.04	0.39	78
1064	0.081	1.13	14.7	73.5	1.19	0.43	87
1357	0.131	1.70	9.8	72.5	1.27	0.44	90
1189	0.120	1.6	10.4	91.0	1.25	0.46	69

[a] Based on mean values.
[b] Not determined.

indicated a normal uptake and release of Fe^{59} in relationship to erythrocyte incorporation with no accumulation of isotopic iron in either the liver or spleens of nonanemic animals (1064, 1188, and 1189).

Whether or not limited intramedullary hemolysis (ineffective erythropoiesis) occurs cannot be stated, although the plasma clearance curves of animals 1357, 1189, and 67 reveal a feedback between the 1st and 3rd

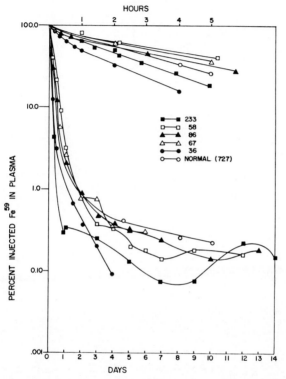

FIG. 9. Plasma clearance of Fe^{59} in anemic cattle with gastrointestinal parasitism.

days that would suggest such an occurrence, as does the lack of effective erythropoiesis in animals 36, 67, and 86. That hemolysis of cells in the peripheral blood stream does occur, however, is indicated by the previously discussed feedback after the 4th day; by the cyclical nature of the red blood cell Fe^{59} content in animal 1189, which corresponds with the feedback into plasma of this animal; and by the fact that the mean life span of red blood cells in animal number 1357 was significantly less than 100 days (Fig. 11).

With regard to the apparent hemolysis of erythrocytes and the reduced plasma copper levels observed in certain anemic animals, the report of

Kaneko *et al.* (1961) on erythrocyte survival in molybdenosis of sheep is of interest. In that study, there developed a condition in which two erythrocyte populations appeared, one having a mean survival of 28 days and the other a surivval of 80–85 days. Whether this alteration was mediated through the influence of molybdenum on copper metabolism, or

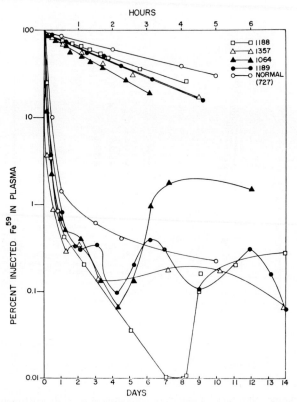

Fig. 10. Plasma clearance of Fe^{59} in nonanemic cattle with gastrointestinal parasitism.

whether alteration of the red blood cell population was the direct result of molybdenum toxicity has not been determined. The observation, however, would appear to be worth investigation in gastrointestinal parasitism of the type presently being discussed.

Certain individuals may progress to a point of bone marrow depression and/or ineffective erythropoiesis. Animals 36, 67, and 86, in which a prolonged hemoglobinization time is noted (Fig. 11), are examples of this. The condition occurred quite late in the syndrome, with animals 36 and 67 succumbing during the trial.

At no time were significant amounts of radioactivity found in the excrement of the experimental animals.

From the foregoing discussion it is obvious that insofar as iron is concerned, there is no metabolic deficiency except in instances of remission or following therapy. Where anemia has not developed, increased iron utilization has compensated for the presence of ineffective erythropoiesis and (or) hemolysis; however, as the disease progresses, a condition occurs in which markedly increased hemoglobinization time, and thus

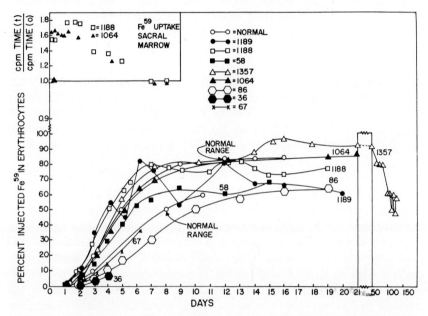

FIG. 11. Erythrocyte uptake of Fe^{59} in anemic and nonanemic cattle with gastrointestinal parasitism.

anemia, appears. The actual rate of hemolysis and its contribution to the degree of anemia has not been established at this time. It would seem rational, however, to remove from the literature all suggestions that blood-sucking habits of these worms are of significance in the production of anemia.

In efforts to determine what factor or factors may be responsible for the initial suppression of effective erythropoiesis and hemolysis, examination of data presented in pure, experimental infections and in mixed infections reveals one change that is common to all animals: hypoproteinemia, especially hypoalbuminemia, and a markedly reduced albumin-to-globulin ratio (Leland, 1961). Limited observations indicate that this depression is greater in anemic than in nonanemic animals. Since protein in the form of amino acids is essential to the normal function of the erythron there may be a relationship between the progressive change in serum proteins and eventual anemia. The report of Cornelius *et al.* (1962) revealed that in such animals there is a reduction of approximately 50 percent in the total synthesis of albumin and indicated the possibility of a deficiency in the amino acid (protein) reserve. Further it has been demonstrated during deficiency states that hemoglobin synthesis has priority over serum and other body proteins for available amino acids (Robscheit-Robbins *et al.*, 1943). It has been suggested that no discrete body protein storage occurs and that there exists only multiple pools with different exchange rates (McFarlane *et al.*, 1962). Thus, the free amino acids in the body fluids would serve as the primary molecular source for protein synthesis. Since, from a chronological standpoint, the serum protein alterations occur prior to anemic changes and progress with the disease, we would like to suggest that the depletion of this amino acid pool may well be responsible for the eventual development of anemia, and that a specific amino acid deficiency, as in swine (Wintrobe, 1961), may also be responsible for the altered copper levels.

Of further significance in this regard is the finding of Baker *et al.* (1965) that the total body water turnover in cattle so parasitized is reduced by approximately one half. This results from a reduction in intake of water, both in the form of fluids and as that available from food. Consequently the assimilation of nutrients absorbed by simple diffusion and (or) active transport would be markedly reduced. Where a limited body reserve, such as that of amino acids, is concerned, a rather rapid depletion might be expected. Such a possibility is further suggested by the work of Spedding (1954) wherein sheep parasitized with *T. axei* experienced a 10 percent decrease in digestive efficiency accompanied by only an 8 percent decrease in appetite.

It is realized that the foregoing studies are not conclusive in all respects, but the finding of (1) normal to increased plasma iron levels, (2) excessive liver iron stores, (3) retention of iron-59 in the body, and (4) no significant amounts of isotope in excrement should without question eliminate hemorrhage as a factor in trichostrongyle infections other than *Haemonchus*. We would like to suggest the hypothesis that when anemia results it is primarily due to a deficient source of amino acids and perhaps, in some instances, partly due to direct or indirect effects of copper deficiency. Such a hypothesis is in agreement with Kates and Turner (1960), who conclude that the anemia caused by *T. axei* is nutritional in origin, and may well explain the varied observations of researchers in regard to the occurrence of anemia in these infections.

REFERENCES

Andrews, J. S. (1939). Experimental trichostrongylosis in sheep and goats. *J. Agr. Res.* **58**, 761-770.

Andrews, J. S. (1942). Stomach worm *Haemonchus contortus* infection in lambs and its relation to gastric hemorrhage and general pathology. *J. Agr. Res.* **65**, 1-18.

Bailey, W. S. (1949). Studies on calves experimentally infected with *Cooperia punctata* (von Linstow, 1907) Ransom, 1907. *Am. J. Vet. Res.* **10**, 119-129.

Baker, N. F. (1960). Unpublished studies.

Baker, N. F., and Douglas, J. R. (1957a). Plasma iron and iron-binding capacity in lambs. *Am. J. Vet. Res.* **18**, 142-146.

Baker, N. F., and Douglas, J. R. (1957b). The pathogenesis of trichostrongyloid parasites. II. Ferrokinetic studies in ruminants. *Am. J. Vet. Res.* **18**, 295-302.

Baker, N. F., Cook, E. F., Douglas, J. R., and Cornelius, C. E. (1959). The pathogenesis of trichostrongyloid parasites III. Some physiological observations in lambs suffering from acute parasitic gastroenteritis. *J. Parasitol.* **45**, 643-651.

Baker, N. F., Osebold, J. W., and Christensen, J. F. (1961). Erythrocyte survival in experimental anaplasmosis. *Am. J. Vet. Res.* **22**, 590-596.

Baker, N. F., Black, A. L., Anand, R. S., and Fisk, R. A. (1965). Body water turnover in cattle with parasitic gastroenteritis. *Exptl. Parasitol.* **17**, 271-276.

Black, A. L., Baker, N. F., Bartley, J. C. Chapman, T. E., and Phillips, R. W. (1964). Water turnover in cattle. *Science* **144**, 876-878.

Boughton, I. B., and Hardy, W. T. (1935). Stomach worms (*Haemonchus contortus*) of sheep and goats. *Texas Agr. Expt. Sta., Progr. Rept.* **48**, 236-239.

Cantarow, A., and Shepartz, B. (1962). "Biochemistry." Saunders, Philadelphia, Pennsylvania.

Cartwright, G. E., Lauritsen, M. A., Humphreys, S., Jones, P. J., Merrill, I. M., and Wintrobe, M. M. (1946). The anemia of infection. II. The experimental production of hypoferremia and anemia in dogs. *J. Clin. Invest.* **25**, 81-86.

Clark, C. H., Kling, J. M., Woodley, C. H., and Sharp, N. (1961). A quantitative measurement of the blood loss caused by ancylostomiasis in dogs. *Am. J. Vet. Res.* **22**, 370-373.

Clark, C. H., Kiesel, G. K., and Goby, C. H. (1962). Measurements of blood loss caused by *Haemonchus contortus* infection in sheep. *Am. J. Vet. Res.* **23**, 977-980.

Cornelius, C. E. Baker, N. F., Kaneko, J. J., and Douglas, J. R. (1962). Distribution and turnover of iodine-131-tagged bovine albumin in normal and parasitized cattle. *Am. J. Vet. Res.* **23**, 837-842.

Doran, D. J. (1955). The course of infection and pathogenic effect of *Trichostrongyles axei* in calves. *Am. J. Vet. Res.* **16**, 401-409.

Faust, E. C. (1955). "Animal Agents and Vectors of Human Diseases." Lea & Febiger, Philadelphia, Pennsylvania.

Fourie, P. J. J. (1931). The haematology and pathology of haemonchosis in sheep. *Dir. Vet. Ser. Animal Ind. Rept., Union S. Africa*, **17**, Part 1, 495-572.

Gallagher, C. H. (1963). Studies on trichostrongylosis of sheep; plasma volume, hemoglobin concentration, and blood cell count. *Australian J. Agr. Res.* **14**, 349-363.

Georgi, J. R. (1964). Absorption of hemoglobin iron-59 in sheep. *Am. J. Vet. Res.* **25**, 952-954.

Hamilton, H. E., De Gowin, E. L., Sheets, R. F., Janney, C. D., and Ellis, J. A.

(1954). Studies with inagglutinable erythrocyte counts. VI. Accelerated destruction of normal adult erythrocytes in pernicious anemia; contribution of hemolysis to the oligocythemia. *J. Clin. Invest.* **33**, 191-205.

Herlich, H. (1957). Preliminary observations on calves experimentally infected with *Trichostrongylus colubriformis. Proc. Helminthol. Soc. Wash., D.C.,* **24**, 139-140.

Herlich, H. (1959). Experimental infections of cattle with the stomach worms *Ostertagia ostertagi* and *Trichostrongulus axei. Proc. Helminthol. Soc. Wash., D.C.* **26**, 97-102.

Herlich, H. (1962). Studies on calves experimentally infected with combinations of four nematode species. *Am. J. Vet. Res.* **23**, 521-528.

Kaneko, J. J. (1963). Erythrokinetics and iron metabolism in bovine porphyria erythropoietica. *Ann. N. Y. Acad. Sci.* **104**, Art. 2, 689-700.

Kaneko, J. J., Cornelius, C. E., and Baker, N. F. (1961). Erythrocyte survival studies in experimental molybdenosis of sheep. *Proc. Soc. Exptl. Biol. Med.* **107**, 924-926.

Kates, K. C., and Turner, J. H. (1953). Experimental studies on the pathogenicity of *Nematodirus spathiger*, a trichostrongylid parasite of sheep. *Am. J. Vet. Res* **14**, 72-81.

Kates, K. C., and Turner, J. H. (1960). Experimental trichostrongylosis (*axei*) in lambs, with a discussion of recent research on this disease in ruminants. *Am. J. Vet. Res.* **21**, 254-261.

Layrisse, M., Paz, A., Blumenfeld, N., and Roche, M. (1961). Hookworm anemia: iron metabolism and erythrokinetics. *Blood* **18**, 61-72.

Leland, S. E., Jr. (1961). Blood and plasma volume, total serum protein, and electrophoretic studies in helminthic diseases. *Ann. N. Y. Acad. Sci.* **94**, Art. 1, 163-182.

Leland, S. E., Jr., Drudge, J. H., Wyant, Z. N., and Elam, G. W. (1960). Studies on *Trichostrongylus axei* (Cobbold, 1879). V. Some quantitatitve and pathologic aspects of experimental infections with a horse strain in sheep. *Am. J. Vet. Res.* **21**, 449-457.

McFarlane, A. S., Garrow, J. S., and Waterlow, J. C. (1962). The use of radioisotopes in the study of protein metabolism and protein deficiencies. *In* "Radioisotopes in Tropical Medicine," pp. 17-26. Intern. At. Energy Agency, Vienna.

Mahrt, J. L., Hammond, D. M., and Miner, M. L. (1964). Changes in serum proteins and other blood values associated with experimental *Ostertagia ostertagi* infections in calves. *Cornell Vet.* **54**, 453-474.

Martin, C. J., and Clunies-Ross, I. (1934). A minimal computation of the amount of blood removed daily by *Haemonchus contortus. J. Helminthol.* **12**, 137-142.

Pollycove, M., and Mortimer, R. (1961). The quantitative determination of iron kinetics and hemoglobin synthesis in human subjects. *J. Clin. Invest.* **40**, 753-782.

Robscheit-Robbins, F. S., Miller, L. L., and Whipple, G. H. (1943). Hemoglobin and plasma proteins; simultaneous production during continued bleeding as influenced by amino acids, plasma, hemoglobin, and digests of serum, hemoglobin, and casein. *J. Exptl. Med.* **77**, 375-396.

Roche, M. (1962). The use of radioisotopes in the study of blood loss due to parasites. *In* "Radioisotopes in Tropical Medicine," pp. 103-118. Intern. At. Energy Agency, Vienna.

Roche, M., and Perez-Gimenez, M. E. (1959). Intestinal loss and reabsorption of iron in hookworm infection. *J. Lab. Clin. Med.* **54**, 49-52.

Schalm, O. W. (1961). "Veterinary Hematology." Lea & Febiger, Philadelphia, Pennsylvania.

Shumard, R. F., Bolin, D. W., and Eveleth, D. F. (1957). Physiological and nutritional changes in lambs infected with the nematodes. *Haemonchus contortus, Trichostrongylus colubriformis,* and *Nematodirus spathiger. Am J. Vet. Res.* **18**, 330-337.

Singer, K., King, J. C., and Robin, S. (1948). The life span of the megalocyte and the hemolytic syndrome of pernicious anemia. *J. Lab. Clin. Med.* **33**, 1068-1076.

Spedding, C. R. W. (1954). The effect of a subclinical worm burden on the digestive efficiency of sheep. *J. Comp. Pathol. Therap.* **64**, 5-14.

Threlkeld, W. L., and Johnson, E. P. (1948). Observations on the pathogenicity and viability of *Ostertagia ostertagi. Vet. Med.* **43**, 446-452.

Todd, A. C., Arbogast, F. M., Wyant, Z. N., and Stone, W. M. (1951). On the blood picture of sheep exposed to the medium stomach worms. *Vet. Med.* **46**, 136-140.

von Bonsdorff, B. (1956). *Diphyllobothrium latum* as a cause of pernicious anemia. *Exptl. Parasitol.* **5**, 207-230.

Whitlock, J. H. (1950). The anemias in the trichostrongylidoses. *Cornell Vet.* **40**, 288-299.

Wintrobe, M. W. (1961). "Clinical Hematology." Lea & Fibiger, Philadelphia, Pennsylvania.

Discussion

Dr. Frank Douvres: Do you believe that the diet of the animals reflects upon whether anemia is or is not apparent? Herlich's animals were laboratory raised!

Dr. Baker: We have produced anemia in laboratory raised sheep. I think there is every possibility that anemia is related to diet and this is concerned with the available amino acids. If one studies other workers' results (for instance, Gallagher's) there has been a definite correlation between the nutrients and the degree of anemia. There is essentially no basic storage of amino acids or protein within the animal and the diet of the animal at the time of infection is probably more important than that prior to infection.

Dr. Mulligan: What is Dr. Baker's current view on the hypoalbuminemia? We have recently carried out some measurements on cattle suffering from type II ostertagiosis and find in every case a hypercatabolic hypoalbuminemia. This is at variance with some of Dr. Baker's earlier work. Has he changed his views on this matter?

Dr. Baker: No! If you will recall the animals we studied, there was a marked hypercatabolic situation near the terminal part of the infection. However, prior to the terminal stage we had no evidence of a hypercatabolic state. Whether this was actually hypercatabolism or loss of the plasma proteins into the body fluids owing to impending death, we do not know. The animals which we have studied have more closely resembled type I ostertagiosis with a less acute onset, more prolonged course of disease, and perhaps a greater tendency toward the steady state condition. It is also possible that our animals early in the course of the disease may have suffered a hypercatabolic hypoalbuminemia.

The Environmental Biology of a Nematode

J. H. WHITLOCK

Department of Pathology, New York State Veterinary College and Division of Biological Sciences, Cornell University, Ithaca, New York

ENVIRONMENTAL BIOLOGY: A FIELD OF STUDY AND A METHOD

The title of this paper was chosen to tie its subject directly to an article by Rene Dubos (1964). Essentially Dubos proposed that there exists a definable field of study in the area where ecology, population genetics, epidemiology, and medicine meet and that development of this area on a rigorous quantitative basis is absolutely essential for further progress in medicine. He recommended that the approach should be wholistic, multidisciplinary, and multifactorial. I not only recommend that you read this article carefully but realize that this is probably one of few general articles in the field that has hit most of the essential problems precisely. Currently one limitation on the development of the area is due to the fact that so many scientific frontiers are involved. There are, of course all kinds of frontiers and barriers between fields of knowledge. Snow's two cultures are an oversimplification. Even science alone is divided into many fields, each with its own jargon, implicit assumptions, status symbols, and dislike of aliens. There are only two definable types of research frontiers left in science: one type where the research is so far out that it isn't related to anything (charity prevents me from naming a type species), and the type that results from the study of grossly neglected borders between the different standard disciplines. We have excellent authority for our belief that the way of the boundary researcher (it can translate as transgressor) is hard. It is, of course, quite difficult simultaneously to cope with several different sets of assumptions, jargons, and historical alienations. Nevertheless there are compensations. There is both the short-term excitement of the new, and the long-term hope that one can find a set of uniform principles underlying the whole of biology.

The basic purpose of this paper is to call attention to the remarkable array of new facts and testable hypotheses that can result from even the most elementary environmental biological approach to parasitological problems.

Both Dr. Dubos and I consider "environmental biology" and "systems biology" largely synonymous, and I must confess that I have a slight preference for the latter term. This is chiefly because a system is inherently predictable and probably constrained or bounded, and our group has found that the preliminary way to analyze a large system is to direct the major attention to the boundaries. Such boundaries can often be measured with a precision that compares with that obtainable with physical systems. I would not wish to imply, however, that all possible host-parasite systems are necessarily bounded. In the first place, man has created unadapted aggregations of plants and animals both in the laboratory and in the field, and the epidemiology of disease in such instances may overwhelmingly represent a truly random process. When host and parasite are thoroughly adapted to each other and to the whole environment, the system becomes tightly constrained and the random elements are apt to be distorted or suppressed.

THE APPARENT SIMPLICITY OF THE HAEMONCHOSIS MODEL

The particular disease model used was haemonchosis, which is due to the blood-letting activities of *Haemonchus contortus,* the commonest and most pathogenic parasite of sheep (and probably goats) in the world. We selected it on the door-step basis: it occurred every year in our experiment station flock. We decided to work on it chiefly because most of the literature on it (except that by N. R. Stoll and H. M. Gordon) did not seem to be particularly relevant to the things we actually saw.

There was one especially relevant piece of literature, and that was Gordon's (1950) prediction that haemonchosis only occurred when the monthly rainfall was over 2 inches and the mean maximal temperature over 65°F. On a superficial basis, therefore, the introduction of sheep into the Americas and the Antipodes had carried with it a stable, well-adapted parasite of sheep whose relatively simple ecological needs could be satisfied by a relatively simple set of environmental circumstances. Both Gordon and Stoll had worked with natural haemonchosis systems and usually things matched in a satisfactory manner; however, by correspondence Gordon and I came to realize that we were dealing with radically different types of sheep populations. We came also to realize that we never saw the anaphylactoid self-cure phenomenon nor could we duplicate Stoll's vaccination experiments. This raised a strong presumption that the parasite populations differed antigenically. Meanwhile, Roberts *et al.* (1954) in Queensland had separated a cattle-adapted species called *H. placei* from the *H. contortus* complex. One especially useful criterion was the characteristics of the vulvular flap in the female, which can be present or absent and which, if present, can be characteristically typical or well developed or only partially developed or knobbed. On the basis of the data we have assembled, this is almost certainly a discontinuous genetic polymorphism such as human blood group types or hemoglobin types in sheep.

EVIDENCE FOR A COMPLEX ECOTYPE SYSTEM IN *HAEMONCHUS*

In the field of ecological genetics such polymorphisms are often especially useful in tracing adaptations of populations to specific environments (ecotypes). Furthermore, it is possible to demonstrate from our studies and from the literature that this polymorphism is distinctly different in incidence in different geographical areas of the world.

Our local subspecies, *H. contortus cayugensis,* is morphologically quite different from *H. contortus contortus* in Australia and from the strain used by Stoll at Princeton.

Not only are there probably morphological and antigenic differences in the ecotypes of *H. contortus,* but bionomic differences appear as well. By extending Cole's (1954) "predictions of the natural consequences of life cycle phenomena," Crofton (1957) was able to demonstrate that Gordon's Cherry Hill data on haemonchosis could be well fitted by assuming a generation time of 34 days. Meanwhile Whitlock (1963a) showed that a 21-day generation time was reasonable for his data. In addition Conway and Whitlock (1965) showed that a culture strain of *H. contortus* from Kentucky reached a maximal fecal egg count significantly later than *H. contortus cayugensis,* Crofton *et al.* (1965) demonstrated significant differences in minimal egg hatching time between *H. contortus cayugensis* and a Bristol, England strain of *H. contortus,* and Crofton and Whitlock (1965) observed a comparable difference between *Ostertagia circumcincta* from Ithaca, New York and Bristol, England. Conway (1964) established that the cultural requirements of *H. contortus cayugensis* to the third-stage larvae are quite different from those reported for *Haemonchus contortus* in the literature. In their analysis of the literature Crofton and Whitlock were able to pick up evidence that this type of shift in phenotype boundary could occur in as little as 40 years; a startling but quantitatively reasonable time for microevolutionary change.

Fundamentally, visualizing the efficacy of reproductive isolation in producing new types, knowing that significant changes can occur in as little as 40 years, and knowing that Skrjabin has pointed out that the trichostrongyles are in their period of greatest evolutionary efflorescence, I suggest the likelihood that the ultimate ecotype system in *Haemonchus* may even rival the *Salmonella* antigenic system in complexity. Meanwhile, I would urge that you take a serious look at the pathogen in your cultures or on your doorstep. You really haven't scratched the fundamental ecological problem when you investigate disease in the manner of a taxonomic lumper.

THE HOST-RECOGNITION SIGNAL FOR *HAEMONCHUS* AND *OSTERTAGIA*

One of the major problems that any surviving parasite has to solve is the recognition of the appropriate host at the appropriate stage of its development. Specifically, in the case of *H. contortus cayugensis,* it has to receive information at the time that it passes from the free living to the parasitic third-stage larvae that "this is a sheep" (or a goat). Apparently *H. contortus cayugensis* gets its essential signal from the rate at which carbon dioxide is converted to carbonic acid, which is, in turn a function of the presence of the inorganic catalysts of this reaction. Although Taylor and Whitlock (1960a,b) reported this as a reasonable hypothesis Rogers (1961) did not mention it in his text, although, by this time, he confirmed our original observations that the concentration and kind of salt did influence ecdysis. The basic problem in determining that *H. contortus cayugensis* ecdysis at the third stage was triggered by the rate of carbonic acid formation was which chemicals to select from the Roughton and Booth (1938) list of catalysts that would not be toxic and would not interfere directly (at the concentration used) with the ions probably present in the incorporation of carbon dioxide into water.

A graduate student in our laboratory, Mr. Arthur Bucknor, has studied the *H. contortus cayugensis* ecdysis reaction in a Warburg apparatus modified to measure the carbon dioxide uptake by the system. Using sodium chloride, sodium selenite, and sodium borate he showed that the molarity of these salts for a standard ecdysis is almost perfectly correlated with the catalytic coefficient under standard conditions. The fact that the Taylor–Whitlock (1960a,b) hypothesis has received substantial confirmation opens up a whole range of problems, testable hypotheses, and explanations of epidemiological facts.

These are even more accessible since it has been shown in our laboratory that our local strain of *Ostertagia circumcincta* ecdyses in carbon dioxide and water but is inhibited by the presence of 0.5 percent NaCl in the water. At the practical level this means that one can take a mixed culture of *Ostertagia circumcincta* and *H. contortus cayugensis* from a natural infection and remove the *O. circumcincta* without affecting the *Haemonchus*. We have already discovered that a few days in an icebox will kill another common contaminant, *Strongyloides* sp. It is obvious that suitable manipulation of the information system can often clear out most contaminants from natural strains. The latter are probably preferable to the artificial strains, maintained in artificially raised lambs. which are used for many studies.

FUNCTION OF HOST-RECOGNITION IN PARASITE POPULATION CONTROL

A second major problem that any successful parasite must face is population limitation, since it cannot succeed biologically if it consistently overwhelms its host. The carbon dioxide concentration in the rumen is a function of the digestible carbohydrate intake of the host. Thus a poorly fed host with adequate sodium chloride intake will also signal the incoming parasite biomass that this host is poorly fed and only a portion of larvae will ecdyse: an animal with a diet richer in fermentable carbohydrates with an adequate salt intake will allow more ecdysis for *Haemonchus*. Even in the case of the more richly fed animal, which is hand-fed a major portion of its carbohydrates either on pasture or in the barn, one can entrain a circadian oscillating system where ecdysis efficiency peaks shortly after the concentrate is fed and goes to near zero efficiency before 8 hours have passed. Conway and Whitlock (1965) have shown that artificially infecting sheep at the low part of the circadian cycle of ecdysis has a marked influence on the parameters of the infection established.

Our standard concentrate ration is an oats, bran, and linseed oil mixture which is not only mineral rich but was selected because it was so trouble free in our experimental flock. One criterion of trouble freeness is that no stiff lamb disease occurs. This is prevented by an adequate intake of selenium which is, in turn, provided by most commercial bran supplements available to commercial farmers.

Therefore, we have a reasonable explanation for our report (Whitlock, 1949) that supplement-fed lambs had more *Haemonchus* and pasture-fed lambs more *Ostertagia* even when exposed to the same pasture. We extrapolate just a little beyond this: *O. circumcincta* has about the same generation time as *H. contortus*; it is reported to be a blood sucker, and it is found in the same host organ; hence when one considers not only the different extrahost temperature adaptation of these two species but also the different information system used by each, it is easily seen that the niche used by each is significantly different. At this point we can add the host recognition signal to the concept of an ecological niche for parasites and perhaps comparable essential signals for free-living forms.

THE HOST-RECOGNITION SIGNAL AND HOST SPECIFICITY

The Trichostrongyloidea and Strongyloidea in general, have the problem of ecdysing the extra second-stage larval sheath at infection and it is known that sodium chloride, borax, chlorine, and bromine are effective larvicides for the group. These are all catalysts of the carbonic acid reaction. There is thus a hint from the literature that the basic mechanism in information and control at the ecdysis period may involve a widespread use of this system in the nemata. We would grant that these nematodes indulge in something like a hunt and stick Markovian regulatory process in the search for new hosts. Nevertheless, the group is remarkably host and organ specific and there must be some mechanism tied genetically to the sheath which is remarkably versatile at the sensing end. The various parameters which have been suggested as the sources of ecdysis information over a series of different host species show more similarities than differences and it would appear that the potential information channel to the ensheathed nema is just too restricted to carry the requisite information in terms of possible configurations of physical and chemical parameters. However, if the actual information-receiving device is rate sensitive to gases or their dissolved ionic products, the potential amount of information that can be carried reaches satisfactory levels of capacity. After all, one can easily distinguish between individual sheep by the oxygen dissociation curves of their hemoglobins and the modern, large information capacity, analytical tools are essentially rate-sensitive devices. We propose as a testable hypothesis that the sensing mechanisms that provide for host specificity, and perhaps for other critical developmental stages of the Strongylina, are essentially rate-sensitive devices for dissolved gases and other parameters and we offer an appropriately adapted Warburg as an instrument.

We do not propose that these devices are the only possible mechanisms. Every truly successful life form probably has a certain amount of redundancy built into its sensing devices. Furthermore, it is probable that the development of geographic races adapted to specific hosts may shift the mechanisms. In testing the hypothesis, one would suggest that the strains of *Haemonchus* that are troublesome in the semiarid regions of the world (places where the rainfall is intermittent and the hosts poorly nourished) would be desirable test objects. At least some of these areas have high concentrations of selenium in the soil. This would assure a rapid carbonic acid reaction even with low carbon dioxide production.

It is, therefore, possible that though the system used by *H. contortus cayugensis* is a specific or generic character it might be quite labile under adaptation. At least it is possible now to get at the essential problem of host specificity with a working hypothesis.

POPULATION CONTROL OF *HAEMONCHUS*

As mentioned before, a second major problem facing a parasite if it is to perpetuate itself is that of finding a system of limiting the parasite biomass in such a way that the drain on the energy of the host population does not place the perpetuation of the host population in serious jeopardy. All populations are constrained, and we have repeatedly demonstrated that the populations of *H. contortus cayugensis* are so tightly constrained that we can handle the whole epidemic and its host components as a predictable machine with error terms that are substantially under 1 percent. When one is dealing with a system as predictable as haemonchosis, it is improbable that the maximal population constraint can be due to a single feedback system or single environmental limiting substance. There almost must be a number of feedback channels or limiting reactions.

If the population of a pathogen is strictly controlled in a host there is a tendency for medically oriented researchers to approach the problem *a priori* as "immunity." As a result, the term immunity has been so badly stretched in parasitology that it has almost lost any force as an operational concept. This is not a trivial matter of semantics. The basic problem comes about because in any natural epidemic almost any measurable parameter is a function of time—that is, the whole system is time dependent. It is a fundamental principle of analysis of such systems that it is almost impossible to establish a causal relationship between time-dependent parameters. For example, suppose one were to discover that concomitant with the onset of a population constraint, the pH of the environment shifted. The correlation is interesting but not proof. Proof would only come if one demonstrated that one could constrain the population at will by altering the environmental pH. A lot of what passes for evidence of immunity in parasitology is based on correlation and not rigorous proof. It is rather like saying that a garden becomes immune to flowers because they go to seed and wither. If one wishes to study the constraints on a natural population, it is necessary to leave that population in its natural ecosystem because one of the results of transferring hosts to laboratory environments and use of laboratory infections is to remove at least some of the signals that acted to control the natural population.

How does a natural population of internal parasites behave? You

would have to search a long time in the literature before you found
much data, and the truth certainly isn't like the descriptions in most texts
and reviews. First, it is necessary to torpedo the myth that there is a
fundamental difference between the growth of a bacterium and a nema
in the host body. In both cases, the parasitism results in a net increase
in parasite biomass and is only comparable on that basis and in terms of
the energy involved.

Contrary to the statement in texts, we just can't find any appreciable
erythrocyte loss while the parasite is maturing from the infective larvae
to adulthood. Similarly, naturally acquired infections of under 100 worms
rarely produce any appreciable blood loss but egg counts may reach
quite high levels for a transitory period of time. Heavier infections start
bleeding the host in measurable amounts synchronously with the onset
of egg production. The gross amounts of eggs produced during an
epidemic can reach about the same biomass as the worms producing
the eggs. For reasons detailed elsewhere (Whitlock *et al.*, 1966), we have
proposed that the relatively large natural *Haemonchus* populations need
the host blood to produce eggs and one of those needs is likely the oxygen
therein.

Except for those hosts whose hemopoietic system collapses, it is improbable that the oxygen is an environmental limiting substance for
either parasites or egg production. We shall not detail the experimental
evidence for these phenomena, but while we can find evidence for feedback and functional relationships between egg biomass, pasture biomass,
adult parasite biomass, and intrahost larval biomass and the host, we
also can find evidence that biological constraints on each component of
the gross parasite biomass are quite independent.

The only period during the whole epidemic that we have been able
to approximate to a stochastic process has been the early period of
infection in new lambs each year. If one assumes that the distribution of
feces on a pasture approximates the negative binomial (a concept that
we owe to A. D. Donald of Australia and that we can confirm) and that
the buildup of infective larvae on the pasture is essentially exponential
(Crofton, 1957; Whitlock, 1963a), one could predict that the actual
infection established in the lambs would tend to approximate to logarithmic normal because as the populations with a basic negative binomial distribution get very large, especially as the result of an exponential buildup, they tend to become logarithmically normal. The natural
result of such a model is that during the buildup of the pasture infection,
there is a marked tendency for lambs exposed during the last 2 weeks
of a period to have adult nema populations that are quite equivalent to
those exposed for the whole time. In other words, lambs exposed to a

natural epidemic from 15 July to 1 August will have about the same number of adult worms as those exposed from 1 May to 1 August.

However, the population of infective forms on the pasture does not build up as one would predict from the fecal egg counts. This population tends to reach an upper limit about 15 July and remain relatively constant at least until 1 October. The population of worms established in the host then follows something like a logarithmic normal distribution appropriate to the exposure time. However, sometime after the appropriate blood loss is established the homeostatic controls lock the system in and in spite of constant natural exposure to infective forms the adult worm population does not increase. If one takes the hosts off the infected pasture, it is possible to detect a parasite mortality rate, particularly among the males. However, if the hosts are left on the pasture after the system locks in, the population of parasites settles down to a relatively constant level.

Now it is a fundamental biological principle that there is a marked tendency for a few egg-laying forms in a given niche to produce more eggs per female than a larger population of worms. This is especially true for *Haemonchus*. For any equivalent exposure period to our natural epidemic the fecal egg counts and erythrocyte losses are good functions of the number of worms present but this does not hold between exposure periods. The easiest host genetic parameter to pick up is one that sets a limit on egg production by the parasite. But since the gross biomass efficiency may range between 1 and 7 percent in terms of volume of erythrocytes lost and volume of eggs produced, it follows that the constraint on egg production is only partially a constraint on erythrocyte loss and adult worm populations.

POSSIBLE ADVANTAGES TO HOST POPULATIONS
FROM HAEMONCHOSIS

One of the incredible things about this epidemic is that when the homeostatic mechanisms have locked in, the clinical blood parameters become independent of the erythrocyte loss and they may diagnose recovery in an animal that is actually losing as much as a liter of whole blood a week.

If by controlled tests of equivalent twins, one tries to estimate the loss in pounds, ignoring the overcompensation cases where the infected animals are gaining faster, one keeps coming up with an estimate roughly equivalent to the net pounds of erythrocytes lost which for the liter of blood loss per week would tend to average out at about 2 lb per month. This raises an interesting question.

Suppose one had 100 lambs which lost an average of 1 lb per month for 3 months, as a cost of a disease, and suppose the disease culled out five disease-prone lambs early in the pasture season and identified their dams so that they could be culled too: Would the net position of the owner be better or worse with the disease in the flock? By every test we have been able to devise the only animals that are likely to die in our epidemic are those that are demonstrably constitutionally inferior. On the basis of what we know about natural selection, it is probable that any elaborately controlled biological system contains biological advantages for all the components. Modern commercial sheep husbandry depends to a large degree upon judicious crossbreeding, that is, heterosis. In fact anyone who has attempted inbreeding sheep is quite likely to be amazed at the size of the genetic load in the average sheep population which usually manifests itself as perinatal deaths. The sheep haemonchosis system has all the earmarks of a steady-state prey-predator system where the prey benefits by the elimination of the genetically unfit and weaklings before they reach breeding age.

In other words, man, by domestication, may have succeeded in getting the lion and the wolf off the backs of his sheep but, in so doing, seems to have constructed a remarkably efficient internal predator. There may be even more subtle advantages of the system. We have pointed out (Whitlock, 1961) that there is a possibility that a lesser blood volume may have a biological advantage for sheep in warm humid climates and we have demonstrated that maximal erythrocyte volume is genetically controlled (Whitlock, 1963b) and related to the AB hemoglobin system (Evans and Whitlock, 1964). A Beltsville group (Lindahl *et al.*, 1963) performed an experiment with three bands of sheep: one in dry lot, one on heavily contaminated pasture, and one on a lightly contaminated pasture. The mortality from parasitosis in the heavily contaminated group matched that from "heat stroke" on the dry lot. This raises the interesting possibility that a little judicious phlebotomy is biologically useful (at least for sheep) in the Washington area.

THE CARRIER STAGE OF *HAEMONCHUS*

Finally, in order to be successful, the parasite, especially if it has the overwintering, flowering type of adaptation built into its population structure, has to assure its survival from one growing season to the next.

The "spring rise" phenomenon is such a mechanism. This assures that the carrier sheep contaminate the pasture just in time to start the new epidemic in the lambs. We have carried our analysis of the system far enough to detect that the phenomenon is basically due to quiescent larval stages which are likely inhibited from growing by a feedback signal from an adult population but which also needs some signal transmitted from, or originated by, the carrier host, which could be roughly translated as "the spring is come, the grass is riz."[1]

SUMMARY

First, we present a testable hypothesis that the host and organ specificity displayed by most of the Trichostrongyloidea and Strongyloidea is due to the fact that these nemas are able to detect the rate of change of the gases (and perhaps other chemicals) in the host tissues and organs especially at the time of infection.

Second, we propose that there is a great deal of microevolutionary change going on in many of the Trichostrongyloidea. We suggest that we need to measure this from both the standpoint of defining a pathogen and also defining the adaptive mechanisms of the free-living stages which are likely to be strongly influenced by culture technics.

Third, we propose that direct competition between parasitic species for the same niche is avoided not only by the flowering phenomenon [Tetley's (1949) "march of the species"], which Crofton (1957) has shown to be due mostly to intrinsic factors, and by different phenotype boundaries in the free-living stages, but also by different sets of receptor sensitivities that enable the parasite to recognize the niche.

Fourth, we propose that the infection of the new lambs can be fitted by a random model, but that some period after infection has started the homeostatic mechanism's lock-in and unless the animal is genetically or physiologically defective, he will not only survive but do reasonably well.

Fifth, we propose that the population constraints on adult worms, larval worms, egg biomass, and infective larvae are all to some degree independent.

Sixth, we propose that small populations of *H. contortus cayugensis* do not need blood to grow and reproduce and large populations do not need blood to reach the egg-laying stage but that egg production for large populations does utilize blood in such a wasteful fashion that the essential need may be the oxygen. In any case, the blood oxygen is not apparently an environmental limiting substance.

Finally, we propose as a possibility that these orderly, tightly constrained diseases may carry with them a biological advantage for the host population. At the practical level, the problem is whether or not a little

---

[1] The remainder of the couplet, "I wonder where my blanket is," obviously applies to the young in heart. The poet has escaped me.

judicious haemonchosis is an assistant or a hazard in the culling operation over several sheep generations.

ACKNOWLEDGMENTS

Support for these researches has come from the State of New York, The National
Science Foundation (GB 2443), The Atomic Energy Commission, and the National
Institute of General Medical Sciences (GM 05900).

The author especially wishes to acknowledge his indebtedness to his colleagues for
many of the ideas expressed herein, especially to Professors H. D. Crofton, Jay R.
Georgi, Douglas Robson, Walter Federer, and LaMont Cole.

REFERENCES

Cole, L. C. (1954). The population consequences of life history phenomena. *Quart.
Rev. Biol.* **29**, 103-137.

Conway, D. P. (1964). Some effects of temperature on the development and activity
of *Haemonchus contortus* larvae. *Cornell Vet.* **54**, 266-270.

Conway, D. P., and Whitlock, J. H. (1965). A study of the variables influencing
artificial infections with *Haemonchus contortus. Cornell Vet.* **55**, 19-54.

Crofton, H. D. (1957). Nematode parasitic populations in sheep on lowland farms.
III. The seasonal incidence of species. *Parasitology* **47**, 304-318.

Crofton, H. D., and Whitlock, J. H. (1965). Ecology and biological plasticity of
sheep nematodes. III. Studies on *Ostertagia circumcincta* (Stadelmann 1894).
Cornell Vet. **55**, 259-262.

Crofton, H. D., Whitlock, J. H., and Glazer, R. A. (1965). Ecology and biological
plasticity of sheep nematodes. II. Genetic *x* environmental plasticity in *Haemonchus contortus* (Rud. 1803). *Cornell Vet.* **55**, 251-258.

Dubos, R. (1964). Environmental biology. *Bioscience* **14**, 11-14.

Evans, J. V., and Whitlock, J. H. (1964). Genetic relationship between maximum
hematocrit values and hemoglobin type in sheep. *Science* **145**, 1318.

Gordon, H. M. (1950). Some aspects of parasitic gastro-enteritis of sheep. *Australian
Vet. J.* **26**, 93-98.

Lindahl, I. L., Kates, K. C., Turner, J. H., Enzie, F. D., and Whitmore, G. E. (1963).
Effect of managements systems on the growth of lambs and development of
internal parasitism. I. Dry lot vs. two pasture rotation systems. *J. Parasitol.* **49**,
209-217.

Roberts, F. H. S., Turner, H. N., and McKeveth, M. (1954). On the specific distinct-
ness of the ovine and bovine "strains" of *Haemonchus contortus* (Rudolphi)
Cobb (Nematoda: Trichostrongylidea). *Australian J. Zool.* **2**, 275-295.

Rogers, W. P. (1961). "The Nature of Parasitism," 287 pp. Academic Press, New
York.

Roughton, F. J. W., and Booth, V. H. (1938). Catalytic effect of buffers on the
reaction $CO_2 + H_2O \rightleftharpoons H_2 CO_3$. *Biochem. J.* **32**, 2049-2069.

Taylor, A. N., and Whitlock, J. H. (1960a). Further notes on the exsheathing
mechanism of the third stage larvae of *Haemonchus contortus. Am. J. Vet. Res.*
21, 318.

Taylor, A., and Whitlock, J. H. (1960b). The exsheathing stimulus for infective
larvae of *Haemonchus contortus. Cornell Vet.* **50**, 339-344.

Tetley, J. H. (1949). Rhythms in nematode parasitism of sheep. *New Zealand Dept. Sci. Ind. Res. Bull.* **96**.

Whitlock, J. H. (1949). The relationship of nutrition to the development of the trichostrongyliduses. *Cornell Vet.* **39**, 146-182.

Whitlock, J. H. (1961). Genetic perspectives in disease resistance and susceptibility (discussion part III). *Ann. N.Y. Acad. Sci.* **91**, 761.

Whitlock, J. H. (1963a). A cybernetic approach to a natural epidemic of strongylatosis in sheep. *Cornell Vet.* **53**, 505-534.

Whitlock, J. H. (1963b). The influence of heredity and environment on maximum hematocrit values in sheep. *Cornell Vet.* **53**, 535-551.

Whitlock, J. H., Georgi, J., Robson, D. S., and Federer, W. T. (1966). Haemonchosis: An orderly disease. *Cornell Vet.* In press.

Pathogenesis of Migrating Stages of Helminths, with Special Reference to *Strongylus vulgaris*[1]

J. H. DRUDGE, E. T. LYONS, AND JOSEPH SZANTO[2]

Department of Veterinary Science, Kentucky Agricultural Experiment Station, University of Kentucky, Lexington, Kentucky

INTRODUCTION

Pathogenesis of helminth infection is a complex of biological interrelationships between the helminth and the host. The type and extent of the parasite's contact with the host's tissues is determined by inherent biological mechanisms in the parasite and is interrelated with the host's physiological processes which respond to the invasion of the helminth. Larval stages of parasitic nematodes are characterized by varying degrees of migrations into the host's tissues and are generally associated with the primary damage produced by helminth infections. Considerable variation in the type and extent of larval migrations exists among the broad range of helminths of veterinary importance; however the acme of migratory propensity of developing larvae is found in the genus *Strongylus*.

Three members of the genus *Strongylus* or the so-called large strongyles are of considerable importance in veterinary medicine. All three are parasites of the horse and are characterized by extensive parenteral migrations for prolonged periods of time. The prepatent periods that have been reported are $6\frac{1}{2}$ months for *S. vulgaris* (Wetzel, 1942), 8 months for *S. equinus* (Wetzel, 1942), and 11 months for *S. edentatus* (Wetzel, 1952).

Strongylus vulgaris is the most pathogenic of the three species. Pathological changes associated with the wanderings of the larvae have been described (Enigk, 1950; Farrelly, 1954; Jubb and Kennedy, 1963;

[1] The investigation reported in this paper (No. 65-4-63) was made in connection with a project of the Kentucky Agricultural Experiment Station, supported in part by a grant made by The Grayson Foundation, Inc., and is published by permission of the Director of the Station.

[2] Present address: Ciba Research Farm, Three Bridges, New Jersey.

Ottaway and Bingham, 1946; Poynter, 1960; Smith and Jones, 1961). Migrating larvae produce inflammation of mesenteric arteries, and changes in the anterior mesenteric artery, commonly referred to as "verminous aneurysm." Additional changes include thrombosis and embolism, primarily of branches of the ileocecalcolic artery and associated inflammation and infarction of the intestinal walls.

The precise migratory route followed by the larvae of S. *vulgaris* remains controversial as indicated in recent publications (Jubb and Kennedy, 1963; Poynter, 1960), even though the association of worm larvae with aneurysms of Equidae was already known to the Romans, and in modern times the specific identity and constant association of S. *vulgaris* larvae with the arterial lesions was pointed out by Loos in 1901. Since then at least four migratory pathways have been described for S. *vulgaris* (Enigk, 1950; Ershov, 1949; Olt, 1932; Ottaway and Bingham, 1946) but only that of Enigk is based on experimental infections in worm-free animals. The others are based on necropsy examinations of naturally infected animals in which such essential factors as numbers of infective larvae involved and time of infection were unknown.

The paucity of experimentally based information on this important host-parasite relationship motivated the present investigations which have continued over a period of 4 years. In the early phases pathogenic effects were of primary concern. Later, the discovery by Drudge *et al.* (1962) and Drudge (1964) that thiabendazole was chemotherapeutically effective against early migrating S. *vulgaris* larvae shifted emphasis to this aspect. Experimental design dictated the inclusion of infected untreated controls in the drug evaluation trials. This report presents data that have accumulated on a series of untreated experimental infections of S. *vulgaris* in foals raised worm-free.

METHODS

ANIMALS

Shetland pony foals were raised worm-free by weaning from the mares within 12 hours after birth and confinement thereafter in elevated wire-bottom cages. A milk formula containing cow's milk, corn syrup, and lime water was given until the foals were three months of age. A protein supplement (36 percent ground corn, 50 percent soybean oil meal, 8 percent molasses, 4 percent alfalfa leaf meal, 1.5 percent bone meal, and 0.5 percent salt) was hand-fed starting the first week and continuing for 3–4 months. At two weeks of age, a pelleted feed (50 percent alfalfa leaf meal, 10 percent oatmeal by-product, 14 percent corn, 14 percent oats, 5 percent soybean oil meal, 5 percent molasses, 1.5 percent bone meal, and 0.5 percent salt) was started. The pelleted feed *ad lib* was the ration at the time the majority of the foals were experimentally infected.

Success of the procedure in raising the foals worm-free and absence of prenatal infection were evidenced by consistently negative fecal examinations, which were done at weekly intervals starting at one week of age. These observations pertained not only to the present experimental animals but also to 6 foals which were raised under these conditions during the year prior to the present investigation. Five of the 6 foals were examined for periods in excess of one year with uniformly negative findings.

INFECTIVE LARVAE

Several sources were resorted to for the infective larvae of S. *vulgaris*. Attempts to establish pure infections of S. *vulgaris* in donor foals using larvae cultured from ground-up adult female worms collected from the ceca of naturally infected horses were not successful. Larvae derived in the foregoing manner were used to infect one animal (Experiment 11) in the present series. The remainder were infected with larvae cultured from the feces of naturally infected horses which were selected by preliminary fecal cultures for the presence of the desirable combination of S. *vulgaris* and small strongyle larvae and treated repeatedly with piperazine at 20 mg base per pound body weight to selectively remove the small strongyles. After this, feces were collected and routinely cultured in an incubator at 80°F, and 80 percent relative humidity for 1 week before the larvae were collected by the Baermann funnel technique. The infective larvae were then stored in a refrigerator at 40°F until used. Prior to administration each infective dose of larvae was examined for viability and purity under a stereoscope at approximately 20× by individual inspection of the larvae in narrow ribbons of the water suspension on glass slides. Extraneous larvae of small strongyles, *Trichostrongylus axei*, and S. *edentatus* were removed by needles. Larvae were administered by stomach tube, which was rinsed several times with water after the larval suspension was poured through.

OBSERVATIONS

Daily clinical observations were made for body temperature, gastrointestinal disturbances, fecal consistency, appetite, and general physical condition. Body weight was measured at weekly intervals. Blood samples were drawn at biweekly or weekly intervals for standard clinical determinations on the cellular components. Observations on the serum proteins were completed in the experiments numbered in the 30 and 40 series.

Total serum protein was measured by the refractive index method and component separations were completed in a Spinco Model R paper electrophoresis system according to the manufacturer's instruction manual. Preinfection observations were made in all cases and an uninfected control animal was included in each experiment for corresponding observations and determinations.

Bacteriological examination of blood was completed on several of the animals in the series 20 experiments by the inoculation of aseptically drawn samples into tryptose agar. Likewise, serum transaminase determinations were made on the cultured animals following the instructions of the reagent manufacturer (Dade Reagents) for serum glutamic oxalacetic transaminase (SGO-T) and serum glutamic pyruvic transaminase (SGP-T).

Necropsy examination included a thorough examination (Rooney, 1963) of the body organs and tissues for gross lesions. Selected tissues and lesions were processed for histological examination using the hematoxylin-eosin staining procedure. Recovery of parasites on a quantitative basis was not feasible because of the location in the thrombosed arteries. Qualitatively, larvae were recovered for morphological examination and measuring by carefully teasing small portions of the affected arteries in physiological saline under stereoscopic microscope.

RESULTS

General data pertaining to the foals, infective larvae, clinical reaction, and necropsy findings are outlined in Table I.

In the series of 11 foals receiving single doses of infective larvae a definite clinical disease entity was apparent. Nine of the 11 developed acute reactions and died or were sacrificed *in extremis*. It was an acute, highly fatal syndrome characterized by (1) marked increase in body temperature, (2) loss of appetite, (3) rapid loss of body weight, (4) mental depression and loss of physical activity, (5) abdominal distress (colic), (6) constipation or diarrhea, and (7) death in 14–22 days. The other two foals became ill but to a lesser degree.

Fever was a consistent reaction exhibited by all of the animals, being sudden in onset. In most of the animals the rise was recorded on the second day after larvae were administered. Levels reached ranged from 104° to 106°F. Several were characterized by a diphasic type of curve; after peaking during the first 10 days of infection, a dip occurred during the 12–16 day interval, which was followed by a secondary rise. Temperature curves on the two surviving animals fluctuated in a restricted

TABLE I

EXPERIMENTAL INFECTIONS OF *Strongylus vulgaris* IN PONY FOALS

Exp. no.	Animal				Larvae		Clinical			Necropsy[a]	
	No.	Age	Weight (lb)	Source horse (no.)	No. administered	Symptoms	Weight loss(%)	Fate[a]	Lesions[b]	Larvae (mm)
Single Dose of Larvae											
11	1-727	2	60	769	2,500	Acute	−12	D–18 days	Severe	1.4–2.2
12	1-729	6	148	802	5,000	Acute	−24	S–19 days	Severe	1.2–2.8
13	1-728	9	260	832	5,000	Acute	−20	D–21 days	Severe	1.6–2.4
24	V2-4	6	137	812	5,000	Acute	−20	S–21 days	Severe	1.5–2.4
25	V2-2	8	185	913	5,000	Subacute	+8	Survived	x	x
33	3-736	3	94	913	5,000	Acute	−13	D–16 days	Severe	1.0–1.5
34	3-12	5	101	913	3,500	Subacute	+9	Survived	x	x
35	3-36	7	135	913	5,000	Acute	−18	S–22 days	Moderate	1.5–2.5
42	4-730	6	150	774	5,000	Acute	−26	S–20 days	Severe	1.8–2.0
43	4-36	4	120	774	5,000	Acute	−13	D–15 days	Severe	1.2–2.3
44	4-7	8	108	774	5,000	Acute	−19	S–16 days	Severe	1.2–2.2
Multiple Doses of Larvae											
32	3-727	2	63	913	25 × 250	Chronic	+32	D–16 weeks	Severe	2.2–16.0

[a] D = Died; S = sacrificed; x = not completed.
[b] Degree of inflammation, infarction, and thrombosis.

range of 100.9°–103.2°F. Representative curves for the acute, subacute, and control animals are presented graphically in Fig. 1.

Inappetence closely followed the temperature curves. Characteristically, the acutely affected foals stopped eating at the outset of the fever and very little interest was shown for the pelleted ration during the remainder of the course of the disease. Any remission of the fever was usually followed by an improvement in the appetite. Impaired appetite was observed in the two subacutely affected animals. In both, this was

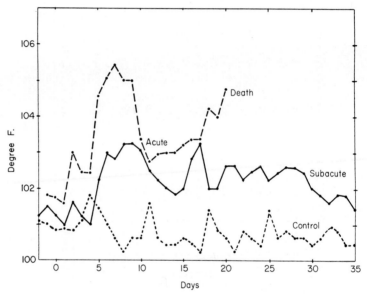

FIG. 1. Body temperature curves associated with acute and subacute reactions to experimental infections of *Strongylus vulgaris* in pony foals.

delayed in onset and transient, and was associated with the moderate rise in the body temperature.

Loss of body weight was rapid in the acutely affected animals (Table I). In relation to the preinfection body weight, the losses ranged from 11.6 to 26.0 percent, for the 2–3 weeks' period between infection and death. Both of the subacutely affected animals gained in excess of 8 percent during a corresponding 3-week period of time after infection which approximated the performance (10 percent) of their respective uninfected controls.

Consistency of feces was variable in the severely affected animals. Reduced fecal output and hardened consistency was generally more typical; however, some animals showed intermittent diarrhea. This usually occurred early in the course of the disease. Abdominal distress or colic was usually not seen until the second week after infection. The colic seizures were intermittent and became progressively more severe.

The acute cases lost physical condition rapidly during the first week. Following this the foals characteristically stood quietly, head drooping in a mentally depressed and physically inactive state. Later, the bulk of the time was spent lying down.

Consistent changes in the cellular components of the blood were also associated with this infection. Typical examples of both an acute and subacute case are presented in Table II. Except for the eosinophiles, similar changes were seen in both types of infection varying mostly in degree. A moderate anemia was characteristic as indicated by the decreases in the hematocrit and hemoglobin values. Sedimentation rates were increased to a moderate degree. Leukocytosis was also a consistent reaction. In the acutely affected animals the increase of both immature and mature neutrophiles was particularly impressive. Eosinophiles were absent or present in relatively small numbers in the acute case, whereas in the subacute reaction the percentage of eosinophiles steadily increased and became a conspicuous feature.

Serum protein changes observed in typical acute and subacute reactions are presented in Table III. Total serum protein (gram percent) increased early, during the first week in the course of the acute reaction; thereafter the higher values were maintained or relatively small additional increases were recorded. Consistent changes in the various components were also associated with the foregoing. Albumin fraction was maintained through the first post-infection week, after which decreases were progressive. Globulin fractions were markedly increased the first week, particularly the alpha component, after which more moderate progressive increases occurred, particularly in the beta and gamma components. In the subacute reaction, the foregoing pattern of change was also characteristic but the development was more gradual. The graphic illustration of the progressive changes in the serum components is presented in Fig. 3.

Of a total of 42 blood cultures prepared, 40 were negative, while *Corynebacterium equi* and *Enterococcus* were recovered from two foals, respectively, on the second day after infective larvae were administered.

Serum transaminase determinations were completed on the same animals and on the same days to correspond with the foregoing blood cultures. Increased values were not associated with the acute clinical reaction except in one foal (V2-4) on the day before death. This was the only foal of the five with a fatal termination to the *S. vulgaris* infection. The remainder were treated with thiabendazole during the second week

TABLE II

BLOOD CELL DATA PERTAINING TO ACUTE AND SUBACUTE REACTIONS OF PONY FOALS TO EXPERIMENTAL INFECTIONS OF
Strongylus vulgaris

Day of infection	Hematocrit	Hgb. (gm %)	Sed.[a] rate	Leukocytes per mm³	Differential (%)					
					YP	P	L	E	M	B
Experiment 24, Foal No. V2-4 (Acute Reaction)										
−10	32.7	10.5	53	8,250	6.5	39.0	53.0	0.0	1.5	0.0
− 2	30.4	10.2	61	8,200	10.5	33.0	56.0	0.0	1.0	0.0
+ 4	27.4	9.0	65	8,750	4.0	17.5	71.5	1.5	5.5	0.0
+ 9	25.4	9.4	66	12,700	14.5	41.0	40.0	0.5	4.0	0.0
+13	24.4	8.4	68	19,500	32.5	41.5	23.5	2.0	0.5	0.0
+16	24.0	8.0	70	22,700	37.0	43.5	16.5	0.0	3.0	0.0
+20	35.0	12.6	1	16,750	54.5	27.5	18.0	0.0	0.0	0.0
Experiment 34, Foal No. 3-12 (Subacute Reaction)										
− 7	33.2	10.6	58	8,150	8.0	35.0	57.0	0.0	1.0	0.0
0	31.7	10.2	59	9,400	7.5	41.0	51.0	0.0	0.5	0.0
+ 7	30.2	11.0	62	11,000	13.0	52.0	32.5	1.5	1.0	0.0
+12	25.0	8.8	69	10,950	14.5	40.5	41.5	2.5	0.5	1.0
+14	27.6	10.0	66	10,350	22.0	39.5	31.0	5.5	2.0	0.0
+21	27.6	10.0	65	10,750	18.5	35.0	35.0	10.0	1.5	0.0
+28	24.0	8.0	70	13,300	21.5	37.5	32.0	8.5	0.5	0.0
+35	24.0	8.0	70	15,000	8.5	25.0	39.0	36.5	0.5	0.0
+42	26.0	8.6	69	14,500	10.0	33.5	38.5	15.5	2.0	0.0
+49	25.0	8.0	66	15,400	15.5	30.5	38.0	14.5	1.5	1.0

[a] Sedimentation per 30 minutes.

after larvae were given and this arrested the course of the disease. The elevated values for foal V2-4 were a fivefold increase for SGO-T and a threefold increase for SGT-P. The range of "normal" values for SGO-T was 300 to 500 and for SGT-P it was 10–20.

At necropsy, the gross pathology was characteristically restricted to the posterior small intestine, cecum, and ventral colon. The walls of these organs presented typical lesions, including (1) small discrete, subserosal

TABLE III

SERUM PROTEIN DATA (GRAM PERCENT) PERTAINING TO ACUTE AND SUBACUTE
REACTIONS OF PONY FOALS TO EXPERIMENTAL INFECTIONS OF
Strongylus vulgaris

Day of infection	Total	Albumin	Globulins		
			Alpha	Beta	Gamma
Experiment 35, Foal No. 3-36 (Acute Reaction)					
− 7	5.70	3.30	1.07	0.91	0.42
0	5.70	3.44	1.00	0.86	0.40
7	7.20	3.31	1.92	1.23	0.74
14	6.60	2.43	1.97	1.19	1.01
21	7.40	2.01	1.85	1.64	1.90
Experiment 34, Foal No. 3-12 (Subacute Reaction)					
− 7	6.40	3.67	1.34	0.88	0.51
0	5.90	3.60	1.13	0.77	0.40
+ 7	6.00	3.25	1.58	0.83	0.34
+12	6.30	2.84	2.06	0.83	0.57
+14	6.50	2.78	1.86	1.03	0.83
+21	6.70	2.65	2.11	0.95	0.99
+28	6.80	2.37	2.20	1.09	1.14
+35	7.40	2.54	2.23	1.63	1.00
+42	7.70	2.34	2.13	2.00	1.23
+49	8.00	2.31	2.10	2.41	1.18

hemorrhages, predominantly in the small intestine; (2) hemorrhagic inflammation of extensive areas of the terminal portion of the small intestine, cecum, and ventral colon, (3) infarction of large areas, particularly of the ileum and cecum, (4) adhesions involving loops of the small intestine and cecum, ventral colon, and the ventral abdominal wall. The anterior mesenteric artery and its branches distributing blood to the foregoing organs also were consistently affected by (1) thrombosis and embolism, (2) enlargement and thickening of the walls, and (3) tortuous fibrin track formations in the intima. In some animals the tracks extended to the abdominal aorta in an area around the origin of the anterior mesenteric artery. Only the youngest animal in the series (1-727) presented an acute peritonitis with an accumulation of sanguinous exudate in the peritoneal cavity. The liver was usually enlarged, with generalized degenerative changes. Discolored areas and small granulomatous lesions were also frequently observed in the liver. The latter type of lesion was seen occasionally in the lungs and rarely in the kidney. Histologically, the lesions of the mesenteric arteries included inflammatory

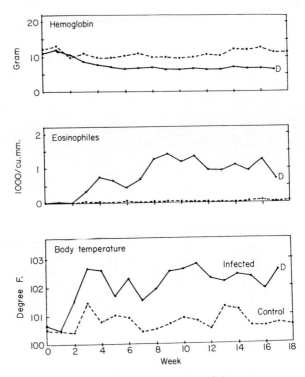

Fig. 2.   Body temperature, eosinophile, and hemoglobin changes associated with chronic *Strongylus vulgaris* infection (pony foal 3-727).

changes in the walls, fibrin deposits on the intima, and varying degrees of thrombosis. Living fourth-stage larvae of S. *vulgaris*, varying in length from 1.2 to 2.8 mm (Table I), were recovered from the arterial lesions.

Multiple Doses

The administration of small numbers of infective larvae repeatedly over a prolonged period of time produces a reaction similar in many respects to the foregoing acute and subacute types, except that the changes become manifest gradually and are generally less dramatic. This chronic type of S. *vulgaris* infection is represented by a foal that received

25 doses of 250 larvae at approximately biweekly intervals over a 16-week period before succumbing.

The clinical symptoms of the chronic reaction include (1) persistent low-grade fever (the weekly average was consistently above the uninfected control after the first week; Fig. 2); (2) generally poor appetite; (3) intermittent periods of abdominal distress; (4) poor weight gain performance (from 63 pounds initially to 83 at death in comparison to

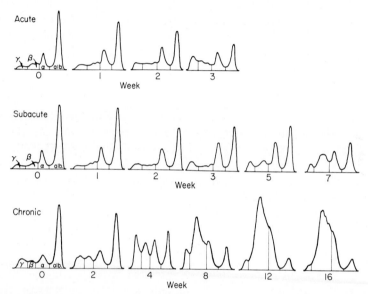

FIG. 3. Profiles of serum proteins associated with acute, subacute, and chronic infections of *Strongylus vulgaris* in pony foals 3-36, 3-12, and 3-727, respectively.

the control's performance of gaining from 48 to 123 pounds over the same period).

Blood cell changes were (1) below-normal hemoglobin (Fig. 2) and hematocrit values after the third week, and (2) persistent leukocytosis characterized by a neutrophilia and eosinophilia (Fig. 2).

Serum protein alterations included (1) progressive increase in total serum protein to a level twice the normal at 12 weeks which was maintained thereafter, and (2) progressive and marked changes in the components (Fig. 3). Albumin decreased throughout. Increases in alpha and beta components were gradual until the profiles were grossly distorted during the last half of the course of the disease in this animal. Gamma globulin increased during the first 4 weeks after which this component declined to relatively small quantities at death.

At necropsy, the gross pathology was somewhat different from that described for the acute infections. Subserosal hemorrhages in the small intestine were scattered and ranged in color from new bright red to old discolored lesions. Hardened nodules were present in the small mesenteric arteries with a distribution pattern of some being close to the small intestinal wall and others located some distance away in the larger arterial branches in the mesentery. The ileal artery was much enlarged and partially thrombosed. The cecal wall was relatively free of hemorrhagic inflammation, but was extensively infarcted. Both cecal arteries were enlarged with thickened walls, and thrombi virtually occluded the lumens. Ventral colon was devoid of infarction and inflammation except for regional involvement at the pelvic flexure. The latter was associated with a regional thickening and thrombosis of the ventral colic artery. Anterior mesenteric and coeliac arteries were distended with thickened walls and accumulations of thrombus material. The dorsal aorta also had small scattered thrombi concentrated mainly near the anterior mesenteric and coeliac arteries which in some cases extended forward to the heart. The liver was enlarged and discolored, and the surface showed scattered granulomas and fibrotic foci. Several-nodular lesions and infarctions were present in the spleen. Many fourth- and fifth-stage forms of S. vulgaris ranging from 2.2 to 16 mm were recovered from the arterial lesions.

DISCUSSION

Pathogenesis of acute S. vulgaris infection is related to the migratory activities of the larvae in the mesenteric arteries. The present observations are in accord with the migratory pathway described previously for S. vulgaris by Enigk (1950, 1951). It is of interest to note that the experimental method in both investigations gives rise to this accord. The three other proposed migratory routes (Ershov, 1949; Olt, 1932; Ottaway and Bingham, 1946) for this parasite were derived from necropsy examinations of naturally infected animals in which the numbers of infective larvae involved, the time of infection, and the receptive state of the host were unknown.

The invasion of arterioles shortly after gut penetration and the migration in the intima of the mesenteric arteries, against the flow of blood and toward the anterior mesenteric artery, account for the characteristic localization of the primary lesions in the walls of the small intestine, cecum, ventral colon, and associated arteries. This is determined by the predilection of the larvae to penetrate these areas. Activities of the early migrating larvae provide extensive contact between the host and the parasite and result in the profound response on the part of the host which is manifested in the clinical symptoms and hematological changes described in this report.

Relatively small numbers of larvae are capable of eliciting an acute reaction. Infections of 5000 larvae were lethal for foals as old as 9 months at the time of infection. This indicates a higher level of pathogenicity than the investigations of Enigk (1950), who used similar infective doses in terms of numbers of larvae; however, the foals ranged from 2 to 6 weeks of age when infected. This is much younger than the 2 to 9 months in the present series. Neither investigation was designed to determine the minimal lethal dose of larvae and further study will be needed to resolve this point.

An increasingly body of evidence indicates that an additional etiological agent is not required in the pathogenesis of this infection. The change in the blood cell picture associated with S. *vulgaris* infection is not unlike that seen in bacterial infections. However, blood culture work in the present study and the bacteriological examination of Enigk (1951) have been negative in determining a consistent isolate. This is not to indicate, however, that bacterial infections do not occur coincidentally or on occasion in specific relation to S. *vulgaris*. Antibiotic therapy of a foal for a 3-day period preceding and continuing for 7 days after infective larvae were administered did not prevent the typical febrile reaction and provided additional evidence against bacterial involvement.

The febrile reaction which was so prominent in the clinical reaction in the present observations was also previously associated with S. *vulgaris* infection (Enigk, 1950). Origin of the fever can be ascribed to the tissue damage inflicted by the migrating larvae and (or) a toxic substance elaborated by the larvae (Ershov, 1956). Evidence in support of the latter hypothesis is apparent in the prompt remission of the fever following chemotherapy of acute S. *vulgaris* infection with high dosages of thiabendazole (Drudge *et al.*, 1962; Drudge, 1964). This therapy was associated with the killing of migrating larvae of S. *vulgaris* and it is doubtful that the tissue repair would be prompt enough to coincide with the remission of the fever which occurs within 24 hours.

Profound changes in serum proteins were observed in the present investigations. The magnitude of the changes was related to the more severe injury produced by the migrating stages of this parasite in comparison with the other helminthic infections that have been studied (Cornelius and Kaneko, 1963; Leland, 1961). An increase in total serum protein concentration has been generally associated with helminthic infection, while decrease in the albumin fraction coupled with increases in the globulin fractions, which characterized the present observations, has also been generally related to experimental helminthic infections

(Leland, 1961). This pattern of change has also been related to tissue injuries of various causes and cannot be used as a reliable means of differential diagnosis of helminth infection (Cornelius and Kaneko, 1963).

The role played by eosinophiles remains to be determined. In the acute infections the rapid culmination and termination of the disease probably did not allow time for their mobilization and appearance in the circulating blood. The subacute reaction provided more time for the appearance and progressive increase in the numbers of circulating eosinophiles and was regarded as an index of a developing resistance by the host. Similarly, the eosinophilia associated with the chronic type of reaction stemming from multiple doses of small numbers of infective larvae was regarded as a response favoring the host. However, the fatal termination indicates that the eosinophilia is not an absolute index of resistance and that additional investigation is necessary to clarify the relationships.

Anemia has been associated with S. vulgaris infection. Usually this is credited to the blood-sucking activities of the adult parasites. The present experimental evidence indicates that the early migrating larvae produce a low-grade normocytic type of anemia which no doubt contributes to the overall picture under natural conditions.

The occurrence of acute S. vulgaris infection as a specific clinical syndrome is probably not generally recognized by practicing veterinarians. The reason for this is readily apparent from a comparison of similarities of the clinical symptoms and blood picture of S. vulgaris infection with bacterial infections. Practitioners have not been alerted to this parasite's role in a clinical syndrome characterized by fever, inappetence, depression, and a mild leukocytosis with a shift to the left in the neutrophilia and have been disposed to regard such a syndrome as a bacterial infection. Unfortunately, the present observations do not present a specific means of differentiating between the two conditions. Until this is possible, the foregoing symptomatology must be regarded as stemming from either cause. Fortunately, successful chemotherapy of acute S. vulgaris infection is possible with thiabendazole (Drudge et al., 1962; Drudge, 1964).

The question of prenatal infection by S. vulgaris has been a matter of conjecture over the years. Although the attempts to demonstrate this by examination of fetuses and newborn foals have been negative (Enigk, 1951), the basis for the persistency of this contention is the natural occurrence of fatal S. vulgaris infections in 4–6 week old foals. Coupled with this is the idea that the prepatent period of 6 months for S. vulgaris must call for an infection in utero. Experimental reproduction of a rapidly developing, fatal disease within 2 to 3 weeks after infective larvae are administered indicates that postnatal infection by ingestion of infective larvae offers a more plausible explanation for the source of the larvae for the naturally occurring disease than the *in utero* route. The absence of *in utero* infection offers evidence against the intraarterial route of migration proposed by Ottaway and Bingham (1946) and Poynter (1960) for *S. vulgaris*. Such a route should provide a mechanism more favorable for *in utero* infection as well as a generalized distribution of the larvae and associated pathology. This has not been substantiated by observations on natural infections or experimental evidence.

REFERENCES

Cornelius, C. E., and Kaneko, J. J. (1963). "Clinical Biochemistry of Domestic Animals." Academic Press, New York.

Drudge, J. H. (1964). New developments in parasite control. *Bloodhorse* 87, 132-133 and 166-168.

Drudge, J. H., Szanto, J., and Wyant, Z. N. (1964). Studies on the anthelmintic thiabendazole in the horse. III. Activity against migrating *Strongylus vulgaris*. Proc. seminar on Parasite diseases with special reference to thiabendazole. *4th Pan Am. Congr. Vet. Med. & Zootech., Mexico City, 1964*. pp. 84-88. Merck & Co., Inc., Rahway, New Jersey.

Enigk, K. (1950). Zur Entwicklung von *Strongylus vulgaris* (Nematodes) im Wirtstier. *Z. Tropenmed. Parasitol.* 2, 287-306.

Enigk, K. (1951). Weitere Untersuchungen zur Biologie von *Strongylus vulgaris* (Nematodes) im Wirtstiere. *Z. Tropenmed. Parasitol.* 2, 523-535.

Ershov, V. S. (1949). Cycle of development of *Delafondia vulgaris* (Loos, 1901) in the horse. *Veterinariya* 26, 26-28.

Ershov, V. S. (1956). "Parasitology and Parasitic Diseases of Livestock," pp. 140-147. State Publ. House Agri. Lit., Moscow.

Farrelly, B. T. (1954). The pathogenesis and significance of parasitic endarteritis and thrombosis in the ascending aorta of the horse. *Vet. Record* 66, 53-61.

Jubb, K. V., and Kennedy, P. C. (1963). "Pathology of Domestic Animals," Vol. 2, pp. 149-154. Academic Press, New York.

Leland, S. E. (1961). Blood and plasma volume, total serum protein, and electrophoretic studies in helminthic diseases. *Ann. N. Y. Acad. Sci.* 94, 163-182.

Loos, A. (1901). The Sclerostomidae of horses and donkeys in Egypt. *Records Egyptian Govt. School Med.* 1, 21-114.

Olt, A. (1932). Das Aneurysma Verminosum des Pferdes und seine unbekannten Beziehungen zur Kolik. *Deut. Tierarztl. Wochschr.* 40, 326-332.

Ottaway, C. W., and Bingham, M. L. (1946). Further observations on the incidence of parasitic aneurysm in the horse. *Vet. Record* 58, 155-159.

Poynter, D. (1960). The arterial lesions produced by *Strongylus vulgaris* and their relationship to the migratory route of the parasite in its host. *Res. Vet. Sci.* 1, 205-217.

Rooney, J. R. (1963). The equine necropsy. *Veterinary SCOPE* 8, 2-11.

Smith, H. A., and Jones, T. C. (1961). "Veterinary Pathology," 2nd ed., pp. 519-522. Lea & Febiger, Philadelphia, Pennsylvania.

Wetzel, R. (1942). Ueber die Entwicklungsdauer der Palisadenwurmer im Korper des Pferdes und ihre praktische Answertung. *Deut. Tierarztl. Wochschr.* 50, 443-444.

Wetzel, R. (1952). Die Entwicklungsdauer (Prepatent-periode) von *Strongylus edentatus* im Pferd. *Deut. Tierarztl. Wochschr.* **59**, 129-130.

Discussion

Dr. Soulsby: You demonstrated marked changes in the serum protein profiles; were the designations alpha, beta, gamma, and so forth based on any information other than electrophoresis on paper?

Dr. Drudge: No! These have been defined according to their mobility on paper.

Dr. Round: At Newmarket we have looked at the serum protein patterns of ponies exposed to natural infections of *Strongylus vulgaris, S. edentatus* and also small strongyles. Exactly the same type of pattern occurred as in Dr. Drudge's experimental infections, at from 5 to 7 months of age. The amount of total serum protein remained fairly constant but there was a great reduction in albumin and a compensating increase in the globulins. This increase occurred mainly in the region of the beta globulins.

Zoonoses, with Particular Reference to Parasites of Veterinary Importance

PAUL C. BEAVER

Department of Tropical Medicine and Public Health, Tulane University School of Medicine, New Orleans, Louisiana

A large number of parasites might be discussed under the title "zoonotic parasitoses." The majority, however, are of little or no veterinary importance, and several of those which do lie within that category have been recently dealt with in other reviews (Cameron, 1962; Witenberg, 1964). I shall discuss here only a few of the zoonoses, mainly toxocariasis, ancylostomiasis, ascariasis, and filariasis. Others which are of special veterinary importance and might have been included are trichinosis, echinococcosis, toxoplasmosis, and certain trematode infections. It should be noted that the monkey, an increasingly popular household pet, is a potential source of infection with *Strongyloides*, *Oesophagostomum*, tapeworms, amebae, and *Balantidium*. In the past few years it has become apparent that malaria can be acquired from monkeys (Chin *et al.*, 1965). A finding of great interest, though not of veterinary importance, is that marine fish harbor worms (anisakids) which normally develop in sea mammals but when ingested by man invade the wall of the stomach or intestine and produce life-threatening disturbances (van Thiel *et al.*, 1960; van Thiel, 1962; Asami *et al.*, 1965; Yokogawa and Yoshimura, 1965). Also of great recent interest is the lungworm of rats which invades the central nervous system (Rosen *et al.*, 1962) and eye of man (Prommindaroj *et al.*, 1962). However, the zoonotic helminths on which newer findings are of prime interest to veterinarians are the *Toxocara*, *Ancylostoma*, and *Dirofilaria* species that are common in dogs and cats, and the large roundworm, *Ascaris suum*, which is commonly present in pigs.

TOXOCARIASIS

Toxocara canis is found in dogs, more commonly young dogs, in nearly all parts of the world. *Toxocara cati* is also common in cats and is cosmopolitan in its distribution. Owing to the extraordinary resourcefulness of *T. canis* in host-to-host transmission, where it occurs at all, it tends to be extremely prevalent. Infection is acquired in four different ways (Sprent, 1958, 1961).

(1) By ingestion of eggs incubated to the infective stage in contaminated soil.

(2) By prenatal transfer of larvae from the tissues of the mother to the lungs of the fetus.

(3) By eating, as prey, paratenic small mammalian hosts who were earlier infected by ingesting eggs in soil, the hatched larvae remaining unchanged in the tissues until eaten by the predator.

(4) By ingestion of voided larvae in the feces of the suckling pup. In this instance the nursing mother who is otherwise immune to intestinal stages of the parasite acquires the infection by ingesting young worms that have undergone partial development in the pup. The passage of viable worms in the feces of pups apparently results from overcrowding in the intestine.

The several modes of infection are mentioned because three of them have some bearing on the nature of infection in man. As is well known, children at the age of 1 to 2 years have a strong tendency to eat dirt and, as is readily appreciated, in areas regularly contaminated by infected dogs the upper layers of the soil bear large numbers of infective *Toxocara* eggs. Thus, children ingesting even moderate amounts of such soil, and over relatively short periods of time, may ingest thousands of infective eggs which hatch in the intestine, liberating larvae which then migrate to the liver and other organs. Beaver (1960) examined a liver biopsy of about 100 mg from a 4-year-old child which contained 32 *Toxocara* larvae. This is approximately 300 per gram of liver. In another case (Dent *et al.*, 1956), autopsy revealed larvae abundantly present in essentially all of the organs. By quantitative estimate there were approximately 60 larvae per gram of liver, 5 per gram of muscle, and 3–5 per gram of brain.

The fact that *T. canis* is adapted for transfer through paratenic hosts is of significance because in the light of this fact we can assume that while man is an unsuitable host for the adult stage he is not an abnormal host for the larval stage. Possibly for this reason, the larvae live in the tissues for very long periods, up to 9 or 10 years in monkeys, and are well tolerated by children except when present in large numbers or located in the brain or eye, or when the infected individual has become hypersensitive. The monkeys referred to were a male and a female, inoculated with massive doses of infective *T. canis* larvae in 1954 and 1955. Biopsies of the liver were taken at 6-month, and later at yearly, intervals. Active, apparently infective larvae were found in all biopsies through 1964, but when the animals were sacrificed in 1965 no larvae were found, in the liver or elsewhere. It is perhaps noteworthy that whereas all larvae after the first year were encapsulated in the male, in the female some of the larvae were free in the tissues even at the 9th year.

In 1962, when the last review of toxocariasis cases was published, 10 years after the first cases were reported, approximately 150 instances of infection with larval *Toxocara* in man had been recorded. (Beaver, 1962). In more recent years only a few new cases have been reported but many more are known to have occurred in this and other countries. Cases not referred to in the above review have been reported by Brain and Allan (1964), Braun-Vallon *et al.* (1964), Falkinburg and Kay (1962), Farber and Craig (1959), Fushimi *et al.* (1963), Moore (1962), Rey (1962), Schoenfeld *et al.* (1964), Shrand (1964), Schrott (1963), and Wong and Laxdal (1958). The decline in reporting is due mainly to the fact that only the cases presenting unusual features are reportable in leading journals, not that the disease isn't observed. Another reason is that without demonstration of the larva in biopsy or autopsy tissues the diagnosis is somewhat uncertain. Nevertheless, there is no uncertainty about the high frequency of illness caused by *Toxocara* in children, and since no specific treatment has been found, preventive measures which consist chiefly in the frequent, thorough, anthelmintic treatment of infected pets, are essentially the responsibility of the veterinary clinician.

It can be mentioned incidentally that *Toxocara canis* larvae also invade the tissues of the pig (Done *et al.*, 1960), sheep (Schaeffler, 1960; Sweatman *et al.*, 1962), chicken, and pigeon (Galvin, 1964). Such infections acquired naturally may possibly be damaging to these animals, but of greater significance is the possibility that human infection may be acquired from eating the infected organs, particularly the liver. It has previously been noted (Beaver, 1956) that during the brief period when raw liver was prescribed for pernicious anemia, a high and persistent eosinophilia was observed in essentially all persons so treated. While it has not been shown that the eosinophilia associated with the raw liver diet was due to larval nematode infections acquired from the liver, it is possible that an observer was closer to the truth than he suspected when he stated, "The eosinophilic reaction with liver treatment is probably well known . . . , but those unaware of the phenomenon are not unlikely to suspect that parasites derived from the raw liver have been implanted in the patient."

The cat *Toxocara* (*T. cati*) differs from *T. canis* both in structure and life cycle (Sprent, 1956). Prenatal infection apparently does not occur in *T. cati*, and the infective-stage larva probably is much less adapted to long survival in the tissues of paratenic hosts. Owing to these differences and probably also to the peculiar defecation habits of cats, larval *T. cati* infection has seldom been reported in man. In one of two cases reported by Karpinski *et al.* (1956) a larva which was thought possibly to be *T. cati* was found in a liver biopsy of a 2-year-old boy in Philadelphia. The larva was tentatively identified as *T. cati* because it appeared to be smaller than *T. canis* and because the child had had contact with an infected kitten and no known contact with a dog. In the other case (Schoenfeld *et al.*, 1964), numerous larvae that were identified as *T. cati* were found in the brain of a 5-year-old girl in Israel who came to hospital comatose, with fever, and in convulsions. As *T. canis* and *T. cati* larvae are closely similar in all respects except size, and even in this character there is some overlap, there is great difficulty in distinguishing one from the other when seen only in microsections of tissue. On the other hand, there usually is no problem in recognizing *Toxocara* larvae as distinct from *Ancylostoma* and other types.

HOOKWORMS OF DOGS AND CATS

Creeping eruption or cutaneous larva migrans is a form of dermatitis caused by the burrowing of nematode larvae, especially those of the dog and cat hookworms, and characterized by a progressive, papulo-vesicular, pruritic lesion which develops in the wake of the migrating larva. Having recently been reviewed (Beaver, 1964), the condition is too well known to merit discussion here except to emphasize two old but often overlooked features and to call attention to a relatively new feature that probably has not yet been referred to in the veterinary literature.

It is generally believed that creeping eruption in this and other parts of the world usually is caused by *Ancylostoma braziliense*. This hookworm is found in cats, and to a lesser extent in dogs, throughout the tropical and subtropical regions. For unknown reasons, its distribution is characteristically discontinuous, at least in the United States. It occurs in Florida and adjacent coastal States and in parts of Texas, but apparently is not found in the intervening zone. A point that is often overlooked is that while *A. braziliense* unquestionably is capable of producing creeping eruption, and possibly is the most common cause of the disease, it has never been identified in the skin of man. It is only by experimental demonstration of its capabilities, and by the fact that it is present in localities where the incidence of creeping eruption is highest, that inferences are made concerning its role. In experiments with human volunteers the larvae of other hookworms penetrate the skin less readily (*Ancylostoma caninum, A. ceylanicum, Uncinaria stenocephala*), or not at all (*A. tubaeforme*), and when they do enter the skin the lesions are less migratory and less persistent (Beaver, 1956; de Carneri and Castellino, 1964). Further studies on the behavior of these and other larvae are needed to clarify the question of which species in any given region are involved in creeping eruption.

Because the larvae causing creeping eruption in individual cases usually are unidentified, it is difficult to satisfactorily interpret the events following the active migratory phase in the skin. In all cases migration in the skin eventually ceases spontaneously. It is often stated that when migration ceases the larvae have died in the skin. This would seem to be a conclusion that is based on faulty logic; thus far evidences of suppuration around dead larvae have not been reported. Whether the larvae ever do die in the skin is unknown but it is clear that in some cases they move into the deeper tissues and reach the lungs. Roentgenographic and clinical evidences of lung invasion have been reported in a number of cases, and in one instance large numbers of the larvae were observed in the sputum coincident with the disappearance of skin lesions (Muhleisen, 1953). In another similar case, although the larvae were not observed, masses of Charcot-Leyden crystals, characteristic of verminous pneumonitis, were found in the sputum. Thus it is appropriate to stress the point that the cutaneous phase of creeping eruption is or may be followed by a pulmonary phase.

About two years ago, a new type of human infection with hookworm larvae was described (Baldone *et al.*, 1964; Nadbath and Lawlor, 1965). In three cases, two in Maryland and one in Alabama, a nematode larva was discovered in a small opacity of the cornea. In two of the cases, after being observed for several days or weeks, the larva migrated into the sclera and was not seen thereafter. In the third case, however, when the larva had moved to the margin of the cornea it was successfully removed in a small wedge-shaped biopsy. After clearing, it was readily identified as an *Ancylostoma* type of larva having all of the characteristics seen in the stage which invades the skin in cases of creeping eruption (Fig. 1). In none of the three cases were there skin lesions suggestive of creeping eruption. Whether the larva entered the cornea directly through the surface of the conjunctiva, or migrated from the skin, or from the deeper tissues, could not be determined. In this connection it is of interest to recall that the larva of *Ancylostoma caninum*, which is the most common hookworm of dogs in this country, persists in the tissues of mice and other experimental animals for more than a year, and tends to migrate to the central nervous system (Nichols, 1956; Soh, 1958). Although in only one case was the larva identified as that of a hookworm, and in this instance it could not be identified with a particular species, it serves to point out that while the skin lesions in creeping eruption cause great

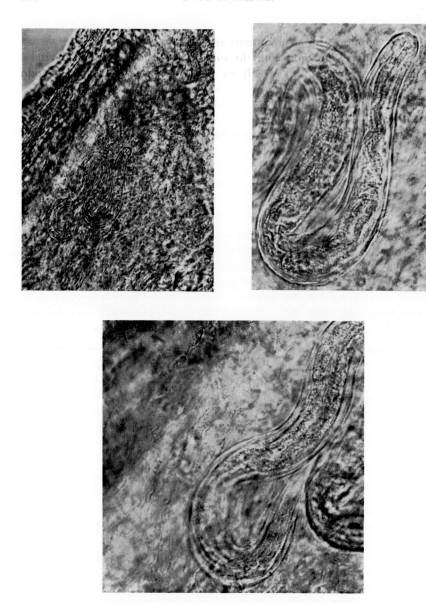

Fɪɢ. 1. *Ancylostoma* larva in cornea of human eye; case reported by Nadbath and Lawlor (1965). Figures printed by permission of publisher and authors. A. Entire larva as it appeared after fixation in 10% formalin and cleared in glycerine jelly (×168). B. Anterior end, showing oral structures and esophagus extending to level of first flexure (×535). C. Posterior end, showing genital anlage, intestine, and lateral ala (evident in curved portion of hind body) (×535).

discomfort, more serious disturbances may result from subsequent migration into other sites.

PIG *ASCARIS*

While the importance of some of the infections acquired from domestic animals is perhaps overestimated, the amount of human disease produced by the common *Ascaris* of pigs probably is underestimated. Great effort has been made to determine the relationship between *Ascaris lumbricoides* of man and *Ascaris suum* of pigs. In its own host each is regarded as an important pathogen, and the diseases caused by both the adult stage in the intestine and the larval stage in the lungs are well recognized. It apparently has been shown that the pig *Ascaris* produces patent infection in man, and that the human *Ascaris* likewise develops to maturity in the pig. What has been lacking is an assessment of the morbidity caused by each when it invades the host of the other.

Probably these two worms should be regarded as separate species. Although, by most workers at least, they are regarded as morphologically indistinguishable, they differ in their ability to develop in man and pig, and when they do develop to maturity the prepatent period appears to be widely different irrespective of the host. Japanese workers have demonstrated that in human volunteers the prepatent periods for the pig and human *Ascaris,* respectively, were 4 to 6 and 8 to 10 weeks (Takata, 1951; Yajima, 1955; Akamatsu, 1958, 1959). Galvin (1964), in the United States, found that in the pig the prepatent periods were 40 to 53 days for *A. suum* and 54 to 61 days for *A. lumbricoides.* Development in the lungs and migration to the intestine (of pigs and rabbits) was faster in *A. suum* than it was in *A. lumbricoides.*

In the above experiments there was no conclusive evidence of differences in pathogenicity of the two types of *Ascaris.* For the present discussion, the main point to be stressed is that pig *Ascaris* larvae unquestionably hatch in the intestine and make the lung migration in man as they do in the pig. This applies as well to many other mammals, including cattle (Kennedy, 1954). In view of these observations, it is noteworthy that the pig *Ascaris* has not been recognized as a cause of naturally acquired pneumonitis in man. Probably if it were looked for among people who have frequent contact with infected pigs it would be found. It may be stated as an hypothesis that a significant proportion of the chest-cold like illnesses experienced in summer among rural people living in the hog-raising regions is caused by the *Ascaris* of pigs. This might be more, or less, true in regions where human ascariasis is endemic.

FILARIASIS

Dirofilaria immitis, the heartworm of dogs, has for many years been a problem to veterinarians. It is found in nearly all tropical and subtropical regions of the world and in this country its geographic range appears to be spreading northward. It is not uncommon in New England, and in some parts of the Great Lakes area it is now one of the more common parasites of the dog (Schlotthauer and Griffiths, 1964). Recently it has been recognized as a parasite which reaches maturity in man (Beaver and Orihel, 1965).

The first case of heartworm infection in man was reported in Louisiana in 1941, the second in South Carolina in 1954, and in the past 5 years nine others have been reported: three from Louisiana, two from other southeastern states, and one each from Massachusetts, Michigan, Wisconsin, and Texas. In two cases the worms were found at autopsy, in the heart and adjacent vessels; in the remainder the worm, dead and folded in a pulmonary artery, was discovered in sections of an infarct-like lesion of the lung, removed surgically on suspicion of cancer. In two of the surgical cases a density had been discovered on routine X-ray of the chest while in the others examination of the chest had been because of symptoms, usually cough and chest pain. In all cases only one worm was discovered. All infected persons were adult and nine of the eleven were women.

Dipetalonema reconditum which also occurs in dogs has not been identified in man. However, three unidentified small filariae removed from subcutaneous tissues of residents of this country, two of which were morphologically similar to this species, have been reported (Beaver and Orihel, 1965).

Inasmuch as the raccoon is occasionally a household pet, and even in the wild state frequently lives close to people, it can be mentioned here that a *Dirofilaria* (*D. tenuis*) which lives in the subcutaneous tissues of this common animal has been found to occur in man. Among 26 *Dirofilaria* removed from subcutaneous nodules or abscesses in residents of the United States, mostly Florida, Louisiana, and adjoining states, 25 probably were acquired from the raccoon (Orihel and Beaver, 1965).

DISCUSSION

Toxocariasis, ancylostomiasis, ascariasis, and dirofilariasis—each a zoonosis of world-wide distribution, and each a cause of human illness which occasionally is severe—are nevertheless of minor importance when considered in relation to other health problems of either man or the animals which harbor the infections. On the other hand, these diseases have several features which, when considered together, command the attention of health workers.

First to be mentioned is the fact that the frequency and severity of human disease caused by these zoonoses has not been fully assessed. Toxocariasis as a cause of disease in man is not even known in many parts of the world. Although it unquestionably occurs in a certain proportion of the people wherever it occurs in a high proportion of the dogs, it is difficult to diagnose even when there is a sharp awareness of its zoonotic character and clinical characteristics. As it has been less than 15 years since it was recognized as a disease of man, there are some parts of the world where visceral larva migrans has not yet gotten into the published guides that are used in either training or practice. Moreover, in countries where helminth infections of various types are still at a high level of endemicity the presence of patent infections tends to mask out the nonpatent ones such as toxocariasis. When, in any country, or even in any given community, an attempt is made to estimate the rate of *Toxocara* infection, usually it is merely stated that the incidence probably is higher than is presently suspected.

The above remarks are almost as applicable to zoonotic ancylostomiasis, ascariasis, and filariasis as they are to toxocariasis. Creeping eruption is, of course, readily diagnosed, but the species of larva invading the skin in essentially all cases will be unknown, and therefore the precise source of infection will be unknown too in many instances. More noteworthy, however, is the fact that the presence or degree of invasion of the deeper tissues usually cannot be known with certainty. On the basis of the known like cycles and the behavior of the infective-stage larvae in experimental animals, any of the *Ancylostoma* species which occur in wild or domesticated mammals may invade the tissues of man. As far as is known, all of these hookworms are infective by the oral route, as much or more so than they are by skin penetration. On the basis of the high prevalence of endemic soil-transmitted helminths, it can be inferred with confidence that ingestion of the infective stages of zoonotic helminths occurs regularly and frequently in some communities.

Examination of dooryard soil has revealed that infective stages of helminths may be present in great variety and in amazing numbers if samples are advantageously selected (Beaver, 1952, 1953). The transport of helminth eggs by splash and flow of water from rains and the sorting action of water currents and sedimentation are powerful forces in the dissemination and preservation of infective stages in the soil.

A second consideration is the disease-producing potential of *Toxocara,* *Ancylostoma, Ascaris,* and *Dirofilaria* in their natural hosts. This point requires no discussion here as the morbidity and mortality among animals infected with these parasites is a matter of high concern to veterinarians.

The third consideration, and one to be stressed especially, is the matter of prevention, that is, the application of preventive measures against transmission of infection from animals to man, and the dissemination of knowledge needed by health workers, and the people, in preventing such infections. From the standpoint of the animals' health it is desirable to eradicate and prevent the re-entry of worms. If it also is fully appreciated that infected animals, even when lightly infected, are reservoirs of infection in man, greater interest will be shown in preventive as well as curative measures against infection in animals. In this connection it comes to mind that in most communities there is a stern disapproval of promiscuous defecation by people. There is also a growing disapproval of the use of human feces in the cultivation of garden crops. On the other hand, there is a lasting indifference toward promiscuous defecation by animals. This attitude represents a lag in the evolution of civilized behavior and should be changed. Having, as he does, a more complete knowledge of the biology of parasites than do others in his community, the veterinary parasitologist can exert a favorable influence toward bringing about this change.

REFERENCES

Akamatsu, T. (1958). Study of the experimental infection with *Ascaris* in babies and infants. I. *Nippon Shonika Gakukai Zasshi* **62**, 1584-1592.

Akamatsu, T. (1959). Study of the experimental infection with *Ascaris* in babies and infants. II. *Nippon Shonika Gakukai Zasshi* **63**, 496-502.

Asami, K., Watanuki, T., Sakai, H., Imano, H., and Okamoto, R. (1965). Two cases of stomach granuloma caused by *Anisakis*-like larval nematodes in Japan. *Am. J. Trop. Med. Hyg.* **14**, 119-123.

Baldone, J. A., Clark, W. B., and Jung, R. C. (1964). Nematode ophthalmitis: Report of two cases. *Am. J. Ophthalmol.* [3] **57**, 763-766.

Beaver, P. C. (1952). Observations on the epidemiology of ascariasis in a region of high hookworm endemicity. *J. Parasitol.* **38**, 445-453.

Beaver, P. C. (1953). Persistence of hookworm larvae in soil. *Am. J. Trop. Med. Hyg.* **2**, 102-108.

Beaver, P. C. (1956). Parasitological reviews. Larva migrans. *Exptl. Parasitol.* **5**, 587-621.

Beaver, P. C. (1960). Unpublished results.

Beaver, P. C. (1962). Toxocarosis (visceral larva migrans) in relation to tropical eosinophilia. *Bull. Soc. Pathol. Exotique* **55**, 555-576.

Beaver, P. C. (1964). Cutaneous larva migrans. *Ind. Med. Surg.* **33**, 319-321.

Beaver, P. C., and Orihel, T. C. (1965). Human infection with filariae of animals in the United States. *Am. J. Trop. Med. Hyg.* **14**, 1010-1029.

Brain, L., and Allan, B. (1964). Encephalitis due to infection with *Toxocara canis*. Report of a suspected case. *Lancet* **I**, 1355-1357.

Braun-Vallon, S., Ashton, N., Duguid, I. M., and Dhermy, P. (1964). Manifestations oculaires de l'infestation par *Toxocara* (larva migrans viscerale). *Ann. Oculist., Paris* **197**, 217-240.

Cameron, T. W. M. (1962). Helminths of animals transmissible to man. *Am. J. Med. Sci.* **243**, 130-157.

Chin, W., Contacos, P. G., Coatney, G. R., and Kimball, H. R. (1965). A naturally acquired quotidian-type malaria in man transferable to monkeys. *Science* **149**, 865.

de Carneri, I., and Castellino, S. (1964). Incapacita delle larvae di *Ancylostoma tubaeforme* di provocare dermatiti nell'uomo. *Riv. Parassitol.* **25**, 31-34.

Dent, J. H., Nichols, R. L., Beaver, P. C., Carrera, G. M., and Staggers, R. J. (1956). Visceral larva migrans—with a case report. *Am. J. Pathol.* **32**, 777-803.

Done, J. T., Richardson, M. D., and Gibson, T. E. (1960). Experimental visceral larva migrans in the pig. *Res. Vet. Sci.* **1**, 133-151.

Falkinburg, L. W., and Kay, M. N. (1962). Visceral larva migrans. Report of a case and review. *Arch. Pediat.* **79**, 155-161.

Farber, S., and Craig, J. M., eds. (1959). Clinical pathological conference. The Children's Medical Center, Boston, Mass. *J. Pediat.* **54**, 707-716.

Fushimi, J. Nishimura, T., and Murakami, K. (1963). On a case which is considered as human toxocariasis cured by dithiazanine iodide. *Japan. J. Parasitol.* **12**, 303-304.

Galvin, T. J. (1964). Experimental *Toxocara canis* infections in chickens and pigeons. *J. Parasitol.* **50**, 124-127.

Galvin, T. J. (1964). Development of human and pig *Ascaris* in the pig. Dissertation. Tulane University, New Orleans, Louisiana.

Karpinski, F. E., Jr., Everts-Suarez, E. A., and Sawitz, W. G. (1956). Larval granulomatosis (visceral larva migrans). *A. M. A. J. Diseases Children* **92**, 34-40.

Kennedy, P. C. (1954). The migrations of the larvae of *Ascaris lumbricoides* in cattle and their relation to eosinophilic granulomas. *Cornell Vet.* **44**, 531-565.

Moore, M. T. (1962). Human *Toxocara canis* encephalitis with lead encephalopathy. *J. Neuropathol. Exptl. Neurol.* **21**, 201-218.

Muhleisen, J. P. (1953). Demonstration of pulmonary migration of the causative organism of creeping eruption. *Ann. Internal Med.* **38**, 595-600.

Nadbath, R. P., and Lawlor, P. P. (1965). Nematode (*Ancylostoma*) in the cornea. *Am. J. Opthalmol.* [3] **59**, 486-490.

Nichlos, R. L. (1956). The etiology of visceral larva migrans. II. Comparative larval morphology of *Ascaris lumbricoides, Necator americanus, Strongyloides stercoralis* and *Ancylostoma caninum. J. Parasitol.* **42**, 363-399.

Orihel, T. C., and Beaver, P. C. (1965). Morphology and relationship of *Dirofilaria tenuis* and *Dirofilaria conjunctivae. Am. J. Trop. Med. Hyg.* **14**, 1030-1043.

Prommindaroj, K., Leelawongs, N., and Pradatsundarasar, A. (1962). Human angiostrongyloidiasis of the eye in Bangkok. *Am. J. Trop. Med. Hyg.* **11**, 759-761.

Rey, A. (1962). Nematode endophthalmitis due to *Toxocara. Brit. J. Ophthalmol.* **46**, 616-618.

Rosen, L., Chappell, R., Laqueur, G. L., Wallace, G. D., and Weinstein, P. P. (1962). Eosinophilic meningoencephalitis caused by a metastrongylid lung-worm of rats. *J. Am. Med. Assoc.* **179**, 620-624.

Schaeffler, W. F. (1960). Experimental infection of sheep with the dog ascarid, *Toxocara canis. J. Parasitol.* **46**, Suppl., 17.

Schlotthauer, J. C., and Griffiths, H. J. (1964). Heartworm infection in dogs in Minnesota. *J. Am. Vet. Med. Assoc.* **144**, 991-993.

Schoenfeld, A. E., Ghitnic, E., and Rosen, N. (1964). Granulomatous encephalitis due to *Toxocara* larvae (visceral larva migrans). *Harefuah* **66**, 337-339.

Schrott, E. R. (1963). Parasitäre Nelzhauterkrankung durch Askaris. (Parasitical retinal affection caused by *Ascaris*). *6th Ann. Meeting, Ost. Ophthalmol. Ges., 1961*. pp. 160-164. Abstracted in *Ophthalmic Lit.* 17, 1641.

Shrand, H. (1964). Visceral larva migrans. *Toxocara canis* infection. *Lancet* I, 1357-1359.

Soh, C. T. (1958). The distribution and persistence of hookworm larvae in the tissues of mice in relation to species and to routes of inoculation. *J. Parasitol.* 44, 515-519.

Sprent, J. F. A. (1956). The life history and development of *Toxocara cati* (Schrank 1788) in the domestic cat. *Parasitology* 46, 54-78.

Sprent, J. F. A. (1958). Observations on the development of *Toxocara canis* (Werner, 1782) in the dog. *Parasitology* 48, 184-209.

Sprent, J. F. A. (1961). Post-parturient infection of the bitch with *Toxocara canis*. *J. Parasitol.* 47, 284.

Sweatman, G. K., Henshall, T. C., and Manktelow, B. W. (1962). Experimental observations on parasitic liver white spot in New Zealand sheep. *New Zealand Vet. J.* 10, 99-107.

Takata, I. (1951). Experimental infection of man with *Ascaris* of man and the pig. *Kitasato Arch. Exptl. Med.* 23, 49-59.

van Thiel, P. H. (1962). Anisakiasis. *Parasitology* 52, 16-17.

van Thiel, P. H., Kuipers, F. C., and Roskam, R. T. (1960). A nematode parasitic to herring, causing acute abdominal syndromes in man. *Trop. Geograph. Med.* 12, 97-113.

Witenburg, G. G. (1964). Chapter VI: Zooparasitic Diseases—A. Helminthozoonoses. *In* "Zoonoses" (J. van der Hoeden, ed.), pp. 529-719. Elsevier, Amsterdam.

Wong, L. C., and Laxdal, O. E. (1958). Visceral larva migrans. *Can. Med. Assoc. J.* 78, 695-699.

Yajima, T. (1955). Studies on the natural and experimental infection of *Ascaris lumbricoides* in man. II. Studies on the experimental infection of pig and human *Ascaris* in man. *Japan. J. Parasitol.* 4, 245-250.

Yokogawa, M., and Yoshimura, H. (1965). *Anisakis*-like larvae causing eosinophilic granulomata in the stomach of man. *Am. J. Trop. Med. Hyg.* 14, 770-773.

Discussion

Dr. Leland: Can you give us some of your experiences with respect to the *Strongyloides* of the domestic animals as they affect man.

Dr. Beaver: Almost all the species from animals which we have studied will invade the skin of the human. I believe that some will actually develop to patency in man, but in any case they cause skin lesions, creeping eruptions, of varying duration. The skin lesions produced by *Strongyloides* are easily recognized, owing to the speed at which they move, several centimeters within 2 to 3 hours.

Dr. Marsden: I would like to thank Dr. Beaver for his fascinating paper. Would he comment on the value of serological tests in the diagnosis of visceral larva migrans. How often are larvae found in liver biopsies of such patients and if these are negative would he consider peritoneoscopy or laparotomy. Finally has he any information in the use of thiabendazole in this infection.

Dr. Beaver: The diagnosis of visceral larva migrans toxocariasis in children offers great problems. It would be nice if we could use a skin test which was infallible but this is not so at the present time. There are many people who have considerable confidence in the indirect hemagglutination test and I suppose one should say it shows some promise. However, I never see a report from the laboratory which convinces me one way or the other; we can get negative serological tests when the liver biopsy is positive. At present the diagnosis of visceral larva migrans due to *Toxocara*, or any other larvae, rests mostly on the blood picture, especially the high eosinophilia, which may remain about 50 percent of 50,000 white cells for more than 50 weeks. Where there is a question of eosinophilic leukemia then laparotomy is the choice for diagnosis. Punch biopsy is employed by only a few people and an additional advantage of laparotomy is that the liver can be examined and material selected for examination. However, in infections in excess of 30 larvae per 100 mg of liver the punch biopsy would generally be positive, but it is very seldom used.

We have only started to assess thiabendazole; the results are interesting but I don't know what to predict.

companied by an increased MHC... and... stimulation... the (Fig. 4) but as the demands... and...

Pathogenesis of Ectoparasites

S. M. Gaafar

Department of Veterinary Microbiology, Pathology, and Public Health,
School of Veterinary Science and Medicine,
Purdue University, Lafayette, Indiana

The association between an ectoparasite and its host results in as varied a reaction as there are parasites and hosts. This reaction may become complicated and obscured by the development of disease conditions not directly related to this pure host-parasite relationship. A few attempts have been made to study some of these uncomplicated relationships but unfortunately much more has to be done in this branch of veterinary and medical parasitology.

Ectoparasites cause damage to their host by several different methods. They suck blood or lymph, feed on tissues, and transmit other parasitic and injurious organisms. Many of these methods of injury have been discussed in leading textbooks and other publications. The purpose of this paper is not to reiterate or even delve into any of these mechanisms. It is rather a review of and to some degree speculation into the basic reaction of the host to the ectoparasite regardless of the type of parasite or host or whatever else it might cause. I am aware of the fact that other disease processes may be influenced by these basic processes and that these basic reactions may be dependent on the diseases produced.

Whether the ectoparasite bites, stings, punctures the skin with its proboscis, defecates on the skin of its host, or migrates through the body tissues, the basic reactions of the host are similar. These reactions are protective mechanisms directed against the parasite itself, its secretions, or its excretions. A review of the volume of literature available on ectoparasitism provides little information on the mechanisms of the early reactions (Arthur, 1962; Brock, 1961; DeMeillon, 1949; Goldman *et al.*, 1952a,b; Horsfall, 1962). It is evident, however, that the differences in the reaction of the host are dependent mainly on the biology and bionomics of the parasite, its location in the host, and the route of migration it follows. The chemical constituents of the parasite, its saliva, or other products are of utmost importance in the development of these reactions.

Since these chemical constituents are not static even within a single species throughout its life cycle, one would expect at least variations in the intensity of reaction.

The four basic reactions of a host to its ectoparasitic invader can be classified in one or more of the following reactions: (1) histamine reaction; (2) enzymatic reaction; (3) hypersensitive or allergic reaction; (4) immune and nonresponsive reaction.

THE HISTAMINE REACTION

Histamine and histamine-like compounds have been described as constitutents of some salivary secretions and venoms of many arthropods and other animals. Whether or not they exist in the saliva of all arthropods remains to be determined. The reaction occurring in an animal following an invasion by an arthropod suggests that histamine or some physiologically similar compound produced these reactions. The development of a wheal, papule, or skin erythema in the area of the invasion substantiates this assumption. The primary wheal appears at the invasion site within a few minutes and usually disappears in 1 or 2 hours. Histamine is a powerful dilator of capillaries and in certain animals (cat, dog, monkey) and in man it dilates the arterioles as well (Halpren, 1960).

The presence of histamine in bee venom has been described by Habermann (1963) and Marshall (1957). There is about 10 mg of this compound per gram of the crude bee venom. Riek (1955) indicated that horses injected with either an extract of *Culicoides* sp. or histamine exhibited lesions identical to those observed in naturally occurring early lesions of equine allergic dermatitis. McKiel (1959) and McKiel and Clune (1960) maintain that there is no free histamine or histamine-like compound in the mosquitoes they investigated, yet they describe cutaneous symptoms similar to those exhibited following histamine injection. Histamine and histamine-like products have been detected in several organs and in excreta of adult as well as immature insects (Clark, 1960; Harrington, 1961; Walle *et al.*, 1954; Welsh and Moorhead, 1960).

Several decarboxylases have been extracted from the bodies of insects and it is very probable that appropriate decarboxylases are found in the salivary glands of insects which synthesize histamine or physiologically similar compounds (Chefurka, 1965). Chefurka has listed a number of pharmacologically active compounds in the different organs and excreta of arthropods. These are the decarboxylation products of amino acids. He stated that, "The precise role of many of these amines in the physiology of mammal is not clearly understood, in insects it is sheer speculation." It is entirely possible that one of these products exerts a physiological reaction similar to histamine.

Tissue destruction due to penetration of the probosces or stingers may be the cause of release of additional histamine at the site of insertions. This is particularly true in the case of those arthropods that probe the skin causing cutaneous or sutcutaneous hemorrhage for their pool feeding.

Whether it is histamine, histamine-like compounds, or some physiologically similar compounds that cause the initial reaction will have to remain mere speculation until more biochemical data are available. The initial reaction, however, is the typical ischemic ring surrounded by a slightly elevated, edematous and reddened wheal. Even in those animals that have not been previously sensitized or those that have become immunologically tolerant, the wheal appears. This has been demonstrated in flea bites where the initial reaction is seen in all animals and man but flea dermatitis or a sustained reaction is only seen in those that are hypersensitive and immunologically competent.

THE ENZYMATIC REACTION

The secretions produced by most insects are intended to aid that particular insect in obtaining its food in a digestible and useful form. Host tissues may or may not be digestible and available to the parasite. They have to be converted or transformed before they can be used. Most of the host tissues are fairly solid and present a barrier to the migration of those forms that have to migrate as part of their life cycle. Secretions of the parasite are used to dissolve parts of these tissues and provide the parasite with an avenue to its predilection site. It is not surprising, therefore, that these secretions and excretions are made up of enzymes with proteolytic, anticoagulant, cytolytic, and spreading action. The types and amounts of enzymes present in any particular arthropod secretion are necessarily dependent on the bionomics of that parasite.

Gregson (1957) showed that the tick *Dermacentor andersoni* can produce up to 34 µg of saliva during a feeding period. This saliva was shown later to contain an anticoagulant and a hemolysin (Riek, 1953; Sabbatani, 1898). The tick also secretes a cement substance that helps to hold the mouth parts stationary. Chiggers secrete a proteolytic enzyme that dissolves cutaneous cells and creates a food canal through which the stylosome is introduced. The larvae of *Hyprodema bovis* penetrate the skin and migrate through the tissues of the hind leg reaching the esophageal epithelium and then migrate to the skin of the back of cattle where they bore holes for breathing and emergence. Myiasis-producing fly larvae secrete enzymes that dissolve the skin and other tissues. The list of these examples could be as long as the list of parasites injurious to animals and man.

Although it is important to know the nature of these enzymes in any given case of ectoparasitism, it is equally important to know the end products of the enzymatic action and the fate of these products. The cytolytic enzymes are known to contain different proteases, lipases, and carbohydrases. In addition some arthropods produce hyaluronidase as a spreading agent (Chefurka, 1965). The presence of anticoagulants and agglutinins in the saliva of many ticks and other blood-sucking, long-feeding arthropods is well known.

The digestion and liquefaction of the host tissue results in the production of substances foreign to the body. One of the first reactions noticed in these sites is the inflammation. The blood vessels are dilated and their walls become permeable. The main infiltrating cells at this stage are polymorphonuclear leukocytes and eosinophiles. A few lymphocytes and plasma cells may be present but not in large numbers. Collagen fibers in the area appear widely separated. The gross appearance of the lesion is that of local inflammation, the surface of the skin is elevated and reddened, and the area becomes itchy and painful. This reaction in the nonsensitized animal is probably a direct result of release of histamine from the damaged tissue. This phase of the reaction usually subsides in a few days and most of the lysed tissue is absorbed. The remaining portion of the lysed tissue, however, spreads throughout the adjacent parts of the skin. Goldman (1963) showed that supposed complete removal of the tick *Dermacentor variabilis* and the local bite area did not prevent the development of a prolonged and progressive tick bite granuloma in man. The saliva or conjugated skin protein apparently persists in the adjacent tissue. If this is a first exposure of the animal or man to such an anthropod invasion, regression of the symptoms is almost complete. Histologically the edema subsides, lymphocytes, plasma cells, and histiocytes become the predominant infiltrating cells. The number of mast cells in the area is increased. Eventually, however, these infiltrating cells disappear as the tissue returns to normal.

On the other hand if the exposure was preceded by several similar exposures and the animal had become hypersensitive, the reaction persists and a typical hypersensitive reaction is observed.

THE HYPERSENSITIVE REACTION

This phase of ectoparasitic reaction manifests itself in several ways, such as localized granuloma, Arthus reaction, and generalized allergic reaction. Since the specialists in hypersensitive reactions are not in complete agreement about the definitions and mechanisms of many of these reactions, it will not be the purpose of this paper to expound on any of the reactions, but rather to describe and use what seems appropriate. Ectoparasite hypersensitivity may be a new phenomenon lending itself to none of the criteria set for any single hypersensitive phenomenon.

This reaction is divided into two phases: (A) the development of hypersensitivity; (B) the hypersensitive reaction.

DEVELOPMENT OF HYPERSENSITIVITY

This is essentially a continuation of the enzymatic reaction described above. The enzymes contained in the secretions of the parasite when injected in the tissues of the host may be cytolytic as well as antigenic in nature. In fact in some instances they are both. Young *et al.* (1963) showed that the saliva of fleas is haptenic and needs conjugation with the skin of the host before it becomes antigenic. Whether a certain secretion is haptenic or antigenic needs to be investigated in each case of ectoparasitism. As a result of absorption of the antigen at the site of infestation, the animal, if immunologically competent, becomes sensitized (Benjamini *et al.*, 1963; Hudson *et al.*, 1960). Of course, the degree of sensitization is increased with every exposure. Explanations of the mechanisms of sensitization are in a great state of flux at present. The prevailing theory, however, is that the macrophages engulf lysed antigenic products and transport them to the regional lymph nodes. The lymphocytes and germinal centers in these nodes are stimulated and sensitized. Some investigators consider the presence of the large pyroninophilic cells in the regional lymph nodes a sign of development of hypersensitivity in an animal. These large pyroninophilic cells are presumably of the lymphocyte series and carry the factor responsible for reaction with the antigen or for sensitizing other cells. These cells have been described in tuberculin reactions and experimental allergic encephalitis as well as other delayed hypersensitivities. Unfortunately, I am not aware of any literature describing the histopathology of the regional lymph nodes in cases of ectoparasitism. The local reaction, however, is very similar to that obtained in tuberculin hypersensitivity or contact allergic dermatitis.

THE HYPERSENSITIVE REACTION

When the animal is hypersensitive to the secretions of a specific ectoparasite, further exposure to these secretions results in the development of hypersensitive reaction. The presence of the antigen in a certain tissue of the body stimulates the accumulation of sensitive lymphocytes, plasma cells, and histiocytes. This reaction is usually similar in appearance to the primary reaction but is more intense, its appearance is delayed for several hours, and it lasts for several days or even weeks. Early in the formation of the reaction nodule eosinophiles and polymorphonuclear cells are predominant, but later lymphocytes, plasma cells, and histiocytes prevail. There is usually an occasional giant cell in older lesions. The capillaries and sometimes the arterioles are dilated and their walls are thin. Extensive areas of extravasated blood may be seen, particularly in cases of pool-feeding insects. The reaction between the residual antigen and the mobilized lymphocytes causes the accumulation of mast cells and the release of histamine (Humphrey, 1961).

Beside the response of the lymph glands, the antigen present in the local site may stimulate the body of the host to produce antibodies. The mechanism of production of these antibodies is probably similar to that in the case of many internal multicellular and protozoal organisms. The reaction of these antibodies with the antigen at the local site produces the Arthus reaction seen at the invasion sites. In highly sensitized animals general allergic and anaphylactic reactions may be seen.

IMMUNE AND NONRESPONSIVE REACTION

This phase of reaction to ectoparasitism is well known to most of us but unfortunately is not well documented by much controlled research. Trager (1939a,b, 1940) in earlier work showed that guinea pigs can acquire immunity against *Dermacentor variabilis* and *D. andersoni*. He demonstrated the presence of antibodies in the sera of experimental animals. Francis and Little (1964) showed that draughtmaster cattle carried about 10 times fewer ticks than did British cattle. They concluded that the hypersensitive reaction in the skin was mainly responsible for differences in susceptibility to infestation. Benjamini *et al.* (1961) demonstrated that in flea bite skin reactivity, the sequence of reaction was induction of sensitivity, predominantly delayed skin reactivity, delayed and immediate responses, predominantly immediate reactivity, and finally a condition of nonreactivity or immune nonresponsiveness.

At present our knowledge of the reasons for the development of a condition of nonresponsiveness or immune tolerance in ectoparasitism is very meager. The production of circulating antibodies could be one of these reasons. This may be related to the well-known phenomenon of spontaneous self-cure in helminth infections.

SUMMARY

The pathogenesis of ectoparasitism was discussed. The occurrence of a four-stage sequence of events was suggested. These four stages were (1) histamine reaction; (2) enzymatic reaction; (3) hypersensitive reaction; (4) immune and nonresponsive reaction.

The initial histamine reaction is only recognized in those ectoparasitisms where the reactions contain histamine or similar compounds. The other three reactions probably occur in most ectoparasitisms.

REFERENCES

Arthur, D. R. (1962). "Ticks and Disease." Harper & Row, New York.

Benjamini, E., Feingold, B. F., and Kartman, L. (1961). Skin reactivity in guinea pigs sensitized to flea bites. The sequence of reaction. *Proc. Soc. Exptl. Biol. Med.* **108**, 700-702.

Benjamini, E., Feingold, B. F., and Kartman, L. (1963). The physiological and biochemical role of the host's skin in the induction of flea-bite hypersensitivity. I. Preliminary studies with guinea pig skin following exposure to bites of cat fleas. *Exptl. Parasitol.* **14**, 75-80.

Brock, T. (1961). Resume of insect allerge. *Ann. Allergy* **19**, 288-297.

Chefurka, W. (1965). Intermediary metabolism of nitrogenous and lipid compounds in insects. *In* "The Physiology of Insecta" (M. Rockstein, ed.), Vol. 2, p. 684. Academic Press, New York.

Clark, E. W. (1960). A comparative study of amino acids and carbohydrates of the pink bollworm *Pectinophora gossypiela. Ann. Entomol. Soc. Am.* **53**, 439.

DeMeillon, B. (1949). The relationship between ectoparasitism and host. IV. Host reactions to the bites of arthropods. *The Leech* **20**, 43-46.

Francis, J., and Little, D. A. (1964). Resistance of Draughtmaster cattle to tick infestation and Babesiosis. *Australian Vet. J.* **40**, 247-253.

Goldman, L. (1963). The bite granuloma failure of prevention of lesions by excision of tick bite area. *Am. J. Trop. Med. Hyg.* **12**, 246-248.

Goldman, L., Rockwell, E., and Richfield, D. (1952a). Histological studies on cutaneous reactions to bites of various arthropods. *Am. J. Trop. Med. Hyg.* **1**, 514-525.

Goldman, L., Jackson, P., and Ramsey, J. (1952b). The insect bite reaction. *J. Invest. Dermatol.* **18**, 403-417.

Gregson, J. D. (1957). Experiments on oral secretion of the rocky mountain wood tick, *Dermacentor andersoni* Stiles. *Can. Entomologist* **89**, 1-5.

Habermann, E. (1965). Recent studies on *Hymenoptera* venoms. *Proc. Intern. Pharmacol. Meeting, Prague, 1963* Vol. 9, pp. 53-62. Macmillan (Pergamon), New York.

Halpren, B. N. (1960). Histamine and processes of histamine liberation. *In* "Fundamentals of Modern Allergy" (S. J. Prigal, ed.) pp. 27-42. McGraw-Hill, New York.

Harington, J. S. (1961). Studies of amino acids of *Rhodnius prolixus*. II. Analysis of the excretory material. *Parasitology* **51**, 319-326.

Horsfall, W. R. (1962). "Medical Entomology, Arthropods and Human Disease." Ronald Press, New York.

Hudson, B. W., Feingold, B. F., and Kartman, L. (1960). Allergy to flea bites. I. Experimental induction of flea bite sensitivity in guinea pigs. *Exptl. Parasitol.* **9**, 18-24.

Humphrey, J. H. (1961). Biochemical aspects of reactions in hypersensitive responses. *In* "Cellular and Humoral Aspects of the Hypersensitive States" (H. Sherwood Lawrence, ed.), pp. 1-42. Harper (Hoeber), New York.

McKiel, J. A. (1959). Sensitization to mosquito bites. *Can. J. Zool.* **37**, 341-351.

McKiel, J. A., and Clune, J. F. (1960). Chromatographic fractionation of the non-dialyzable protein of mosquito extract and intracutaneous reactions of mosquito-bite-sensitive subjects to the separated components. *Can. J. Zool.* **38**, 478-487.

Marshall, T. K. (1957). Wasp and bee stings. *Practitioner* **178**, 712-722.

Riek, R. F. (1953). Allergic dermatitis of the horse. *Proc. 15th Intern. Vet. Congr., Stockholm 1953* Part I, pp. 664-669. Gernandts Boktryckeri.

Riek, R. F. (1955). Studies on allergic dermatitis (Queensland) itch of the horse; the origin and significance of histamine in the blood and its distribution in the tissues. *Australian J. Agr. Res.* **6**, 161-170.

Sabbatani, L. (1898). Fermento anticoagulate dell *Ixodes ricinus. Gioin Accad. Med. Torino* **61**, 9-11.

Trager, W. (1939a). Acquired immunity to ticks. *J. Parasitol.* **25**, 57-81.

Trager, W. (1939b). Further observations on acquired immunity to the tick *Dermacentor variabilis. J. Parasitol.* **25**, 137-139.

Trager, W. (1940). A note on the problem of acquired immunity to argasid ticks. *J. Parasitol.* **26**, 71-74.

Walle, J. R., Zuleka, P., Picarelli, Z. P., and Prado, J. L. (1954). Histamine content and pharmacological properties of crude extracts from retal or urticating caterpillars. *Arch. Intern. Pharmacodyn.* **98**, 324-334.

Welsh, J. H., and Moorhead, M. (1960). The quantitative distribution of 5-hydroxy-tryptamine in the invertebrates especially in their nervous systems. *J. Neurochem* **6**, 146-169.

Young, J. D., Benjamini, E., Feingold, B. F., and Noller, H. (1963). Allergy to flea bites. V. Preliminary results of fractionation, characterization, and assay for allergenic activity of material derived from the oral secretion of the cat flea, *Ctenocephalides felis felis. Exptl. Parasitol.* **13**, 155-166.

Discussion

Dr. Riek: There are wide variations in the number of *Boophilus microplus* ticks recovered from cattle on the initial infestation. This so-called innate resistance is supplemented by an acquired state on exposure to subsequent infestations. Have you any indication from your work on the nature of this innate state?

Dr. Gaafar: It is possible that this innate mechanism may have something to do with the genetic status of the animal; however, in a group of animals of approximately the same genetic status the hypersensitive response may be of especial importance.

Dr. Andrews: I would like to comment on a situation that is peculiar; there is apparently a great difference in the susceptibility of normal and dwarf cattle of the same breed. This has often been noticed where dwarf cattle in a herd are covered with lice but other animals in the same herd have almost none. Has any work been done on this? It would seem a good area to study factors affecting the susceptibility to lice. Do you know if anyone has studied this phenomenon?

Dr. Gaafar: No! I have heard about it and it would seem an area where a lot of work should be done.

Pathogenesis of Blood Protozoa

Frans C. Goble

Research Department, CIBA Pharmaceutical Co.,
Summit, New Jersey

INTRODUCTION

Whereas pathogenesis is a term which can be rather readily defined and most will accept it as referring to the development of morbid conditions or disease, the definition of blood protozoa is not so simple. Some of the so-called hemoflagellates are relatively rare in the peripheral blood and exert their main pathogenic effects in other tissues and even those genera that are commonly known from their presence in numbers in the blood occur there only during certain periods of their life cycles and may have important stages elsewhere (Table I).

If certain genera that are of doubtful pathogenicity, such as *Endotrypanum* (which occurs in the red cells of sloths), *Spirogregarina* (a rare parasite of birds), and *Hepatozoon* (of rats and dogs) can be excluded, there are 13 genera of so-called blood protozoa which we can consider from the standpoint of pathogenesis. Recognized here with full generic status are *Haemamoeba* Feletti and Grassi, 1889, which Bray (1957) recently resuscitated to include the avian and saurian malaria parasites, and *Schizotrypanum* Chagas, 1909, which includes the causative agent of Chagas' disease and has a number of characters that differentiate it from the genus *Trypanosoma*. Three genera, *Leishmania, Toxoplasma*, and *Schizotrypanum* appear in the blood as transients, using it as a vehicle for their migration to new foci of tissue invasion within the body of the host. Four, *Haemoproteus, Hepatocystis, Leucocytozoon*, and *Theileria* multiply in various other tissues and invade the red cells only to form gametocytes, which are then available to blood-sucking arthropod vectors. Only five genera, *Babesia, Cytauxzoon, Gonderia, Haemamoeba*, and *Plasmodium*, actually multiply in the intraerthrocytic environment and these along with the plasma-inhabiting genus *Trypanosoma* might be considered to be the blood protozoa, *sensu stricto*. We shall not, however, limit our discussion to these but will attempt to consider all 13 of the pathogenic genera which spell bad luck for warm-blooded animals.

TABLE I

BLOOD PROTOZOA (*Sensu Lato*) OF HOMOTHERMS. GENERA THAT
MULTIPLY AT THE SITES INDICATED

| Plasma | Blood or Hematopoietic System | | | Endothelium | Parenchyma of other organs |
	Erythrocytes	Lymphocytes	Histiocytes		
Trypanosoma	*Endotrypanum*		*Leishmania* *Schizotrypanum*		*Leishmania* *Schizotrypanum*
	Babesia	*Theileria*			
	Gonderia *Cytauxzoon*	*Gonderia*	*Cytauxzoon* *Toxoplasma*		*Toxoplasma*
			Leucocytozoon	*Haemoproteus*	*Leucocytozoon* *Hepatocystis*
	Haemamoeba *Plasmodium*	*Haemamoeba*	*Haemamoeba*	*Haemamoeba*	*Haemamoeba* *Plasmodium* *Hepatozoon*
Spirogregarina					

The disease processes which ensue following invasion of a host by a protozoan parasite result from both direct and indirect effects (Table II). The distinction between those which are exerted by the parasite on the host and those which develop more deviously is readily apparent. With these types of action in mind, we can look briefly at how or whether each

TABLE II

PATHOGENESIS OF BLOOD PROTOZOA

Direct effects	Indirect effects
Mechanical	Competitive
Physicochemical	Inflammatory
Consumptive	Circulatory
Toxic	Immuno-allergic

of them is involved in the pathogenesis of infections with the hematophilous genera we have listed.

MECHANICAL EFFECTS

It is doubtful if protozoa in extracellular locations (for instance, trypanosomes in the plasma) produce mechanical effects detrimental to the host, but in intracellular sites where multiplication of parasites results in increased internal pressure, mechanical rupture of the cells is the rule in many genera. This occurs in glial, reticuloendothelial, and muscle cells, both cardiac and skeletal, in animals infected with *Schizotrypanum cruzi*, in the RES of animals with *Leishmania* infections, in the agranulocytic leukocytes with *Cytauxzoon*, *Gonderia*, and *Theileria*, in erythrocytes infected with asexual stages of *Babesia*, *Haemamoeba*, and *Plasmodium*, in livers and brains infected with the exoerythrocytic stages of *Haemamoeba*, *Plasmodium*, *Hepatocystis*, and *Leucocytozoon*, in the vascular endothelium with *Haemoproteus*, and in a wide variety of cell types with *Toxoplasma*.

In those genera that invade the erythrocytes for the purpose of gametogenesis, the development of the sexual forms may disturb the architecture of the erythrocyte in minor or major ways, the most spectacular of which is the distortion produced by the gametocytes of *Leucocytozoon* in the blood cells of birds. The purpose of the gametocytes, however, is best served by their longevity and their presence in the blood over considerable periods of time attests to their innocuousness for the cells that they occupy. The major pathology in infections with Haemoproteidae and Theileridae, therefore, occurs not as a result of damage to red cells but rather to the attacks on the white cells, endothelium, and liver parenchyma during schizogony in those organs. (De Kock, 1957.)

PHYSICOCHEMICAL EFFECTS

Only in *Babesia* infections and in the schizogonic stages of the malarias are the red cells destroyed by the multiplicative and predatory actions of the parasites. The mechanism of the hemolytic process is complex and not well understood and is thought to involve changes in the physico-chemical properties of the red cell surface as well as mechanical effects resulting from the presence of the parasites (Devakul and Maegraith, 1959). Studies on canine babesiosis (Maegraith, 1954) have shown that both the red cells and the plasma are involved. During the lytic phase, infected erythrocytes are readily lysed by plasma either from normal animals or from infected animals in the prelytic stage. Infected erythro-cytes in the prelytic stage are as resistant to lysis by normal serum as uninfected erythrocytes. Normal red cells, however, lyse readily in plasma from an animal in the lytic phase. These results, indicating that infected erythrocytes become unusually labile during the lytic phase, and that the plasma during this phase, but not before, acquires lytic properties toward both normal and infected red cells, may be representa-tive of a principle that may apply not only to *Babesia* infections but also to the malarias, both avian and mammalian. (Maegraith *et al.*, 1957.)

Another physico-chemical effect that may be mentioned is that sug-gested by Laser (1948), who believes that a lytic substance, probably an unsaturated monocarboxylic fatty acid, accumulates in parasitized cells and may be the cause of lysis, this process being accelerated by hematin. Still another example of a physicochemical effect is the way in which malarial parasites alter the surface of the erythrocytes so that they no longer pass smoothly through the capillaries, this sludging effect being at the basis of many of the pathological lesions of malaria and babesiosis (Knisely *et al.*, 1964).

A change in membrane permeability in liver cells during the early stages of experimental Chagas' disease has recently been suggested as the cause of increased serum levels of five different liver enzymes in guinea pigs with acute infections with *Schizotrypanum cruzi* (Waks, 1965). This provides an example of a physicochemical effect in a flagel-late infection.

CONSUMPTIVE EFFECTS

While we are still not too far from the consideration of ways in which erythrocytes may be attacked and damaged, we might look at the process known as phagotrophy. As Rudzinska and Trager (1957) have pointed out, it is generally believed that cytozoic or intracellular parasites prepare their food for diffusion through the membrane by hydrolysis or liquefication of host cytoplasm. Their studies on plasmodial and babesial species, however, showed that this was not the only way that intracellular parasites get their food supply for their hosts. In the process known as phagotrophy, the parasite lying within the host cell cytoplasm actually pinches off bits of the host cytoplasm and engulfs them, the resulting globules of host cytoplasm becoming food vacuoles within the body of the parasite, which then digests the contained hemoglobin. This direct effect on the host we have termed consumptive. It has been observed in experimental infections with *Babesia rodhaini, Haemamoeba lophurae, Plasmodium berghei, P. falciparum,* and *P. gonderi* (Rudzinska and Trager, 1962) and can be assumed to be a process common to the forms that undergo schizogony in the red cell. (Malherbe, 1956.)

TOXIC EFFECTS

The identification of specific toxic substances in protozoa has been rare, although toxins have repeatedly been suggested as being responsible for various lesions. The existence of true protozoal exotoxins has not been proved and it appears that the metabolic waste products that are liberated during normal parasitic existence are relatively innocuous. Toxic reactions attributable to the lysis or destruction of large numbers of trypanosomes have been noted both in human subjects with African trypanosomiasis, following therapy (McComas and Martin, 1944), and in pigs with *Trypanosoma simiae* infections, at the point when their immunological response had reached a level which precipitated a crisis, during which most of the trypanosomes in the blood were destroyed. Presumably the severe but nonfatal symptoms are caused by disintegration products of the trypanosomes which had undergone lysis and their nature is a matter for speculation (Desowitz and Watson, 1953).

In the blood and urine of rodents experimentally infected with *Babesia rodhaini* and *Trypanosoma rhodesiense,* there occur pharmacologically active peptides which act on smooth muscle and are possibly associated with some of the more obscure aspects of protozoal pathogenesis. It has been suggested that these may result from fragmentation of plasma proteins by enzymes derived from the parasites (Goodwin and Richards, 1960).

Toxic substances have been postulated to account for the degeneration of nerve cells in the muscular organs attacked by *Schizotrypanum cruzi* (Köberle, 1961), but their presumed origin from the destruction of leishmanial forms upon rupture of their intracellular nests cannot be readily investigated or proved. Other evidence that toxins may exist that are capable of effecting tissue changes in organs which are not actually invaded by the parasite is offered by studies on the thyroids of dogs with experimental Chagas' disease in which the follicles become smaller than normal and colloid disappears with evidence of colloidophagy such as that stimulated by excess of thyrotropic hormone. These changes, occurring in the absence of parasite invasion of the gland, suggest that soluble substances responsible for the lesions are elaborated at some other site (Goble, 1954).

TABLE III
SITES OF DIRECT EFFECTS OF BLOOD PROTOZOA

Genus	Mechanical	Physico-chemical	Con-sumptive	Toxic
Trypanosoma	—	—	—	?
Schizotrypanum	Muscle, RES, CNS	Liver	—	ANS, thyroid
Leishmania	Liver, RES	—	—	—
Cytauxzoon	Histiocytes	—	—	—
Gonderia	Lymphocytes	—	—	—
Theileria	Lymphocytes	—	—	—
Babesia	RBC	RBC	RBC	—
Haemamoeba	RBC, CNS	RBC	RBC	—
Plasmodium	RBC	RBC	RBC	—
Hepatocystis	Liver	—	—	—
Leucocytozoon	Liver, lung, CNS	—	—	—
Haemoproteus	Endothelium	—	—	—
Toxoplasma	Various	—	—	—

The effects we have considered so far are summarized in Table III, which may reflect not as much the actual distribution of the sites affected as the amount of attention that has been directed to the various effects produced by the organisms listed. The indirect effects will be considered under the categories listed as competitive, inflammatory, circulatory, and immuno-allergic.

COMPETITIVE EFFECTS

While it can be assumed that parasites, whether intra- or extracellular, make use of nutrients of the host to support their own metabolism, clearcut cases of competition for a substrate are few. In most infections, the host is able to supply such an excess of metabolites that the parasite can be supplied without deficiencies appearing in the host.

One striking example of competition for a vital factor, however, is seen in artificial infections with trypanosomes in rodents, as illustrated by the study of Hoppe and Chapman (1947) in rats with *Trypanosoma equiperdum*.

In rats and mice, there is very little resistance to the trypanosomes of the *T. brucei* group. Following inoculation a progressive fulminating infection develops in which the parasitemia rises without interruption until the trypanosome population exceeds a tolerated level and the animals die.

Hoppe and Chapman concluded that the deaths were attributable to hypoglycemia resulting from the high glucose consumption of the parasites and produced evidence in favor of this view by injecting glucose into rats at the time that the parasite population approached the maximal tolerated level, effecting a prolongation of several hours in survival time in such animals and allowing the parasitemias to rise to heights far beyond those attainable in animals without such glucose supplement.

This demonstration, which points to a simple competition between the host and parasite for an essential metabolite, is not completely accepted by von Brand (1952) and it is certain that the host-parasite relation in the rat with *T. equiperdum* is quite different from that obtaining in non-rodent hosts with other species of trypanosomes, in which immunological responses are both invoked and involved. It may be, therefore, that this type of factor in pathogenesis is not only unique but also unimportant.

There is some question as to whether the eyelid lesions which Becker *et al.* (1949) observed in chicks infected with *Haemamoeba lophurae* while on deficient diets are a result of competition of the host with the parasite for biotin or pantothenic acid, either of which alleviated the condition when added to the ration.

INFLAMMATORY EFFECTS

As we begin to consider the last three types of indirect effects in hemoprotozoal pathogenesis, it will soon become apparent that these factors are interrelated and not easily separated. Inflammatory processes involve the circulation and affect it, noninflammatory circulatory changes may lead to inflammation, and both these factors may be influenced by immune and allergic phenomena.

The best adapted parasites or best adapted stages of parasites do not stimulate inflammatory processes. This is illustrated by the exoerythrocytic stages of *Plasmodium cynomolgi* in rhesus monkeys which attain a size several times that of the liver parenchyma cells without provoking any inflammatory reaction (Eyles and Coatney, 1962). This lack of inflammation or a minimum of reaction seems to be typical of the exoerythrocytic stages of mammalian malarial parasites (Shortt *et al.*, 1954).

In *Hepatocystis* infections in monkeys, the characteristic cysts in the liver may become quite large and the architecture of the parenchyma distorted by the pressures of the multiplying parasites without the development of inflammation, and even when in later stages some reaction appears, it is localized and does not involve more than a limited portion of liver (Edeson, 1953; Garnham, 1961). Likewise, little reaction seems to be provoked by the schizonts of *Haemoproteus* in the vascular epithelium but in *Leucocytozoon* infection in ducks, moderate to marked local cellular response occurs around megaloschizonts in the brain and lung although not in other organs (Newberne, 1957).

At the other end of the pathological spectrum, we find the intensive myocarditis provoked by the presence of *Schizotrypanum cruzi* in the heart, the encephalitides resulting from invasion of the nervous system by trypanosomes or *Toxoplasma* (Innes and Saunders 1962), and the reticuloendotheliosis induced by the presence of *Leishmania* or *Theileria* and its related genera. During the acute phase of theileriasis in cattle, more than 60 percent of the lymphocytes may be infected and proliferation of the lymphoid system can be observed in all organs in which that tissue exists, including liver and kidney, where perivascular foci of lymphocytes are visible on the surface of the organs (Cowdry and Danks, 1933). Sometimes parasitized lymphocytes localize by embolization or sequestration in the cerebral vessels, producing hemorrhagic infarcts and lymphocytic cuffing, with external manifestations that are described by the expression "turning sickness" (Carmichael, 1939; Schulz and Schutte, 1957).

CIRCULATORY EFFECTS

In trypanosomiasis of the nervous system the mechanism of pathogenesis is unclear and descriptions of the processes too involved to be considered here but the perivascular cuffing by agranulocytic cells in the brain may be cited as a lesion which may effect profound changes in the blood supply to the CNS. In leishmaniasis, the histiocytotic proliferation is accompanied by lymphocytic and plasmocytic infiltrations which tend to be concentrated around blood vessels and nerves, and hyperplasia and parasitism of the endothelial cells of blood vessels lead to obstructive or semiobstructive phlebitis. Intravascular micropolyps formed by collections of parasitized macrophages on the valves of dilated lymph vessels also occur and provide a further example of the circulatory results of inflammation (Coutinho-Abath and Coelho, 1965).

Circulatory disturbances may also be of neural origin as is exemplified by the consequences of the destruction of autonomic nerve cells in the heart and blood vessels in Chagas' disease. Köberle has postulated that the underlying lesion in Chagas' cardiopathy is the decrease in parasympathetic ganglia resulting in dilatation, hypertrophy-decreased contractility, and decreased coronary flow, with subsequent ischemia of the myocardium. Similar lesions in the walls of peripheral blood vessels may result in widespread circulatory defects.

Less direct but equally serious circulatory effects are observed in infections with the blood-destroying genera *Babesia, Haemamoeba,* and *Plasmodium.* Probably much of what has been described in malarial infections in both mammals and birds is also applicable to piroplasma infections, the main differences being attributable to the absence of pigment formation in the latter. The destruction and phagocytosis of parasitized and unparasitized erythrocytes may lead to severe anemia and, although Maegraith (1954b) feels that anemia and anoxemia are unlikely to be pathogenic factors in malaria, there is evidence for the existence of tissue anoxia possibly of a histotoxic type. Fever and shock may initiate local changes in tissue depending on the organs involved. Disturbances in the liver (Maegraith, 1959) varying from lobular congestion to centrilobular degeneration and necrosis, occur in both plasmodial and babesial infections (Paget *et al.,* 1962; Gilles *et al.,* 1953). Reduction in renal circulation may result in severe kidney damage (Giglioli, 1962) and adrenal involvement may also occur, leading to more remote effects too devious to be considered here (Golden and Overman, 1949; Maegraith, 1954).

IMMUNO-ALLERGIC EFFECTS

Immunological response is, of course, a common phenomenon in infection and often acts as defense for the host against a parasite and in this way is a factor influencing pathogenesis. Here, however, it will be considered only when it reinforces or contributes to the pathogenic effect of the protozoan invader, becoming a factor unfavorable rather than protective to the host.

In the condition known as blackwater fever which occurs in malarious patients under quinine treatment, severe lysis of erythrocytes occurs presumably as the result of the parasitized red cells becoming autoantigenic, stimulating the production of autoantibodies, which act in the presence of complement against the host's own erythrocytes (Gear, 1946). Observations of McGhee (1964) on ducklings experimentally infected with *Haemamoeba lophurae* and treated with quinine seem to confirm this proposed explanation, and Zuckerman (1960) has also suggested that parasitemia is not the only factor concerned in destruction of red cells and that in both rodent and simian malarias the host's own red cells are altered by infection and rendered antigenic, giving rise to autoantibodies which are involved in the blood loss.

The possibility that plasmodial parasites may also serve as a stimulus for the production of antibodies capable of attacking the kidney has also been suggested by Keitel *et al.* (1956) in their discussion of the nephrotic syndrome in malaria. Allergic reactions have been proposed as the cause of the lesions of myocarditis which are sometimes observed in Chagas' disease in the absence of numbers of parasites commensurate with the severity of the tissue reaction (Muniz and Azevedo, 1947; Jaffe *et al.*, 1961). Liberation of *Toxoplasma* into sensitized tissues and into ventricular fluids of the brain during subacute congenital toxoplasmosis results

TABLE IV

SITES OF INDIRECT EFFECTS OF BLOOD PROTOZOA

Genus	Competitive	Inflammatory	Circulatory	Immuno-allergic
Trypanosoma	Plasma	RES, CNS	—	?
Schizotrypanum	—	RES, CNS, muscle	Muscle, CNS, veins	Heart, ANS
Leishmania	—	RES, Liver, skin	Liver, kidney	—
Cytauxzoon	—	RES	—	—
Gonderia	—	RES	—	—
Theileria	—	RES	—	—
Babesia	—	—	Liver, kidney, CNS, RES, skin	—
Haemamoeba	?	—	CNS	—
Plasmodium	—	—	Liver, kidney, Cns, RES, skin	RBC, kidney, adrenal
Hepatocystis	—	—	—	—
Leucocytozoon	—	Lung, CNS	—	—
Haemoproteus	—	—	—	—
Toxoplasma	—	Various	—	CNS, eye

in sloughing of the ependymal lining and scar formation that blocks the aqueduct of Sylvius, with internal hydrocephalus as the result (Frenkel, 1949). Similar pathogenesis occurs in the eye in chronic toxoplasmic chorioretinitis (Frenkel and Jacobs, 1958) and the fact that specific chemotherapy does not control this type of lesion is taken as evidence for the concept that it is allergic in nature.

It has also been suggested that the Jarisch–Herxheimer type of reaction observed in patients with African trypanosomiasis following arsenical treatment (Manson-Bahr, 1945) may be an allergic phenomenon attributable to the release of parasitic antigen in a body sensitized by the chronic disease, rather than a mere toxic reaction to substances derived from the dying organisms as mentioned previously. In Table IV are summarized the indirect effects on the host resulting from parasitism by hemoprotozoa and the relative importance of inflammatory, circulatory, and immuno-allergic factors can be noted. It should be remembered that these indirect effects as well as the direct ones are influenced by host factors (Table V) and these will be considered briefly

TABLE V

HOST FACTORS AFFECTING PATHOGENESIS

1. Species	5. Endocrine state
2. Strain	6. Concurrent infection
3. Age	7. Previous infection
4. Nutrition	a. Homologous
	b. Heterologous

and illustrated by a few examples taken from work done in our laboratories.

HOST FACTORS INFLUENCING PATHOGENESIS

Species is, of course, of obvious importance both in natural infections and in experimental ones. Breed of domestic animals (Chandler, 1952, 1958; Desowitz, 1959) or strain of laboratory animal (Pizzi and Prager, 1952) may also be important, great differences being possible in both natural resistance and ability to develop acquired resistance. In Fig. 1 can be seen not only the difference in strain susceptibility to experimental Chagas' disease but also the difference in response attributable to sex of the host and mode of inoculation.

Greater resistance of females can be noted in a number of infections. Reflected in Fig. 2 are the relative parasitemias in seven male mice and eight female mice with benign *Babesia rodhaini* infections.

Not only are parasite populations influenced by sex but the development of pathological conditions may also be affected. In the experiment in Fig. 3, the development of edema in hamsters with visceral leishmaniasis is shown to be influenced by sex as well as time, the anasarcous condition being a result of concurrent kidney and adrenal damage.

That sex differences are often not attributable to the hormones of the adult gonads is shown by experiments in which adult and juvenile mice, with experimental Chagas' disease, were treated with sex hormones, females with testosterone and males with progesterone, esterone, and diethylstilbestrol (Figs. 4 and 5). These products did not affect the course of the infection. Age appears here as another host factor, juveniles succumbing more rapidly than adults.

Nutrition of the host may affect pathogenesis either synergistically or antagonistically (Scrimshaw *et al.*, 1957). In our experiments (Fig. 6) mice infected with *Trypanosoma congolense* were protected from the development of rapidly developing fatal parasitemia by a diet deficient in vitamin E.

Intercurrent infections also may affect each other synergistically or antagonistically. When *Plasmodium berghei* and *Trypanosoma lewisi*

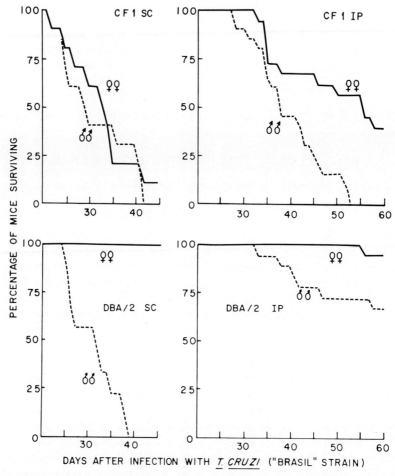

FIG. 1. Influence of sex strain and mode of inoculation upon the course of experimental Chagas' disease in mice. Strains: CF1 and DBA/2. Routes: subcutaenous (SC) and intraperitoneal (IP).

are developing simultaneously in rats the grade of infection with each organism is increased and higher mortality results than would occur with either infection alone (Hughes and Tatum, 1956). On the other hand, in mixed infection in mice with *Trypanosoma brucei* and certain species of *Borrelia,* particularly the *duttoni-microti* group, the latter organisms interfere with the development of the trypanosome infection, effecting significant delays in mortality and sometimes complete protection (Galliard *et al.,* 1958).

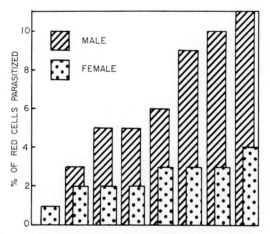

Fɪɢ. 2. Differences between the sexes in parasitemia observed in subacute infection of mice with *Babesia rodhaini.* Represented are the levels attained in seven male and eight female individuals.

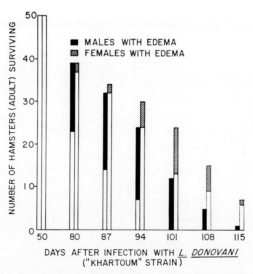

Fɪɢ. 3. Influence of sex on the development of edema and rate of mortality in golden hamsters with experimental kala azar.

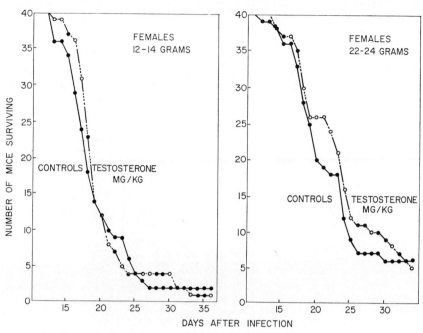

Fɪɢ. 4. Lack of effect of testosterone on course of experimental Chagas' disease in immature and adult female mice.

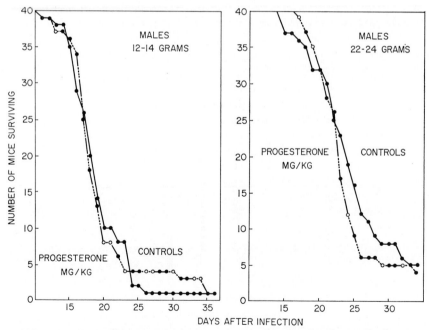

Fɪɢ. 5. Lack of effect of progesterone on course of experimental Chagas' disease in immature and adult male mice.

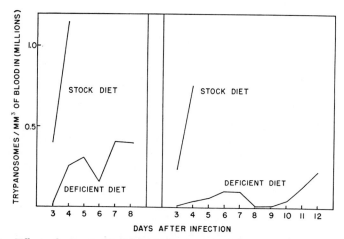

Fig. 6. Effect of vitamin E-deficient diet on parasitemia in mice infected with *Trypanosoma congolense*. Values indicated represent means of ten mice in each group.

CONCLUSION AND SUMMARY

The influence of immunity, acquired as a result of vaccination or previous infection, whether homologous or heterologous, on the course of subsequent infections need only be mentioned here without elaboration. In concluding, it should be emphasized that our view of this subject has had to be panoramic and we could only hint at some of the areas that have been or still need to be explored in depth.

In trying to maintain the distinctions between pathogenesis, pathogenicity, and pathology and to regard disease as a process rather then a condition, we have had to omit reference to a number of detailed descriptions of tissue changes and biochemical lesions and to minimize parasite factors in favor of a more complete view of host factors.

In summary a few generalizations can be made.

In *Babesia, Haemamoeba,* and *Plasmodium* infections, most of the pathogenesis is based on the alteration and destruction of erythrocytes, which results in the release of products into the blood stream which effect fever, shock, vasoconstriction, and a variety of secondary changes.

In *Cytauxzoon, Gonderia,* and *Theileria* infections, the agranulocytes and other cells of the reticuloendothelial system are the primary sites of invasion and destruction, although some red cell damage may also occur.

The genera in which only gametocytes are found in the blood, *Haemoproteus, Hepatocystis,* and *Leucocytozoon,* effect minor mechanical and inflammatory changes in the other tissues they infect.

The genera *Leishmania, Schizotrypanum,* and *Toxoplasma,* which appear in the blood only as transients, effect severe damage in a number of other tissues by intracellular multiplication and cellular necrosis.

The mechanisms by which relatively small numbers of the plasma-dwelling genus *Trypanosoma* effect debilitating and fatal disease in man and other mammals remain poorly understood and insufficiently studied.

REFERENCES

Becker, E. R., Brodine, E. E., and Marousek, A. A. (1949). Eyelid lesion of chicks in acute dietary deficiency resulting from blood-induced *Plasmodium lophurae* infection. *J. Infect. Diseases* 85, 230-238.

Bray, R. S. (1957). Studies on the exo-erythrocytic cycle in the genus *Plasmodium. London School Hyg. Trop. Med. Mem.* 12, 192 pp.

Carmichael, J. (1939). Turning disease of cattle and *Trypanosoma theileri. Parasitology* 31, 498-500.

Chagas, C. (1909). Nova tripanosomiase humana. Estudos sobre a morphologia e o ciclo evolutivo do *Schizotrypanum cruzi* n. gen., n. sp, ajente etiolojico de nova entidade morbida do homem. *Mem. Inst. Oswaldo Cruz* 1, 159-218.

Chandler, R. L. (1952). Comparative tolerance of West African n'dama cattle to trypanosomiasis. *Ann. Trop. Med. Parasitol.* 46, 127-134.

Chandler, R. L. (1958). Studies on the tolerance of n'dama cattle to trypanosomiasis. *J. Comp. Pathol. Therap.* 68, 253-260.

Coutinho-Abath, E., and Coelho, M. (1965). Experimental cutaneous leishmaniasis. *Rev. Inst. Med. Trop. Sao Paulo* 7, 145-155.

Cowdry, E. V., and Danks, W. B. C. (1933). Studies on East Coast Fever. II. Behavior of the parasite and the development of distinctive lesions in susceptible animals. *Parasitology* 25, 1-61.

De Kock, G. (1957). Studies on the lesions and pathogenesis of East Coast fever (*Theileria parva* infection) in cattle with special reference to the lymphoid tissue. *Onderstepoort J. Vet. Res.* 27, 431-452.

Desowitz, R. S. (1959). Studies on immunity and host-parasite relationships. I. The immunological response of the resistant and susceptible breeds of cattle to trypanosomal challenge. *Ann. Trop. Med. Parasitol.* 54, 293-313.

Desowitz, R. S., and Watson, H. J. C. (1953). The maintenance of a strain of *Trypanosoma simiae* in rabbits. The effect of splenectomy on the course of infection. *Ann. Trop. Med. Parasitol.* 47, 324-334.

Devakul, K., and Maegraith, B. G. (1959). Lysis and other circulatory phenomena in malaria. *Ann. Trop. Med. Parasitol.* 53, 430-450.

Edeson, J. F. B. (1953). Presumed exo-erythrocytic schizonts or *Plasmodium knowlesi* in the liver of a Malayan monkey (*Macaca irus*). *Trans. Roy. Soc. Trop. Med. Hyg.* 47, 399-400.

Eyles, D. E., and Coatney, G. R. (1962). Effect of certain drugs on exo-erythrocytic parasites of *Plasmodium cynomolgi. Am. J. Trop. Med. Hyg.* 11, 175-185.

Frenkel, J. K. (1949). Pathogenesis, diagnosis and treatment of human toxoplasmosis. *J. Am. Med. Assoc.* 140, 369-377.

Frenkel, J. K., and Jacobs, L. (1958). Ocular toxoplasmosis. *A. M. A. Arch. Ophthalmol. (Chicago)* 59, 260-279.

Galliard, P. H., Lapierre, J., and Rousset, J. (1958). Comportement specifique de differentes especes de *Borrelia* au cours de l'infection mixte avec *Trypanosoma brucei* son utilisation comme test d'identification des spirochetes recurrents. *Parasitol. Humaine Comparee* 33, 12-208.

Garnham, P. C. C. (1961). Mesocysts of *Hepatocystis semnopitheci* from *Macaca irus* Southern Thailand. *Trans. Roy. Soc. Trop. Med. Hyg.* **55**, 10.

Gear, J. (1947). Autoantigens and autoantibodies in the pathogenesis of disease with special reference to blackwater fever. *Trans. Roy. Soc. Trop. Med. Hyg.* **39**, 301-314.

Giglioli, G. (1962). Malaria and renal disease, with special reference to British Guiana. *Ann. Trop. Med. Parasitol.* **56**, 101-109.

Gilles, H. M., Maegraith, B. G., and Andrews, W. H. (1953). The liver in *Babesia canis* infection. *Ann. Trop. Med. Parasitol.* **47**, 426-430.

Goble, F. C. (1954). Thyroid changes in acute experimental Chagas' disease in dogs. *Am. J. Pathol.* **19**, 599-607.

Golden, A., and Overman, R. R. (1949). Experimental cortical necrosis of adrenal gland in the monkey in diphtheria and in malaria. *Am. J. Clin. Pathol.* **19**, 900-905.

Goodwin, L. G., and Richards, W. H. G. (1960). Pharmacologically active peptides in the blood and urine of animals infected with *Babesia rodhaini* and other pathogenic organisms. *Brit. J. Pharmacol.* **15**, 152-159.

Hoppe, J. O., and Chapman, C. W. (1947). Role of glucose in acute parasitemic death of the rat infected with *Trypanosoma equiperdum*. *J. Parasitol.* **33**, 509-515.

Hughes, F. W., and Tatum, A. L. (1956). Effects of hypoxia and intercurrent infections on infections by *Plasmodium berghei* in rats. *J. Infect. Diseases* **99**, 38-43.

Innes, J. R. M., and Saunders, L. Z. (1962). "Comparative Neuropathology, 839 pp. Academic Press, New York.

Jaffe, R., Dominquez, A., Kozina, C., and Gavallei, B. V. (1961). Bemerkungen zur Pathogenese der Chagaskrankheit. *Z. Tropenmed. Parasitol.* **12**, 137-146.

Keitel, H. G., Goodman, H. C., Havel, R. J., Gordon, R. S., and Baxter, J. H. (1956). Nephrotic syndrome in congenital quartan malaria. *J. Am. Med. Assoc.* **161**, 520-523.

Knisely, M. H., Stratman-Thomas, W. K., Eliot, T., and Bloch, E. (1964). Knowlesi malaria in monkeys. *Angiology* **15**, 411-416.

Köberle, F. (1961). Pathologia y anatomia pathologico de la enfermedad de Chagas. *Bol. Ofic. Sanit. Panam.* **51**, 404.

Laser, H. (1948). Haemolytic system in the blood of malaria-infected monkeys. *Nature* **161**, 560.

McComas, G., and Martin, N. H. (1944). Trypanosomiasis treated with pentamidine: A fatal case. *Lancet* **246**, 338-339.

McGhee, R. B. (1964). Autoimmunity in malaria. *Am. J. Trop. Med. Hyg.* **13**, 219-224.

Maegraith, B. G. (1954). Physiological aspects of protozoan infection. *Rev. Microbiol.* **8**, 273-287.

Maegraith, B. G. (1954b). The pathogenicity of plasmodia and entamoebae. *In* "Mechanisms of Microbial Pathogenicity," pp. 207-229. Cambridge Univ. Press, London and New York.

Maegraith, B. G. (1959). Some pathological process in malaria as exemplified in the development of hepatic lesions in acute infections. *Riv. Parasitol.* **20**, 317-326.

Maegraith, B. G., Gilles, H. M., and Devakul, K. (1957). Pathological process in *Babesia canis* infection. *Z. Tropenmed. Parasitol.* **8**, 485-514.

Malherbe, W. D. (1956). The manifestations and diagnosis of *Babesia* infections. *Ann. N. Y. Acad. Sci.* **64**, 128-146.

Manson-Bahr, P. H. (1945). "Tropical Diseases," 12th ed., p. 134. Cassell, London.

Muniz, J., and Azevedo, A. P. (1947). Novo conseito da pathogenia da doenca de Chagas (Trypanosomiasis americana). *Hospital* (*Rio de Janeiro*) **32**, 165-183.

Newberne, J. W. (1957). Studies on the histopathology of *Leucocytozoon simondi* infections. *Am. J. Vet. Res.* **18**, 191-199.

Paget, G. E., Alcock, S. J., and Ryley, J. F. (1962). The pathology of *Babesia rodhaini* infections in mice. *J. Pathol. Bacteriol.* **84**, 218-220.

Pizzi, T., and Prager, R. (1952). Estabilizacion de la virulencia de una cepa de *Trypanosoma cruzi* por pasaje seriado en ratones de constitucion genetica uniforme. *Biologica* (**16-17**), 3-12.

Rudzinska, M. A., and Trager, W. (1957). Intracellular phagotrophy by malaria parasites, an electron microscope study of *Plasmodium lophurae. J. Protozool.* **4**, 190-199.

Rudzinska, M. A., and Trager, W. (1962). Intracellular phagotrophy in *Babesia rodhaini* as revealed by electron microscopy. *J. Protozool.* **9**, 279-288.

Schulz, K. C. A., and Schutte, J. R. (1957). "Turning sickness." Bovine theileriosis in the Rustenburg district. *J. S. African Vet. Med. Assoc.* **28**, 279-289.

Scrimshaw, N. S., Taylor, C. E., and Gordon, J. E. (1957). Interactions of nutrition and infection. *Am. J. Med. Sci.* **237**, 367-403.

Shortt, H. E., Bray, R. S., and Cooper, W. (1954). Further notes on the tissue stages of *Plasmodium cynomolgi. Trans. Roy. Soc. Trop. Med. Hyg.* **48**, 122-131.

von Brand, T. (1952). "Chemical Physiology of Endoparasitic Animals," 339 pp. Academic Press, New York.

Waks, J. (1965). Enzyme changes in experimental American trypanosomiasis (Chagas-Mazza disease) Amsterdam. *Progr. Protozool., Intern. Congr., 1965,* Ser. No. **91**, p. 81. Excerpta Med. Found., Amsterdam.

Zuckermann, A. (1960). Blood loss and replacement in plasmodial infections. III. *Plasmodium cynomolgi, Plasmodium gonderi* and *Plasmodium knowlesi* in *Macaca mulatta mulatta,* the rhesus monkey. *J. Infect. Diseases* **106**, 123-140.

Discussion

Dr. Stone: In relation to anemia from the destruction of erythrocytes as a cause of death in avian malaria we have found that in *Plasmodium pinottii*, run in pigeons, that the hematocrit drops rapidly at the final segmentation before death. Roughly, the hematocrit goes from 52 to about 30 at death several hours later. We have been able to withdraw large quantities of blood from uninfected pigeons by heart puncture. In a matter of minutes, the plasma plus saline to make up the volume lost by discarding the red cells was transfused back into the pigeon. The birds easily survived this rapidly produced artificial anemia which was as bad or worse than those seen at death in infected birds.

We have transfused large amounts of hemoylzed plasma taken from pigeons just prior to death of *P. pinottii* malaria into uninfected pigeons from which an equal quantity of blood had already been withdrawn. So far the hemolyzed plasma has been well tolerated although quantities up to 40 percent of the total blood volume have been given. This seems to eliminate the possibility of any potent toxin in the plasma of birds infected with *P. pinottii*.

Dr. Beaver: It would be interesting to know on what basis Dr. Goble included *Toxoplasma* and excluded *Sarcocystis*.

Dr. Goble: I do not know that *Sarcocystis* circulates in the blood at any time, whereas we do know that this happens with *Toxoplasma*.

The Mechanisms of Immunity to Gastrointestinal Nematodes

E. J. L. SOULSBY

*Department of Parasitology, University of Pennsylvania,
Philadelphia, Pennsylvania*

INTRODUCTION

It may be somewhat hazardous to attempt a critical examination of the immunity mechanisms which operate against gastrointestinal nematodes at a time of great upsurge of interest in the subject, albeit with a limited number of facts and an almost total absence of chemical data. Nevertheless it has become clear from a review of the recent literature that an evaluation of some of the aspects of the subject is much desired. To search for a unified hypothesis, if one exists, is full of special treachery and it is wise at this stage to accept the proposal that the mechanisms may differ widely from one parasite to another. The best one can do is to place the phenomena in the chronology of their occurrence, though of course this is based on the *effect* of immunity on parasite population and gives little indication of the mechanisms that lead to the effect.

INDUCTION OF THE IMMUNE RESPONSE TO GASTROINTESTINAL NEMATODES

While it is well established that a good immune response occurs in mature animals there is little information on the factors that determine the evolution of the immune response to gastrointestinal parasites in the young animal, which is well known to suffer more severely from parasitism than the old. This of course is as important in man as it is in animals and constitutes an important aspect of herd immunity.

Critical work in this direction was performed by Manton *et al.* (1962), who demonstrated an inability of lambs below 2 to 4 months of age to become immune to *Haemonchus contortus* while those over 9 months did so readily. This situation is also exemplified under natural conditions, where it can be shown that high egg counts are present in lambs until about 6 months of age, when infections are terminated by a curative mechanism. This phenomenon is fairly constant year after year and reflects the difference between a young susceptible population and an older resistant population (See Fig. 1).

Recent studies of the immune responses of young lambs may throw some light on the process. Weekly serum samples were collected from a flock of ewes and their lambs and these were examined by the hemagglutination, complement fixation, and agar gel diffusion precipitation

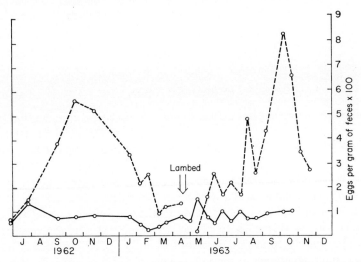

Fig. 1. Mean fecal egg counts of a flock of sheep in Cambridge, England, over a period of 18 months. Solid line: mean eggs per gram of feces of ewes (mean of at least 40 sheep). Dashed line: mean of lambs (number varied from 40 to 160 during the study). At the time of "Lambed" the lambs of the first part of the study are considered to be adult and are included in the mean figures for the ewes.

techniques, the results of which are shown in Fig. 2. Hemagglutinating antibodies were poorly transferred maternally (via colostrum) but the synthesis of new immunoglobulin responsible for hemagglutination was quite rapid (it being assumed that lambs would ingest larvae about 2 weeks after birth), high levels of hemagglutinins being achieved within 2 months. This situation is to be compared with the good maternal transfer of complement-fixing antibody and the subsequent long delay before synthesis of autologous globulin of this type occurred. The delay was of the order of 10 to 12 weeks and substantial levels were not reached until some time afterward. Though the ability to synthesize antibodies which fix complement (and precipitate) coincides with the commencement of an ability on the part of lambs to induce protective immunity to their gastrointestinal nematodes, it is not yet known whether the relationship can be extended further. Nevertheless there may be other antibodies which take even longer to be synthesized in an adequate manner and such a situation would provide an explanation for the inability of lambs to become immune until they are several months of age.

It is not known whether the delay in the production of these antibodies is a natural consequence in lambs or whether the passive transfer of immune globulin inhibits the subsequent synthesis of the same type of immune globulin. This mechanism has been suggested to occur in

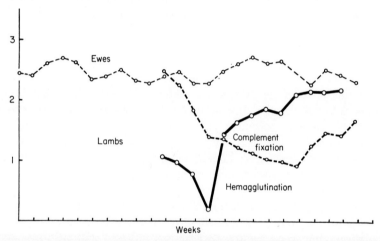

Fig. 2. Complement fixation and hemagglutination antibody levels in a flock of ewes (60) and lambs (120) at the birth of the lambs and for the subsequent 14 weeks. The upper dashed line is the mean complement fixation values for the ewes, hemagglutination levels in the ewes being similar.

the man (Osborn *et al.*, 1952) and more recently Finkelstein and Uhr (1964) have demonstrated in guinea pigs that intravenously administered 7S antibody is markedly effective in inhibiting the formation of that type of antibody to a bacteriophage while 19S antibody has no significant effect. The sedimentation characteristics of the two types of antibody seen in the sheep study have yet to be determined but at least it can be clearly seen that one form of antibody can be readily synthesized without being affected by the other. Other work with fetal lambs (Silverstein *et al.*, 1963) has shown that animals stimulated with antigens such as diphtheria toxoid, bacteriophage, ovalbumin, and so forth are capable of producing significant amounts of antibody (probably 19S) as early as the 66th day of gestation. A similar early production of 19S gamma globulin by young animals has been reported by several authors (see

review by Good and Papermaster, 1964). It will be of interest to determine whether the early response in lambs is of the 19S type. In any case
this study has indicated that the antibodies detectable by the hemagglutination test are probably not concerned in the protective immunity
mechanism.

A further consideration is the ability of various antigens of gastrointestinal parasites to induce antibody formation, since recent developments in the study of antibody formation in embryos and neonates have
shown that striking differences are revealed when different antigens
are used, potent ones such as hemocyanin inducing antibody formation
while others such as serum proteins do not (Good and Papermaster,
1964).

There is at present little critical information on the amount of parasitic infection that is required to initiate an immune response, especially
of the protective kind. An attempt has been made by Dineen (1963a) to
explain this in terms of "fitness characters." He envisaged that there is
a minimal threshold of antigenic information necessary for the stimulation of the immune response, this being dependent on the degree of
antigenic disparity between host and parasite and the rate of flow of
antigenic information. A reduction of antigenic disparity is postulated
to result in a "subliminal tolerance" of an increased population of parasites while an increased flow of antigenic information (by way of additional worm burdens) will tend toward a reduction of the subliminal
tolerance levels (that is, development of acquired immunity) for a given
population. Dineen postulated that the natural host will fail to recognize
the "fitness antigens" (those which influence the survival of the parasite), and using sheep and rabbits immunized with homogenates of larvae
and adult *Haemonchus contortus* he demonstrated (Dineen, 1963b) a
specificity of larvae and adults that was not seen in rabbits. In the latter,
antigens were shared between larvae and adults and Dineen suggested
that these represent the fitness antigens, being unrecognized by the
sheep. Though it was not clearly stated it was implied that the fitness
antigens are the protective antigens. If such fitness antigens induce a
relatively poor immune response, whereas those not concerned with
fitness characters induce a vigorous response, then this may explain
why there is no general correlation between the humoral response and
resistance to infection. However, there may be many other explanations
of this, the obvious one being that the right kind of antibody has yet to
be demonstrated, and the work of Ogilvie (1964) with respect to reaginlike antibodies in helminth infections is an indication of this.

Furthermore the experimental situation described by Dineen (1963b)
may not pertain under natural conditions. Thus a sharing of antigens

between the adult and various larval stages of *H. contortus* can be readily demonstrated in the serum of sheep naturally infected with the parasite (See Fig. 3) and one of the major systems in this is due to antigens which appear to play an important part in the immunological response and the survival of the parasite. Since these antigens, which occur in exsheathing fluid, appear to be concerned with the fitness of the parasite they could certainly be regarded as "fitness antigens" but they stimulate a vigorous immune response rather than a poor one. Sera of sheep which have undergone self-cure show at least five antigen-antibody systems with exsheathing fluid (Soulsby and Stewart, 1960)

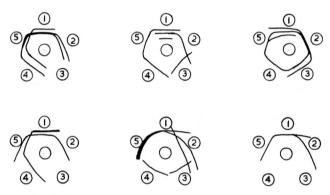

Fig. 3. Agar diffusion precipitin reactions of sera from various sheep, naturally infected with gastrointestinal nematodes. In each case the center well contains serum, the antigens being the following preparations of *Haemonchus contortus*: 1, Exsheathing fluid from 1 million infective larvae in 10 ml of saline. 2, Homogenate of infective larvae. 3, Homogenate of parasitic larvae aged 5 days, obtained from mucosa. 4, Homogenate of parasitic larvae aged 10 days. 5, Homogenate of adult worms. Agar contained 12% NaCl and plates were incubated for 5 days at room temperature.

while sera from rabbits artificially immunized with exsheathing fluid show five and possibly six such systems (Rogers and Sommerville, 1960). There appear to be discrepancies between the artificial and the natural situations and obviously more work is necessary to clarify ideas on the subject.

Specific immunological unresponsiveness to a variety of antigens is now a well-known phenomenon and can be induced before or soon after birth and even in mature animals. This aspect of parasitic infection has received very little study despite the fact that it might be thought that early exposure in an endemic area might lead to a degree of specific immunological unresponsiveness. Evidence in this direction was presented by Gibson (1952), who showed that lambs exposed to excessive infections at an early age developed a lower degree of immunity than those with light infection. Kerr and Robertson (1954) showed that large amounts of *Trichomonas foetus* antigen given to young calves would suppress the subsequent expected antibody response to the antigen. Experiments designed to induce actively acquired immunological unresponsiveness in mice to *Trichinella spiralis* have been conducted by Ewert and Olsen (1960) and Olson and Ewert (1961). Foetal or neonatal mice were injected with various antigens from *Trichinella spiralis* and then challenged with infective larvae, but no acquired tolerance was demonstrated; however these experiments did not show whether the injections of antigen induced an antibody response or whether injected mice would fail to become immune at a later stage in life.

Definite evidence of an acquired immunological unresponsiveness was presented by Soulsby (1963) with *Cysticercus bovis* infection in cattle, in that calves infected at birth failed to develop a good antibody response and an immunity to reinfection, whereas animals infected at 4–6 months of age responded well to both. The latter group behaved as would be expected and were comparable with the animals studied by Penfold and Penfold (1937), who stated that animals exposed to infection developed a strong immunity to reinfection within a few months of infection.

Undoubtedly other examples of specific induced immunological unresponsiveness in helminth infections will be forthcoming and where these are demonstrated to occur under natural conditions it is likely that animals (and human beings) so affected will be placed at a much greater disadvantage than their fellows. Where helminth disease is endemic it might be expected that pathogenic parasites could accumulate in a host, being unhindered by an immune response.

EFFECTS OF IMMUNITY ON DEVELOPMENTAL STAGES

One of the most common responses in immunity to gastrointestinal nematodes is the inhibition of development resulting in a retardation or cessation of growth and differentiation. This effect, under conditions of repeated infection, as seen in natural infections, may result in the total population in an animal being retarded in development. Studies of this were carried out by the author using a flock of sheep in Cambridge, England. Members of the flock, with their lambs, were killed at intervals during the year and total counts of parasites in the abomasum and small intestine were made, including the larval stages which were in the mucosae of these organs. Figure 4 illustrates the results of this study from which it is seen that almost all the parasite burden of adult sheep during the winter months and thereafter consisted of inhibited larval stages. This situation is to be compared with that of the lambs, the susceptible portion of the flock: little retardation of development was seen initially but later it became more marked as immunity became apparent and ultimately terminated the majority of the helminth burden. Detailed examination of the inhibited larvae showed them all to be

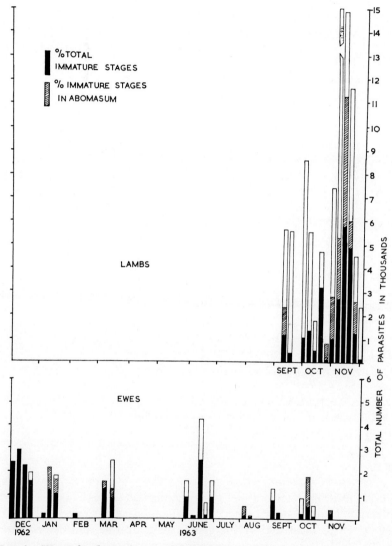

Fig. 4. Worm burdens of ewes and lambs in a flock of sheep in Cambridge, England. Each column represents the total burden in the abomasum, small intestine, and mucosae of these of one animal.

retarded in much the same stage of development (early fourth stage). Attempts to modify the status of the inhibited larvae by large doses of corticosteroids failed to cause any significant growth or development. However, Soulsby and Owen (1965) found that the alkylating agent

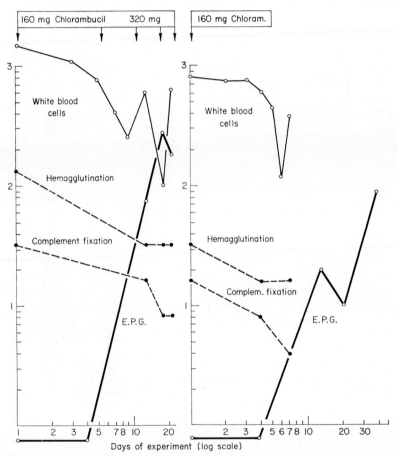

FIG. 5. White blood cell, hemagglutination, and complement fixation levels and fecal egg counts (eggs per gram, E.P.G.) of two sheep given chlorambucil as indicated.

chlorambucil produced a definite response in some sheep (Fig. 5). Chlorambucil treatment caused a fall in total white cells and in antibody levels as measured by the complement fixation and hemagglutination techniques and a marked rise in the number of eggs per gram of feces. In these cases at least, the elimination of the immune response resulted in a relatively rapid development of the parasites. Work with other nematodes indicates that immunity mechanisms are chiefly responsible for inhibition of development and that when the immune influence is removed, either by transplanting worms to a new host (Sarles and Taliaferro, 1936) or by total body irradiation (Dunsmore, 1961), normal development occurs.

Usually the host is considered the chief determinant in the phenomenon of inhibition of development; however, recent work by Anderson *et al.* (1965) with *Ostertagia ostertagi* in cattle has suggested a marked difference exists in the behavior of larvae acquired from pasture during spring and summer as compared with those acquired in the fall. The latter show an enhanced tendency to become inhibited in the abomasal mucosa. There is no evidence yet available to indicate whether this is a function of the larvae or of the physiology of the host (excluding immunological responses), but the question naturally arises whether other instances of inhibition of development are due to a similar mechanism and essentially independent of immunological factors. This might be especially so under conditions of natural exposure to gastrointestinal nematodes. In the case of sheep nematodes the available evidence suggests an immunological basis for the mechanism, since when it is removed there is a swift response on the part of the parasite.

The phenomenon of inhibition of development has important implications in the epidemiology of parasitic infections, since dormant larvae subsequently may develop to maturity, either causing clinical disease in the animal or providing a source of infection for other, more susceptible, members of the host species. The first eventuality is illustrated in the case of *Haemonchus placei* in cattle, where removal of an adult worm population by anthelmintics will allow larvae, inhibited in the abomasal mucosa, to develop, possibly to a pathogenic level (Roberts and Keith, 1959). The second is illustrated by the bovine lungworm, *Dictyocaulus viviparus,* where inhibited larval stages are thought to play an important role in the year-to-year maintenance of infection in a herd (Taylor and Michel, 1953) and in the spring rise phenomenon of sheep where there is strong circumstantial evidence that dormant larval stages contribute substantially to the increased parasitism in the spring (Field *et al.,* 1960). Parnell (1962), working in Western Australia, has described a similar phenomenon which, although occurring at different times of the year, has all the attributes of a spring rise phenomenon, and appears to be due to the reactivation of dormant larval stages when the immune status of the animal falls to a low level.

To ascertain how long dormant larval stages could remain viable and inhibited in sheep, animals from pasture (comparable to those in which a large number of larval stages was found at post-mortem) were placed

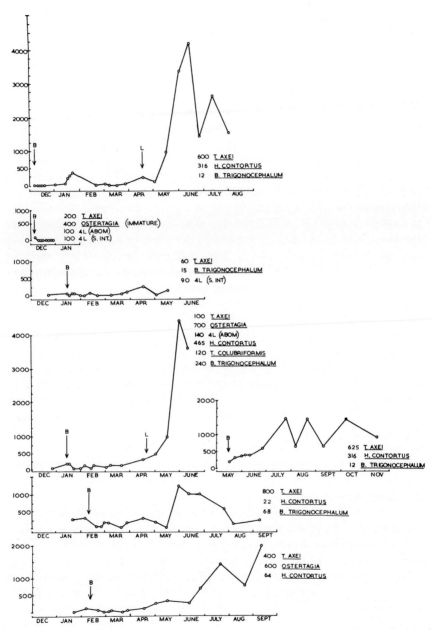

FIG. 6. Fecal egg counts and post-mortem data of seven sheep housed under "worm-free" conditions. B, Time when animals were placed in housing. L, Lambed. Post-mortem worm counts include parasites in the lumina of abomasum and small intestine and the digested mucosae of these.

in stalls under conditions designed to prevent reinfection. Test worm-free lambs were placed in the stalls as controls for the "worm-free" conditions and were uninfected at the end of the experiment. Figure 6 illustrates the results of this experiment. It was found that egg counts remained low for several weeks but after 2 to 3 months a marked rise in egg counts occurred. On post-mortem of these animals it was seen that *H. contortus* and *Bunostomum phlebotomum* took part in this response and it would therefore appear that both these parasites can undergo periods of prolonged retardation of development comparable with other gastrointestinal nematodes. It has been suggested that *H. contortus* does not undergo such an inhibition, but Field *et al.* (1960) produced circumstantial evidence for it and the present results would clearly indicate that this species can be inhibited for some considerable time. Such results raise the interesting question of the epidemiological significance of inhibited larval stages in the maintenance of infection from one grazing season to another. Whether this aspect is of more importance than the survival of larvae on herbage from season to season remains to be determined but at least the persistance of infection in a host can no longer be disregarded in this respect.

The association between parturition and the reactivation of larval stages is clear in the above study (Fig. 6). However it is not an obligatory prerequisite for the phenomenon. A similar situation pertains in the spring rise phenomenon in which Crofton (1958) has demonstrated a correlation between parturition and the maximal egg production, so much so that he prefers to call the phenomenon the "post parturient" rise. Nevertheless it is to be remembered that nonparturient animals equally take part in the phenomenon.

The basic question must be asked as to how the immunological mechanisms inhibit the growth and development of nematodes. There is no satisfactory answer to this at present. Whatever the system, it is of a reversible nature, since removal of the inhibiting mechanism results in continuation of development. That inhibition frequently occurs at a specific stage of development suggests that the inhibition of, for example, a receptor mechanism responsible for further development may be concerned. In the case where a small population of adult worms produces inhibition of larval stages, a feedback mechanism effective on antigens as they first become apparent in the larval stages may also be a possible explanation.

A further unresolved question is the mode of entry of the immune bodies into the parasite, or whether, in fact, entry is necessary. It has been shown with *Nippostrongylus braziliensis* that the worms do not suck large quantities of blood (Mulligan *et al.*, 1965) and hence presumably they do not acquire quantities of immunoglobulin in this way. The self-cure reaction with this parasite is initiated by a fall in egg production and though it may be that environmental changes are responsible for this it might be thought that a more intrinsic mechanism is operable.

Whether antibody alone can affect and ultimately destroy a nematode is by no means clear. It is well known that reactions between immune

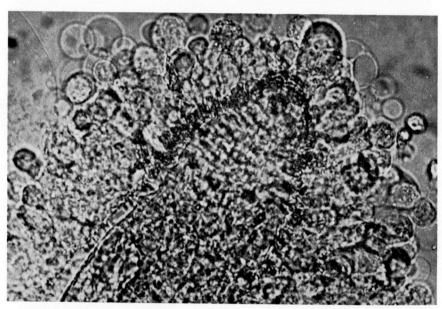

FIG. 7. *Ascaris suum* third-stage larva, sensitized with antibody, then washed and exposed to peritoneal cavity cells from an immune rabbit. Eosinophils and pyroninophils adhere to the surface and the eosinophils have undergone degranulation.

serum and larval stages can be produced with ease; some of these consist of antigen antibody precipitates at the orifices of larvae, a decrease in oxygen consumption (Schwabe, 1957), and a coating phenomenon when larvae are grown in immune substances (Douvres, 1962). There is, however, no direct evidence that these reactions are primarily responsible for the immune rejection of the parasite by the host, though it would be natural to surmise that they were. The work of Douvres (1962) demonstrated immunological reactions with advanced third-stage larvae, these being equivalent to the stages of *Oesophagostomum radiatum* that are found in the mucosa of the bovine digestive tract. Under natural conditions however, Roberts *et al.* (1962) showed that the major immune reaction to this parasite occurred when fourth-stage larvae migrated from the mucosa into the gut lumen. The two findings are, of course, not incompatible. An impressive failure of antibodies to affect nematodes was reported by Jackson (1961). Working with *Neoplectana glaseri,* which can be maintained in culture for several generations, he found that worms grown in the presence of antisera to *N. glaseri* (prepared by immunizing rabbits) failed to be affected in growth or reproduction despite an abundance of precipitates both on the parasites and in the medium.

The primary role of antibody in the specificity of the reaction and the initiation of subsequent immunological events is undoubted but there is great need to investigate the importance of such things as complement and lymphoid cells in the immune reaction. It has been shown, for example, that the antibody-sensitized parasitic larval stage of *Ascaris suum* is a potential target for cells (eosinophils and pyroninophils) and that these can undergo degranulation at the cuticle surface (Fig. 7). It is not unlikely that this results in the release of pharmacologically active substances which may affect the structure or the function of the cuticle.

THE SELF-CURE REACTION

This curative mechanism has been demonstrated in several nematode infections but it is best known in the case of *H. contortus* and *Nippostrongylus braziliensis.* It is doubtful that the component parts of the mechanism in the different infections are identical and to illustrate this the two species named are discussed in detail.

The self-cure reaction in *H. contortus* infection occurs when a challenge dose of infective larvae is superimposed as an existing infection in a sensitized sheep. This results in elimination of the burden of adult worms and may also cause the elimination of the challenge infective larvae, but in some cases the shocking dose of larvae may grow to maturity and themselves be "self-cured" by a further challenge infection. The basic mechanism, which will be considered below, appears to cause a "mechanical" removal of the adult worm burden, rather than the parasites being directly affected by the immune response. This in turn appears to differ from the situation with *N. braziliensis* where no challenge infection of larvae is necessary to initiate the self-cure reaction and which is the terminal response of an increasing immune state.

The component parts of the self-cure in *H. contortus* infection are as follows. It occurs in sheep which have been exposed to frequent spaced doses of infective larvae whereas continuous infection with mature worms does not induce the state conditional for the reaction. Normally the reaction can be induced only by the intake of live larvae; thus the intraperitoneal injection of living larvae, while producing a good antibody response, fails to induce the self-cure reaction. Similarly, dead infective larvae given by mouth or injected parenterally fail to induce the response and the addition of heated *H. contortus* antigen to strips of the abomasum of sheep, which had regularly exhibited the self-cure response, failed to induce contraction (Stewart, 1953). A dependence on antigens associated with living larvae and acting locally is therefore characteristic of the response. More generalized reactions associated with the response consist of an immediate type skin reaction, an increase in circulating antibody (as measured by complement fixation and precipitation techniques), and a significant rise in blood histamine at the time of the reaction. The latter has given evidence of the time of the initiation of the mechanism, since assuming the phenomenon is a local hypersensitive response, a release of histamine would be expected to determine within a matter of hours when the antigen was supplied to initiate the reaction. That the histamine response occurs between the 2nd and 4th day after the administration of the shocking dose of larvae strongly indicates that the antigen is associated with larval stages which have undergone some degree of development. Soulsby and Stewart (1960) demonstrated, by killing sheep serially after a challenge dose of larvae, that an adult population of worms remained intact in the abomasum, along with a population of developing larvae; however, when the challenge larvae underwent moulting to the fourth larval stage much of the adult population was located in the small intestine and in a state of disintegration. Since moulting of *H. contortus* third-stage larvae to the fourth stage is initiated 48 hours after infection (Veglia, 1915), the association of the self-cure reaction with the moulting process is strongly suspected. The importance of the moulting period in immunity to nematodes has been stressed (Soulsby, 1959) and evidence of an association between the self-cure reaction and materials specifically functional in the process of moulting or exsheathment was provided by a strong serological response to exsheathing fluid shortly after the self-cure reaction. Figure 8 shows such a reaction 5 days after self-cure. It is seen that the reaction with exsheathing fluid is also present in a homogenate of infective larvae: this is to be expected since exsheathing fluid is known to be present in such preparations (Rogers and Sommerville, 1960). These reactions were obtained with exsheathing fluid produced at the time of ecdysis of infective larvae, which would normally be released in the rumen (Rogers, 1962), where appropriate conditions of pH and oxygen tension occur. It is unlikely that the serological response observed was due to exsheathing fluid released in the rumen for the following reasons. Self-cure occurs at least 2 days after initial exsheathment, the locale of exsheathment is far removed from the mucosa of the abomasum, and it is likely that great dilution would occur before exsheathing fluid reached the abomasum. The marked serological response with exsheathing fluid would, however, strongly suggest that a comparable material (antigenically and also probably physiologically) is released at an additional time in the life cycle and the moult from the third to the fourth larval stage would appear to be an acceptable time for this.

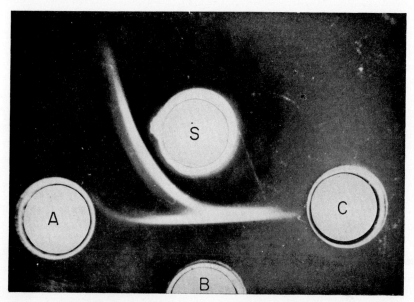

FIG. 8. Agar diffusion precipitin response 5 days after the self-cure reaction with *Haemonchus contortus.* S, Serum. A, Exsheathing fluid. B, Homogenate of infective larvae. C, Metabolic products of *H. contortus* infective larvae.

Though the origin of the antigen (or antigens) in the self-cure reaction seems explicable, their nature is still an open question. There is no evidence that the specific components in exsheathing fluid which stimulate exsheathment also initiate the self-cure reaction. The recent work of Rogers (1963) should, however, help to resolve this question. He has demonstrated that an enzyme similar to leucine amino peptidase, which attacks L-leucyl-*p*-naphthylamide at pH 9.5, is contained in the exsheathing fluid of *H. contortus.* In agar diffusion precipitin tests with various preparations of exsheathing fluid and antisera to exsheathing fluid (prepared in rabbits) Rogers and Sommerville (1960) ascribed several precipitating systems to cuticular components while one antigen-antibody system was missing when inactivated (mercuric chloride 10^{-3} M) exsheathing fluid was used as antigen. It would of course be interesting to know whether self-cure could be induced with such inactivated material and whether precipitin lines would be absent from the precipitin response at the time of self-cure if inactivated material was used as an antigen.

The basic immunological mechanism on the part of the sheep has occasioned speculation. Some time ago, Soulsby (1958) likened the response to the Arthus reaction; however, Augustin and Ridges (1963) objected to this and strongly suggested that there was "good indirect evidence that hypersensitive reactions of the immediate type" were responsible. The latter authors stated that Stewart (1953) found no relationship with precipitin titers; however, though such antibodies were not searched for by Stewart there is some relationship to precipitins, since a striking response, especially to exsheathing fluid, is seen shortly after the reaction and precipitating antibodies increase in amount prior to the self-cure reaction under natural conditions. Whether the level of these is sufficient to allow widespread deposition of antigen-antibody complexes in the local blood vessels and their epithelium has yet to be determined.

The information available on the timing of the self-cure response is not sufficiently clear for critical evaluation. Though Stewart found that the injection of exsheathed larvae into the exposed abomasum, caused increased peristalsis, paleness, and edematous thickening of the mucosa, there is no direct evidence that this was associated with the self-cure reaction. Even with the skin reactions conclusions are difficult to draw since Stewart (1953) reported them to be maximal in 1 to 2 hours. This appears intermediate between immediate-type hypersensitivity (maximal in 10–20 minutes and resolving within 1 to $1\frac{1}{2}$ hour; Pepys, 1963) and the Arthus reaction (edema in 10 to 15 minutes, maximal in 2 to 6 hours; Ovary, 1958; Osler, 1963). While the resolution of the situation is of importance in understanding the basic phenomenon it may be unwise at present to extrapolate phenomena known to occur in the man, rabbit, guinea pig, and so on, to sheep or other animals, since major differences in the behavior of immunoglobulins may occur in these animals. One need only consider the great variation seen in passive cutaneous anaphylaxis to appreciate this.

The response of the self-cure reaction to antihistamines may also be difficult to equate with immediate-type hypersensitivity or the Arthus reaction since Stewart (1953) noted that antihistamine drugs were not invariably inhibitory to the reaction. If the histamine involvement was not an intrinsic part of the reaction, but rather a secondary effect, and almost any tissue damage will induce histamine release with edema, then though antihistamines might not affect the basic immunological reaction they may well affect the secondary response and edema. Furthermore partial inhibition of the Arthus reaction may occur with large doses of antihistamines (Ovary, 1958; Brocklehurst et al., 1955).

Of course the two basic reactions may well be operating in the self-cure reaction, thus giving a rather unclear picture.

The self-cure reaction in N. braziliensis infection shows many superficial differences from that in H. contortus infection; nevertheless, the mechanisms may be much the same. When rats are infected with a suitable number of N. braziliensis the resulting adult infection is lost between the 10th and the 20th day of infection, this being heralded by a fall in egg production. That the whole phenomenon is due to an immune response is illustrated by the fact that if worms are removed from a rat at 10 days and transplanted to a normal rat they will persist for 8 to 10 days and then be eliminated by the self-cure reaction (Chandler, 1936; Mulligan et al., 1965). Furthermore the reaction is passively transferable by serum (Mulligan et al., 1965) and can be inhibited by cortisone therapy (Weinstein, 1958; Ogilvie, 1963). When cortisone is discontinued the immune rejection is re-established. Such component parts might suggest that an Arthus-type reaction was in operation; however, the general lack of association with precipitins and the recent demonstration by Ogilvie (1964) that reaginlike antibodies are associated with the infection may indicate that the response is nearer to the immediate-type hypersensitivity.

Reagins are demonstrable shortly after the self-cure reaction to N. braziliensis and may persist for several months. At present they can be induced solely by an active infection and not by vaccination with homogenized worms, which similarly does not induce any protective immunity. The reagins are detected by the use of the PCA[1] reaction in rats. The shocking antigen is preferably homogenates of adult worms, but infective larvae are also affective. The occurrence of immediate-type hypersensitivity with N. braziliensis infection in rats may be especially fortunate since the rat gut is probably the principal "shock" organ (West, 1959) and, among other things, when shocked, may allow an increased permeability of the bowel mucosa for immunoglobulins, which would have a more direct action on the parasite. Ogilvie (1964) has indicated that anaphylactic shock can be induced in rats following the acquisition of immunity to N. braziliensis.

A common method of experimental induction of reagins and anaphylactic shock in the rat is the combination of antigen with Bacillus pertussis, reactions being more intense than when B. pertussis is not used as an

[1] PCA stands for passive cutaneous anaphylaxis.

adjuvant. Similarly extensive mast cell disruption is seen in the rat when B. pertussis is used with an antigen and Wells (1962) has shown that mast cell disruption is marked during the immune rejection of a N. braziliensis infection. Histamine release is significant in active anaphylaxis in animals sensitized with antigens plus B. pertussis but little is known of this in N. braziliensis infection and it remains to be seen whether the self-cure reaction can be inhibited by antihistamines.

Other entities also require consideration, such as serotonin (5-hydroxy-tryptamine) since in murine anaphylaxis at least this may play a more important role that histamine (Gershon and Ross, 1962; Austen and Humphrey, 1963). Briggs (1963), working with Trichinella spiralis infected mice, showed that marked generalized reactions of immediate-type hypersensitivity were demonstrable about 1 month after infection with 200 T. spiralis larvae, 300 µg of antigen producing severe signs of anaphylaxis. Similarly, mast cell disruption in the subcutaneous tissues was slight during the 2nd week of infection but maximal reactions were seen 1 month after infection. Briggs (1963) attempted to induce host resistance to T. spiralis by the administration of 5-hydroxytryptophan (the precursor of serotonin). This was partially successful when given 90 minutes post infection, that is, before the mechanism of acquired immunity had developed. Experiments such as these are invaluable in characterizing the immune reactions in helminth infections and could be extended to such substances as lysergic acid and reserpine: this is especially important since the mechanisms of immediate-type hypersensitvity differ widely from one animal species to another (see Austen and Humphrey, 1963) and in reality each system may have been regarded as unique for the individual host and the individual species of parasite.

Whereas with H. contortus self-cure there is much to indicate the origin of the antigen responsible for the reaction, no such information exists for N. braziliensis, but the development of a test system which equates protective immunity with a demonstrable immunoglobulin should allow an early resolution of this.

FUTURE PROSPECTS

There is an urgency for a clarification of the immune phenomena which occur in helminth infections: much of this will depend on the purification of antigens so that quantitative techniques can be adopted; nevertheless the existing information does lend itself to a degree of critical assessment. Such a clarification would allow a greater understanding of the immunological mechanisms in helminth infections and a more rational approach to the application of the phenomena for control measures.

The recent advances have depended greatly on the use of sound immunological techniques but the future will also utilize techniques which are a combination of immunology, biochemistry, and physiology since studies of the effect of immunity in gastrointestinal nematodes will undoubtedly require these.

REFERENCES

Anderson, N., Armour, J., Jennings, F. N., Ritchie, J. D., and Urquhart, G. M. (1965). Inhibited development of *Ostertagia ostertagi*. *Vet. Record* 77, 146-147.

Augustin, R., and Ridges, A. P. (1963). Immunity mechanisms in *Eimeria meleagrimitis*. In "Immunity to Protozoa" (P. C. C. Garnham, A. E. Pierce, and I. Roitt, eds.), p. 296. Blackwell, Oxford.

Austen, K. F., and Humphrey, J. H. (1963). *In vitro* studies of the mechanisms of anaphylaxis. *Advan. Immunol.* 3, 1-96.

Briggs, N. T. (1963). Hypersensitivity in murine trichinosis: Some responses of *Trichinella-infected* mice to antigen and 5-hydroxytryptophan. *Ann. N.Y. Acad. Sci.* 113, 456-466.

Brocklehurst, W. E., Humphrey, J. H., and Perry, W. L. M. (1955). The role of histamine in cutaneous antigen-antibody reactions in the rat. *J. Physiol. (London)* 129, 205-224.

Chandler, A. C. (1936). Studies on the nature of immunity to intestinal helminths. III. Renewal of growth and egg production in *Nippostrongylus* after transfer from immune to nonimmune rats. *Am. J. Hyg.* 23, 46-54.

Crofton, H. D. (1958). Nematode parasite populations in sheep on Lowland farms. V. Further observations on the post parturient rise and a discussion of its significance. *Parasitology* 48, 243-250.

Dineen, J. K. (1963a). Immunological aspects of parasitism. *Nature* 197, 268-269.

Dineen, J. K. (1963b). Antigenic relationship between host and parasite. *Nature* 197, 471-472.

Douvres, F. W. (1962). The *in vitro* cultivation of *Oesophagostomum radiatum*, the nodular worm of cattle. II. The use of this technique to study immune response of host tissue extracts against the developing nematode. *J. Parasitol.* 48, 852-864.

Dunsmore, J. D. (1961). Effect of whole body irradiation and cortisone on the development of *Ostertagia* spp. in sheep. *Nature* 192, 139-140.

Ewert, A., and Olson, L. J. (1960). Immunological tolerance studies with mice and *Trichinella*. *J. Parasitol.* 46, 849-854.

Field, A. C., Brambell, M. R., and Campbell, J. A. (1960). Spring rise in fecal worm-egg counts of housed sheep, and its importance in nutritional experiments. *Parasitology* 50, 387-399.

Finkelstein, M. S., and Uhr, S. W. (1964). Specific inhibition of antibody formation by passively administered 19S and 7S antibody. *Science* 146, 67-69.

Gershon, M. D., and Ross, L. L. (1962). Studies on the relationship of 5-hydroxytryptamine and the enterochromaffin cell to anaphylactic shock in mice. *J. Exptl. Med.* 115, 367-382.

Gibson, T. E. (1952). The development of acquired resistance by sheep to infestation with the nematode, *Trichostrongylus axei*. *J. Helminthol.* 26, 43-53.

Good, R. A., and Papermaster, B. W. (1964). Ontogeny and phylogeny of adaptive immunity. *Advan. Immunol.* 4, 1-96.

Jackson, G. J. (1961). The parasitic nematode, *Neoplectana glaseri*, in axenic culture. I. Effects of antibodies and anthelmintics. *Exptl. Parasitol.* 11, 241-247.

Kerr, W. R., and Robertson, M. (1954). Passively and actively acquired antibodies for *Trichomonas foetus* in very young calves. *J. Hyg.* **52**, 253-263.

Manton, V. J. A., Peacock, R., Poynter, D., Silverman, P. H., and Terry, R. J. (1962). The influence of age on naturally acquired resistance to *Haemonchus contortus*. *Res. Vet. Sci.* **3**, 308-313.

Mulligan, W., Urquhart, G. M., Jennings, F. W., and Neilson, J. T. M. (1965). Immunological studies on *Nippostrongylus braziliensis* infection in the rat: The "self-cure" phenomenon. *Exptl. Parasitol.* **16**, 291-299.

Ogilvie, B. M. (1963). *Nippostrongylus braziliensis* (Travassos, 1914; Travassos and Darriba, 1929). A study of the life cycle and the immunological response of the host. Ph. D. Dissertation, University of Cambridge.

Ogilvie, B. M. (1964). Reagin-like antibodies in animals immune to helminth parasites. *Nature* **204**, 91-92.

Olson, L. J., and Ewert, A. (1961). Further studies on immunological tolerance with mice and *Trichinella*. *Texas Rept. Biol. Med.* **19**, 866-868.

Osborn, J. J., Dancis, J., and Julia, J. F. (1952). Studies of the immunology of the newborn infant. *Pediatrics* **10**, 328-334.

Osler, A. G. (1963). Skin reaction of the immediate and delayed types of hypersensitivity: Some aspects of their mechanisms. *In* "Immunodiagnosis of Helminthic Infections" (L. A. Jachowski, ed.), Am. J. Hyg. Monograph Ser. No. 22. Johns Hopkins Press, Baltimore, Maryland.

Ovary, Z. (1958). Passive cutaneous anaphylaxis in the guinea pig: Degree of reaction as a function of the quantity of antigen and antibody. *Intern. Arch. Allergy Appl. Immunol.* **14**, 18-26.

Parnell, I. W. (1962). Observations on the seasonal variation in the worm burdens of young sheep in Southern Western Australia. *J. Helminthol.* **36**, 161-188.

Penfold, W. J., and Penfold, H. B. (1937). *Cysticercus bovis* and its prevention. *J. Helminthol.* **15**, 37-40.

Pepys, J. (1963). Skin tests in diagnosis. *In* "Clinical Aspects of Immunology" (P. G. H. Gell and R. R. A. Coombs, eds.), p. 133. Blackwell, Oxford, and F. A. Davis, Philadelphia.

Roberts, F. H. S., and Keith, R. K. (1959). Observations on the effect of treatment with phenothiazine on the development of resistance by calves to infestation with the stomach worm, *Haemonchus placei* (Place, 1893) Ransom, 1911. *Australian Vet. J.* **35**, 409-414.

Roberts, F. H. S., Elek, P., and Keith, R. K. (1962). Studies on resistance in calves to experimental infection with the nodular worm, *Oesophagostomum radiatum* (Rudolphi, 1803) Railliet, 1898. *Australian J. Agr. Res.* **13**, 551-573.

Rogers, W. P. (1962). "The Nature of Parasitism." Academic Press, New York.

Rogers, W. P. (1963). Physiology of infection with nematodes: Some effects of the host stimulus on infective stages. *Ann. N.Y. Acad. Sci.* **113**, 208-216.

Rogers, W. P., and Sommerville, R. I. (1960). The physiology of the second ecdysis of parasitic nematodes. *Parasitology* **50**, 329-348.

Sarles, M. P., and Taliaferro, W. H. (1936). The local points of defense and the passive transfer of acquired immunity to *Nippostrongylus muris* in rats. *J. Infect. Diseases* **59**, 207-220.

Schwabe, C. W. (1957). Effects of normal and immune rat sera upon the respiration of free living and parasitic *Nippostrongylus muris* larvae. *Am. J. Hyg.* **65**, 338-343.

Silverstein, A. M., Uhr, J. W., Kraner, K. L., and Lukes, R. J. (1963). Fetal response to antigenic stimulus. *J. Exptl. Med.* **117**, 799-812.

Soulsby, E. J. L. (1958). Immunity to helminths. *Vet. Rev. Annotations* **4**, 1-16.

Soulsby, E. J. L. (1959). The importance of the moulting period in the stimulation of immunity to helminths. *Proc. 16th Intern. Vet. Congr., Madrid, 1959* Vol. 2, pp. 571-573.

Soulsby, E. J. L. (1963). Immunological unresponsiveness to helminth infections in animals. *Proc. 17th World Vet. Congr., Hannover. 1963* Vol. 1, pp. 761-767. Hahn-Druckerei, Hannover.

Soulsby, E. J. L., and Owen, L. N. (1965). Lowering of immunity in sheep following injections of chlorambucil. *Nature* **205**, 719-720.

Soulsby, E. J. L., and Stewart, D. F. (1960). Serological studies of the self cure reaction in sheep infected with *Haemonchus contortus*. *Australian J. Agr. Res.* **11**, 595-603.

Stewart, D. F. (1953). Studies on resistance of sheep to infestation with *Haemonchus contortus* and *Trichostrongylus* spp. and on the immunological reactions of sheep exposed to infestation. V. The nature of the "self cure" phenomenon. *Australian J. Agr. Res.* **4**, 100-117.

Taylor, E. L., and Michel, J. F. (1953). The parasitological and pathological significance of arrested development in nematodes. *J. Helminthol.* **28**, 199-205.

Veglia, F. (1915). The life history and anatomy of *Haemonchus contortus* (Rud.). *3rd and 4th Ann. Rept. Dir. Vet. Res. Union S. Africa*, pp. 347-500.

Weinstein, P. P. (1958). The effect of cortisone on the immune response of the white rat to *Nippostrongylus muris*. *Am. J. Trop. Med. Hyg.* **4**, 61-74.

Wells, P. D. (1962). Mast cell, eosinophil and histamine levels in *Nippostrongylus braziliensis* infected rats. *Exptl. Parasitol.* **12**, 82-101.

West, G. B. (1959). Some factors involved in anaphylactic shock. *Intern. Arch. Allergy Appl. Immunol.* **15**, 231-236.

Discussion

Dr. Bennett: Apparently when a lamb infected with *Haemonchus contortus* is exposed to infective larvae one of two things can happen. Either there may be a self-cure or the new larvae may be inhibited. Can you tell us under what conditions the self-cure and under what conditions the inhibition reactions are likely to occur?

Dr. Soulsby: I suspect there are two completely different mechanisms operative. To create a potential self-cure condition the animal needs to be sensitized several times, possibly to induce a satisfactory level of "hypersensitivity" in the mucosa. The inhibition of larvae is directed more to the parasite than the host and may depend more on different antigen-antibody reactions than in the self-cure reaction.

Dr. Damian: Your observation of eosinophils becoming opposed to the cuticle of the nematode is interesting in reference to Spiers' contention that the eosinophil has a very fundamental role in the antibody-forming mechanism.

Dr. Soulsby: Yes! Our results fit well with Spiers' postulates.

Dr. Douvres: In *in vitro* grown parasitic larvae of *Oesophagostomum radiatum* in the 3L, 3M, and fourth stage in unheated sera from infected (single) and multiply infected calves (*O. radiatum*) we get a coating precipitate response, but recently we have found that this also occurs in some, but not all, noninfected calf sera.

Dr. Soulsby: Your "coating" effect is most interesting and I think it may be related to the immune adherence phenomenon with which we have been working. With the latter, an antibody-complement sensitized larva will attract primate cells and thrombocytes of other species and sometimes other particulate matter. This is a specific immunological reaction which is extremely sensitive, and using it we have detected anti-*Ascaris* antibody in normal sera. The same kind of normal specific antibody has been found in rabbit and human sera against *Turbatrix aceti* using the mixed antiglobulin agglutination test, this also being a sensitive technique. Consequently, I feel, with your "coating" effect you are detecting the same type of "normal" antibody. Is the "coating" response more marked in serum from infected animals?

Dr. Douvres: Yes! The reaction is more intense in sera from infected or resistant animals.

Dr. Mulligan: I would like to say a word about our work in Glasgow on self-cure of *Nippostrongylus braziliensis* in the rat. We have been interested for some time in the possible role of local anaphylaxis in this immune expulsion. Recent work by a colleague (Ellen Barth) has shown that the production of ovalbumin-induced anaphylaxis in rats passively immunized with antiserum to *N. braziliensis* brings about a significant reduction in the numbers of a transplanted adult population compared with rats passively immunized alone or rats subjected to ovalbumin anaphylaxis alone.

This suggests a two-stage mechanism, the first stage being associated with increased capillary permeability in the gut, which promotes greater antibody-parasite contact.

Mechanisms of Immunity in Trematode Infection

Irving G. Kagan

U.S. Department of Health, Education, and Welfare,
Public Health Service, Communicable Disease Center,
Atlanta, Georgia

INTRODUCTION

In 1940 Taliaferro reviewed the mechanisms of acquired immunity in infections with parasitic worms and concluded that "immunity rests immediately on humoral factors with secondary cellular cooperation." This statement was based on various studies of immunity for the cestodes, *Taenia taeniaeformis* and *T. pisiformis,* the nematodes, *Nippostrongylus brasiliensis* and *Ancylostoma caninum,* and a few other species. Immunological data on the trematodes were not included.

The schistosomes, because of their medical importance, have attracted the greatest attention in the study of trematode immunity. The bulk of the experimental work has been made with *Schistosoma mansoni* and *Schistosoma japonicum.* This discussion on mechanisms of immunity in parasitic infections will be limited largely to a review of the status of schistosome immunity with some reference to recent work with *Fasciola hepatica* and other trematode species.

SCHISTOSOMA IMMUNITY

In 1958 the speaker reviewed contributions to the immunology and serology of schistosomiasis. Subsequently, a number of excellent summaries of the literature were published (Lincicome, 1962; Soulsby, 1962; Sadun, 1963; Smithers, 1962a; Stirewalt, 1963; H. F. Hsü and Hsü, 1962), but only the more recent contributions will be stressed in this review. Smithers (1962a) concluded that little was known relative to the mechanisms of resistance in animals infected with schistosomes. He emphasized that it had not been proven conclusively that sera from resistant animals possessed protective properties and pointed out that none of the demonstrable antibodies had been shown to have a protective function. He also stated that the stimulus for resistance appeared to be related to the metabolic activity and survival time of living worms in the host. This suggested to him that resistance is stimulated by a metabolic antigen produced by the living worm.

To establish a classical antibody basis for schistosome immunity, three criteria must be fulfilled: (1) Antibodies must be demonstrably present when immunity is proven; (2) passive transfer of protective antibodies should be possible; and (3) the protective property should be absorbable or fractionated from the serum and in consequence the serum should lose its ability to transfer resistance. To date there has been no conclusive evidence for all three of the above postulates for schistosome immunity. Parts (1) and (2) have been tested but part (3) has yet to be investigated.

SERUM PROTEIN CHANGES MEDIATED BY INFECTION

In animals infected with schistosomes, precipitin or bivalent antibodies can be demonstrated by a variety of serological methods (Kagan and Pellegrino, 1961; Soulsby, 1962, 1963). In the rhesus monkey (*Macaca mulatta*) antibodies such as circumoval precipitins (COP), *Cercarienhüllenreaktion* (CHR) antibodies, and agar gel precipitins develop in the serum of susceptible as well as immune animals (Smithers, 1962b). Jachowski *et al.* (1963) concluded that complement fixation, circumoval precipitins, slide flocculation, and fluorescent antibody tests do not indicate the immunological status of monkeys infected with *S. mansoni*.

S. Y. Hsü and Hsü (1964) could find no significant difference in total serum protein of normal monkeys and animals infected with irradiated cercariae of *S. japonicum*. Smithers and Walker (1961) noted a rise in total serum proteins 6–7 weeks following infection with *S. mansoni* in monkeys. This coincided with the appearance of circulating antibody in the host. Sadun and Walton (1958) reported a rise in serum protein in rabbits and human beings approximately 6 weeks after infection with *S. japonicum*. Bénex *et al.* (1960) reported an increase in gamma globulin and decrease in albumin for the sera of individuals infected with *S. mansoni* and *S. haematobium*. Kagan and Goodchild (1961) observed an increase in serum proteins that was correlated with the appearance of CHR antibodies in hosts experimentally infected with *S. mansoni*. Lee and Lewert (1960) fractionated immune serum and located the relative position of some of these antibodies by starch electrophoresis.

In summary, the serum protein changes reported in animals and man infected with schistosomes represent an antibody response to the presence of eggs, schistosomules, or adult worms in the host or a response to damage to the liver and impairment of the synthesis of albumin. These changes, however, have not been correlated to resistance or immunity in the host.

PASSIVE TRANSFER EXPERIMENTS

Passive transfer of immunity has been the subject of many experiments to demonstrate an antibody basis for resistance. Stirewalt (1963) in a review concluded that demonstration of protective schistosome anti-bodies has been elusive. Her attempts (like many others) to transfer high-titer heterologous antisera (immune rabbit to rat or mouse) were negative. She concluded, however, that negative results in passive trans-fer experiments do not indicate an absence of antibody, but rather indicate our inability to understand or handle the antibody that may be present.

Sadun and Lin (1959) successfully transferred serum from rabbits, infected 8–12 weeks earlier with S. japonicum, to normal mice prior to challenge with cercariae of S. japonicum. They found a slight but sig-nificant reduction in the number of worms recovered between con-trols and the mice that had received the immune serum. Meisenhelder et al. (1960) reported passive transfer experiments with relatively mas-sive doses of immune monkey blood (S. mansoni) (approximately one-third the blood volume of the recipient monkey) with negative results. Bruce and Sadun (1964) reported that passive transfer of the blood of monkeys immunized with irradiated cercariae of S. mansoni conferred immunity to rats challenged with S. mansoni. Weinmann and Hunter (1961) studied the effect of immune mouse serum on worm development, egg production, and distribution of eggs in the tissues of the mouse infected with S. mansoni and found no difference between mice that had received injections of normal serum or saline and those that had received immune serum. Weinmann (1960a) also found no statistically significant differences in susceptibility between neonatal mice born of mothers in-fected with S. mansoni and normal mothers toward a challenge exposure. Hunter and Moore (1964) reported experiments with S. mansoni by Crandall in which immunity could not be transferred by parabiotic union between isologous infected and normal mice.

In summary, passive transfer of immunity has been demonstrated with serum from rabbits infected with S. japonicum and monkeys infected with S. mansoni in the rat. Absorption experiments, however, have not been carried out to prove that the antibodies in the serum transferred were responsible for the reduction in worms in the recipient animals.

VACCINATION EXPERIMENTS

Vaccination studies and attempts to induce resistance in experimental animals have produced apparently conflicting results. The evidence to date suggests that some protection can be detected in mice (slight prolongation of life) vaccinated by metabolic products of S. *mansoni* (Levine and Kagan, 1960); but mice vaccinated with eggs, cercariae, or adult worms of S. *mansoni* have not been protected (Thompson, 1954; Ritchie *et al.*, 1962; Moore *et al.*, 1963; Sadun, 1963). Smithers (1962b) was unable to immunize monkeys with eggs, cercariae, and adult worms of S. *mansoni*. Sadun and Bruce (1964) reported that 1-day and 14-day-old rats, vaccinated with worm homogenates of S. *mansoni*, were immune to a challenge of 500 cercariae. Fewer worms developed in young rats that had received worm homogenates than in controls. It is of interest to note that in three of the four experiments just cited, young rats immunized with bovine serum albumin (as a control) developed significant immunity comparable with that developed in rats inoculated with worm homogenates. The development of resistance in the control group suggests a nonspecific basis rather than an antibody basis for the resistance demonstrated in this experiment.

Vaccination experiments in mice with eggs, cercariae, and adult worms of *Schistosomatium douthitti* were uniformly negative (Kagan, 1958). In contrast, experiments with another schistosome species, S. *japonicum*, in mice, dogs, and rabbits have been successful with homogenates of adult worms, cercariae, and metabolic products (Ozawa, 1930; Kawamura, 1932; Sadun and Lin, 1959). Attempts to vaccinate the monkey (*Macaca mulatta*) with worm homogenates of S. *japonicum* were unsuccessful (Vogel and Minning, 1953). In summary, vaccination experiments in some hosts with the various life cycle stages of S. *japonicum* have been more successful than with other schistosome species. The question of specificity of these experiments is still unanswered.

ACQUIRED IMMUNITY

Acquired immunity in hosts infected with S. *japonicum*, S. *spindalis*, S. *haematobium*, S. *mansoni*, and S. *douthitti* subject to homologous and heterologous challenge has been demonstrated by many workers. Stirewalt (1963) summarized her excellent review of this subject with the following statement:

"Some degree of protection has been described in most hosts but it is erratic and sometimes absent. It appears that S. *japonicum* is more effective immunologically than S. *mansoni;* that unisexual infection of some hosts with either sex of schistosome protects partially to completely

against lethal bisexual challenges; that eggs are not a necessary antigenic stimulus; that small serial exposures confer some protection against
subsequent infection although single exposures may at least be equally
effective and that penetration of the skin may produce at least a transient
partially protective local parakeratosis."

Smithers (1962a) added the following in his summary of acquired
resistance: "Absolute resistance in the absence of a patent infection has
rarely been achieved, but it should be possible to achieve it provided
the immunizing dose is sufficiently large."

In monkeys (*M. mulatta*) a year or longer is necessary before resistance
can be demonstrated (Vogel and Minning, 1953; Naimark *et al.*, 1960).
Smithers (1962a) concluded that because of this long period of development, the number of worms, their metabolic activity, and the survival
time within the host constituted the stimulus. The stimulating antigens,
he believes, are highly labile, for they dissociate rapidly upon the death
of the worms. In the monkey (*M. mulatta*), it appears that a sterile
immunity may persist for 34 months following chemotherapeutic cure
of an *S. mansoni* infection (Vogel, 1962).

Can one summarize the conclusions reached in the large number of
acquired immunity experiments that have been carried out and find a
unifying mechanism for this immunity? If a single mechanism were operative in all schistosome host-parasite relationships, this would be possible.
Stirewalt (1963) suggested that standardization of procedure might lead
to more conclusive answers. The writer doubts whether this can be
achieved. A single mechanism for acquired immunity in various host
species may simply not exist. For example, in mice infected with *S.
douthitti,* schistosome eggs play an important role in stimulating immunity in this host. In a series of 12 experiments with 69 mice initially
infected with male worms and challenged over a 2-year period, a
significant immune response was not found in any of the animals. This
contrasted sharply with the mice that had been infected with female
worms (which produce eggs parthogenetically) and with worms of both
sexes (Kagan, 1952). These observations have been supported in part
by work of Crandall and Hunter (1961) and Hunter and Crandall (1962).

Hunter *et al.* (1962), in their studies with *S. mansoni*, confirmed that
a substantial period of time is required, after initial exposure, before increased resistance to challenge can be demonstrated. The results of their
experiments support the hypothesis that maturity of the initial infection
with egg deposition is necessary before immunity can be demonstrated.
Von Lichtenberg *et al.* (1963) reported that the eggs of *S. mansoni* were
important in stimulating delayed hypersensitivity in the host but not
immunity. The egg plays no role in stimulating resistance in mice (Ritchie

et al., 1962; Moore *et al.*, 1963) or monkeys (Smithers, 1962b) infected with *S. mansoni* or in mice and monkeys infected with *S. japonicum* (Vogel and Minning, 1953; S. Y. Hsü and Hsü, 1961; Sadun *et al.*, 1961). Male worms can stimulate immunity in rhesus monkeys infected with *S. japonicum* (Vogel, 1949) but not in mice infected with *S. douthitti* (Kagan, 1952). These data suggest that different mechanisms of acquired immunity may be active in various host-parasite relationships.

IRRADIATION EXPERIMENTS

Recent work with irradiated cercariae demonstrated that not only do adult worms stimulate resistance, but schistosomules and immature worms are effective life cycle stages for this purpose. Smithers (1962c) found that large numbers of irradiated cercariae were necessary to stimulate immunity in monkeys. Resistance in animals exposed to irradiated cercariae is greater than in animals exposed to normal cercariae (Radke and Sadun, 1963). The observations of H. F. Hsü *et al.* (1963a) that up to four repeated doses of irradiated cercariae of *S. japonicum* shifted the site of cercarial destruction from the liver to the lung and in the hyperimmune animal to the skin is reminiscent of the immune response to *Nippostrongylus brasiliensis*. With this nematode a similar sequence of larval destruction takes place in the immune and hyperimmune animals (Taliaferro and Sarles, 1939).

Von Lichtenberg and Sadun (1963) observed the destruction in the skin of cercariae that had been irradiated with 50,000 roentgens. Cercariae irradiated with 5000 roentgens were destroyed in the lung while those that had received 2500 roentgens were destroyed in the liver. Moreover, they noted that the tissue response to irradiated cercariae in susceptible hosts was very similar to the tissue response noted with normal cercariae in resistant or abnormal hosts and similar to the response in the immune host challenged with normal cercariae. H. F. Hsü *et al.* (1963a) also noted that cercariae of *S. japonicum* irradiated with 48,000 roentgens died in the skin, that cercariae irradiated with 24,000 roentgens died in the skin and lungs, and those irradiated with 6000 roentgens or less were destroyed only in the liver. H. F. Hsü *et al.* (1963b) were able to solidly protect monkeys with several immunizing exposures of irradiated cercariae of *S. japonicum*. Sadun *et al.* (1964) were not able to accomplish this in monkeys immunized with irradiated cercariae of *S. mansoni*. They found no correlation with respect to immunity between levels of antibody or levels of cercarial irradiation.

Erickson and Caldwell (1965) demonstrated acquired resistance in rats and mice exposed to irradiated cercariae, and an enhanced tissue response in animals receiving repeated exposure. These workers suggested that the irradiated cercariae must reach the liver in order to stimulate a strong immunity. They also speculated that immunity to irradiated cercariae is greater than immunity to normal cercariae because the irradiated cercariae had been retarded in their development and, as a result, may produce greater amounts of specific immunogenic substances with a less debilitating effect on the host. The only conflicting reports in this area of research are the studies of Perlowagora-Szumlewicz and Olivier (1963) and Perlowagora-Szumlewicz (1964). Immunity was equivocally demonstrated in their experiments with mice infected with irradiated cercariae of S. mansoni. They found that if animals were autopsied in 6–8 weeks, an apparent immunity (reduction in worm burden) was evident, but if necropsy was delayed several weeks, a significant reduction in worm burden was not evident. This suggested that irradiation resulted in arrested development of the worms. Studies by Erickson and Caldwell (1965) and Sadun (1963) and Sadun et al. (1964) did not confirm this observation. A recent report by S.Y. Hsü et al. (1965) indicated that mice exposed to irradiated cercariae of S. japonicum were not protected.

Ogilvie (1964) demonstrated that reaginlike antibodies developed in monkeys and rats infected with S. mansoni. She noted that the appearance of these nonprecipitating antibodies demonstrated by the passive cutaneous anaphylaxis test of Ovary (1958) was closely correlated with immunity to reinfection. In addition, she showed that a patch of skin saturated with these antibodies prevented the normal development of cercariae exposed to this area 3 days later. Vaccination experiments failed to produce the reaginlike antibody.

REAGINLIKE ANTIBODIES

Reaginlike antibodies were demonstrated in individuals infected with S. mansoni by Prausnitz-Kuestner (PK) reactions by Taliaferro and Taliaferro (1931), Guerra et al. (1945), Coker and Oliver-Gonzalez (1956), and Mendes and Amato Neto (1963). The studies of Mendes and Amato Neto (1963) with sera of patients infected with S. mansoni in Brazil indicate that PK antibodies were demonstrable in five of nine infected individuals whereas precipitin antibodies in some of these proven infections were difficult to demonstrate. PK antibody has been difficult to study because of the lack of a suitable laboratory model. The use of the passive cutaneous anaphylactic (PCA) technique may overcome this difficulty provided it can be demonstrated that the same type of antibody is reactive in both tests. Further studies of this type may give an insight into the mechanism of trematode immunity. Are these reaginlike antibodies solely responsible for the skin test reaction in individuals exposed to infection with schistosomes? If they circulate in the blood long after the disappearance of classical antibody demonstrable by serological test, could this account for the persistence of skin reactivity in the absence of serological activity?

IMMUNITY IN MAN

Thompson (1954) suggested that the basis of resistance in man and experimental animals may be natural resistance. He also suggested that the enhancement of natural resistance, rather than acquired immunity, may account for man's survival in regions where schistosomiasis is endemic. Evidence that man does develop an acquired immunity has not been conclusively proven and the belief that this phenomenon does take place is based on epidemiological data.

Schistosoma haematobium primarily infects children. In adults evidence of infection is very difficult to demonstrate (Nelson, 1959; Gothe, 1963). Skin test studies in Ethiopia in an area endemic for *S. mansoni* revealed a rise to 100 percent skin reactivity in males at age 19 with only 71 percent passing eggs in single stool evaluations (Buck *et al.,* 1964). In Southern Rhodesia, Clarke (1965) studied seven native communities for evidence of the development of acquired resistance. In all, a pattern of decreasing incidence of infection and decrease of egg production correlated with increasing age was found. In such communities, persistence of skin-sensitizing antibodies may be high (85 percent positive) with only 13 percent passing eggs of *S. mansoni* or *S. capense.* Such epidemiological patterns are believed due to the development of acquired resistance in the population. From data accumulated in areas before and after effective bilharzia control was initiated, Clarke concluded that resistance in man appears to be biphasic. In early infection immunity is dependent on the presence of an active infection (premunition) which in time is replaced by a true immunity that is not dependent on the living worm. Racial differences in susceptibility (between European and African) were found and individual differences in the ability to acquire resistance were noted. Acquired resistance in man may be species specific (an infection with *S. capense* does not protect against *S. mansoni*) and the rate and degree of resistance developed are influenced by the pattern of transmission in the area. In a community where initial exposure was moderate and was followed by regular moderate re-exposures, maximal resistance, as determined by decrease in egg production in older age groups, occurred.

Fisher (1934) in his classical experiment with human volunteers was unable to infect all six subjects who were exposed to a challenge infection with viable cercariae of S. *intercalatum*. Gothe (1963) claimed to have immunized himself to infection with S. *haematobium* by exposure to 16 doses of attenuated cercariae. Clarke (1965) exposed himself and a laboratory technician to 3000 cercariae of S. *mattheei* that were infective for a baboon. Despite repeated exposure to cercariae of S. *mansoni* and S. *capense* under natural conditions, Clarke has never become infected. The technician's resistance was not as strong and she developed a very light infection with S. *mansoni* on a collecting trip at a later date. Both individuals grew up in the endemic area. H. F. Hsü and Hsü (1956), in Formosa, were unable to infect volunteers with a zoophilic strain of S. *japonicum*. DeMorais (1962) reported, however, that in Mozambique there is no evidence that man acquires immunity. A high percentage of infection is found in all age groups and in both sexes. This situation may be due to the pattern of infection in Mozambique, which does not favor the development of immunity.

INNATE AND NONSPECIFIC FACTORS IN IMMUNITY

Lewert and Mandlowitz (1963) reviewed their work on innate immunity to S. *mansoni*. They concluded that the state of organization of the acellular polysaccharide protein substances that form the intercellular cement and subepithelial basement membranes of the host is of fundamental importance in resistance and establishment of an infection. The organization of the acellular elements of the connective tissue correlates directly with the degree of innate immunity in the susceptible host.

Active innate resistance probably depends on a number of factors such as the skin, phagocytosis, the stimulation of the reticuloendothelial system, inflammation, and the presence of such substances as properdin in the body and cidal substances in the blood. Some of the factors that may effect innate immunity were studied by Lewert and Mandlowitz (1963). The genetic constitution of the mouse is important. The observations of Coker (1957) and Weinmann and Hunter (1959) were verified and extended with regard to the effect of cortisone on susceptibility to schistosome infection. Cortisone increases resistance not only in young animals as shown by Coker (1957), but in older animals as well. Stirewalt (1956) showed that when cercariae are placed on the skin of 1 to 3-day-old rats little to no penetration occurs. Other nonspecific factors that were studied by Stirewalt (1963) are repellent skin secretions, epidermal agents, corneal thickening, and compactness of the skin resulting in hyperkeratosis.

Kagan and Levine (1956) tested the serum of 18 animal species and noted that some sera were cercariacidal, others inhibited the locomotion of cercariae, and two agglutinated cercariae. The sera of hosts with a high degree of resistance to infection with S. *mansoni* were more cercariacidal than the sera of hosts susceptible to infection. The role that these substances may play in enhancing resistance is not well defined.

Stimulation of the reticuloendothelial system ("mesenchymal activation") may be another factor in the nonspecific resistance of the schistosome species (Magalhães Filho and Coutinho-Abath, 1961). The observation by Yoeli (1956) that an infection with S. *mansoni* alters the course of infection of *Plasmodium berghei* in the field vole (*Microtus guentheri*) suggested that a schistosome infection may stimulate the RES system which, once stimulated, may be responsible for the resistance to *P. berghei*. The observations of Sadun and Bruce (1964) that injections of bovine serum albumin stimulated resistance in experimental hosts may also be due to nonspecific stimulation of the RES system. Hunter and Moore (1964) suggested that nonspecific factors per se may be important in schistosome immunity.

INDUCTION OF THE IMMUNE RESPONSE
AND HETEROLOGOUS INFECTIONS

Resistance in an infected host takes a relatively long time to develop. In monkeys this appears to be related to the number of cercariae used to infect the animal. Smithers (1962c) developed resistance in monkeys in 6 months with an infecting dose of 1000 cercariae. Naimark *et al.* (1960) found that with a dose of 500 cercariae, approximately 8 to 9 months were required to develop immunity in the monkey. In the mouse infected with S. *douthitti*, approximately 30 days were necessary for resistance to develop (Kagan, 1952). In the mouse infected with S. *mansoni* approximately 60–90 days are required (Hunter *et al.*, 1962). Campbell (1963) found that resistance to challenge infections was eliminated by subjecting mice to large and sometimes repeated infections with cercariae of S. *mansoni* and then aborting the infection by chemotherapy. Cheever *et al.* (1965) found little difference in the histological responses of animals cured by chemotherapy and rechallenged. Ritchie *et al.* (1963a) reported that prolonged infection with S. *mansoni* in rats and hamsters resulted in a decrease in resistance to a challenge exposure. Are all of these observations tied in with the role of the RES system and resistance in the host?

The immunological role of infections with heterologous schistosome and helminth species on resistance to challenge has been studied. Infection with S. *douthitti* in the monkey (Kagan, 1953) and in the mouse (Hunter *et al.*, 1961; Stirewalt, 1963) did not protect against infection with S. *mansoni*. An infection with S. *mansoni* in the mouse, however, did protect against a challenge with S. *douthitti* (Hunter *et al.*, 1961). *Schistosoma douthitti* slightly protected against a challenge with S. *japonicum* in the monkey (H. F. Hsü *et al.*, 1964). An infection with S. *haematobium* in the monkey did not protect against a challenge with S. *mansoni* (Meleney and Moore, 1954), and an infection with S. *japonicum* in the monkey was also nonprotective against a challenge infection with S. *mansoni* (Liu and Bang, 1950). Infections with *Trichinella spiralis* (Weinmann, 1960b) or *Ascaris suum* and immunization with BCG did not induce resistance in mice against S. *mansoni* (Hunter *et al.*, 1963). An infection with A. *suum* protected against a challenge with S. *douthitti* (Hunter *et al.*, 1963). Jachowski and Bingham (1961) found that an initial infection with T. *spiralis* protected slightly against a challenge with 200 cercariae of S. *mansoni* but not against a challenge with 50 cercariae. These studies suggest that the degree of tissue damage and nonspecific stimulation of the host may be important in resistance against a challenge infection.

CELLULAR ASPECTS OF IMMUNITY

Of late the cellular aspects of schistosome immunity have been receiving increasing attention. The spectrum of cellular responses invoked by different hosts is striking. Studies of the cellular response of different species of monkeys to S. *mansoni* by von Lichtenberg (1964) indicate a variation of responses. Magalhães Filho and Coutinho-Abath (1961) reported slight lymphatic and reticular hyperplasia in the spleen of mice 3 days after infection with S. *mansoni* which became progressively more intense until day 15. The cercariae of S. *douthitti* when penetrating the skin of mice invoked a diffuse and slight inflammatory reaction (Kagan and Meranze, 1955). Immune mice respond with a greater and more intense response composed mainly of small mononuclear cells. A similar sequence of events takes place in the skin of mice exposed to cercariae of S. *mansoni* (Magalhães Filho and Coelho, 1957; Coutinho-Abath, 1962), rabbits, mice, and monkeys exposed to S. *japonicum* (Davis *et al.*, 1963; Sadun and Lin, 1959).

The cellular reactions in 14 species of wild mammalian hosts were studied by von Lichtenberg *et al.* (1962). The reactions were varied but the hosts' cellular responses could be characterized as typical of "very susceptible," "partly susceptible," "poorly susceptible," and "resistant" animals. The cellular reactions observed in the abnormal hosts resembled, in many aspects, the reactions observed in immune susceptible hosts. The authors concluded that the cellular response was one of the mechanisms by which abnormal hosts prevented the development of infection with schistosomes. An antibody basis for this response has not been demonstrated.

Raslavicius (1965) utilizing parabiosis studied the tissue response in the noninfected parabiotic twin. Although some alteration in the lymphatic tissue of the uninfected twin was noted, parenchymal changes in the liver and granulomata formation were absent. This investigation suggested that tissue damage in the infected host is a result of direct action of antigen released by the worm or perhaps the activity of antigen-antibody complexes or the egg in the organs of the infected host. Schistosome antigen in tissues has been demonstrated by fluorescent antibody methods in mesenchymal cells of liver and spleen of infected hosts (Andrade *et al.*, 1961; Magalhães Filho *et al.*, 1965). Free schistosome antigen has also been demonstrated in the urine of infected animals and man (Okabe and Tanaka, 1958, 1961).

Lengy (1962) reported that some mice, sensitized to S. *bovis* cercariae 8–12 weeks earlier, died 1–2 days following re-exposure to the same species of cercariae due to anaphylactic shock. Allergic shock is believed responsible for the eosinopenia and eosinophilia of chronic bilharziasis in man following intracutaneous injection with schistosome antigen (Pautrizel *et al.*, 1964). Fernex and Fernex (1963) reported that in helminth infections, including schistosomiasis, an increase in mast cells in the connective tissue is evident. The whole question of the role of hypersensitivity and resistance in schistosome infections requires further study.

IMMUNOLOGY OF *FASCIOLA HEPATICA* AND PARAGONIMUS SPECIES

Mechanisms of immunity for other trematode species have not been studied as intensively as the schistosomes. Dawes and Hughes (1964) reviewed the contributions made for infection with *F. hepatica* in experimental animals. Attempts to alter the course of infection in experimental animals by injections of immune serum and vaccination have been reported by several workers with negative results. Animals infected with *F. hepatica* develop many circulating antibodies that can be demonstrated by a variety of serological tests. However, correlation of circulating antibody with resistance to infection or acquired immunity has not been unequivocally demonstrated. Urquhart *et al.* (1954) did report some inhibition of development of flukes, but not a decrease in the number of worms developing in rabbits following vaccination with antigen. Studies on the use of X-ray irradiated metacercariae indicate that the metacercariae are weakened and are more susceptible to destruction by the host's cellular response than normal metacercariae. Attempts to immunize animals by this technique have been unsuccessful (Dawes, 1964). The work of Thorpe and Broome (1962) (who reported successful immunization in rats) has been severely criticized because of the absence of suitable control groups of animals (Dawes and Hughes, 1964).

Studies on clonorchiasis have dwelt mainly on the epidemiology of the infection, serology, preparation of purified skin test antigens, and development in experimental animals. Nagamoto (1959) reported isolation of an antigen from the urine of infected animals and patients which is active in serological tests.

S. Yokogawa et al. (1960) briefly reviewed studies on immunity to *Paragonimus* species. The few reports indicated that infected hosts do develop some degree of acquired resistance. Yokogawa (reviewed in S. Yokogawa et al., 1960) was unable to demonstrate any difference in the infectivity of metacercariae placed in immune serum from metacercariae bathed in normal serum prior to challenge. M. Yokogawa et al. (1957) did demonstrate PK antibodies in serum of individuals infected with *Paragonimus*. Araki (1959) demonstrated Schwartzman and Arthus-type reactions in the skin of guinea pigs sensitized with protein extracts of *Paragonimus* worms. He also confirmed the presence of PK antibodies in the sera of all infected patients examined. A species-specific antigenicity between *Paragonimus ohirai* and *P. westermanii* in the Arthus and PK tests was reported.

NONCLASSIC ANTIBODY MECHANISMS
IN TREMATODE IMMUNITY

Is it possible to have resistance in a host in the absence of protective precipitating antibodies? There are a number of host-parasite relationships which suggest this possibility. Acquired immunity to *Bacillus anthracis*, an aerobic spore-forming bacillus that causes anthrax in man and animals, does not follow classical antibody mechanisms in rabbits and sheep. In these hosts acquired resistance to the bacillus follows the same pattern as the resistance found in nonsusceptible resistant hosts. This consists primarily of an interference with the formation of capsular substance and death of the bacterial organisms by disorganization and disintegration in the absence of specific antibodies. In the mouse, however, the mechanism of acquired resistance is dependent upon the activity of anticapsular antibodies and follows more classical patterns (passive transfer, absorption, and so forth) (Raffel, 1961). In tuberculosis, in spite of a tremendous amount of research, a role for humoral antibodies in acquired immunity against *Mycobacterium tuberculosis* has not been conclusively demonstrated (Raffel, 1961). Sera of animals resistant to infection contain many antibodies as do the sera of animals vaccinated with bacillary substances who are not resistant. In leishmaniasis, Adler (1964) stated that "classical antibodies cannot as yet be demonstrated with certainty as participants in this immunity."

The schistosomes may occupy a similar position in parasite immunity in that some infected hosts do not follow classical immunological patterns while others do. The possibility must also be considered that more than one mechanism of resistance may be operative in this large complex of species, depending on the species of the schistosome parasite and the host being infected.

HOST-PARASITE RELATIONSHIPS IN SCHISTOSOME IMMUNITY

The host-parasite relationships of a few schistosome species have been carefully studied. To provide a base line for studies on natural resistance in the rat, Ritchie *et al.* (1963b) re-evaluated this animal as a host for *S. mansoni*. They found a susceptibility much greater than previously reported (Stirewalt *et al.*, 1951). Bruce *et al.* (1961) tested the susceptibility of a series of 14 wild mammal species for *S. mansoni*. The studies of von Lichtenberg *et al.* (1962) on tissue responses confirmed groupings into resistant, partially susceptible, and susceptible hosts made on biological grounds. Stirewalt (1963) reviewed this work and listed other hosts susceptible and resistant to infection with *S. mansoni*. Recent studies on four strains of mice (Stirewalt *et al.*, 1965) and 15 species of German rodents (Loos, 1964) with *S. mansoni* indicated similar groupings into susceptible and resistant hosts.

Of the three human schistosome complexes, the *S. japonicum* group has the greatest range of mammalian hosts. The virulence of this species is very high and few hosts are innately resistant. *Schistosoma mansoni* is not as limited in its host specificity as previously thought. It is found in a number of rodents and primates as well as man. *Schistosoma haematobium* appears to be the most highly specialized. Aside from man it is found in nature only in the higher primates. The evolutionary recency of a species for a host may have important pertinence with regard to stimulation of the immune response. This may explain why *S. japonicum*, whose host specificity is not as limited, is far more invasive than *S. mansoni*. Unfortunately, we know very little about immunity to *S. haematobium*. It is not as pathogenic as *S. mansoni*, and *S. mansoni* is less pathogenic than *S. japonicum* for man.

In a host-parasite relationship of long standing, it would be to the benefit of the parasite to share many antigens that are so similar to the antigens of the host that they would not invoke a foreign body response. Dineen (1963a,b) suggested that those parasites that do share antigens in common are selected since by invoking no immunological response they have a closer and better host-parasite relationship than an organism that invokes a defense response on the part of its host.

Damian (1964) discussed the whole problem of eclipsed antigens and molecular mimicry with special reference to the helminths. Host and parasites do share antigens. Whether these antigens are eclipsed or antigenic determinants of parasite origin and not contaminating antigens of host origin is difficult to determine. Successful host-parasite relationships are developed through a long history of selection acting on similar antigenic determinants (Damian, 1964). With regard to the schistosomes, Damian (1962) reported that at least six antigen-antibody systems are shared in common between the mouse host and *S. mansoni*. Rabbits immunized with whole worm homogenates produce Forssman antibody. This antigen may be a host contaminant in the parasite since it occurs naturally in the endothelium of the mouse. An agglutinin for mouse red cells and at least four common bands detectable in Ouchterlony agar gel between worm antigen, normal mouse serum, and an antischistosome serum have been reported. The antigenic complexity of the schistosome life cycle stages, as demonstrated by agar gel methods, suggests that there may be 20–25 antigen-antibody systems active in antigens prepared from *S. mansoni* (Kagan and Norman, 1963; Caetano da Silva and Guimarães Ferri, 1965).

Why are irradiated cercariae better stimulators of immunity in experimental hosts than normal cercariae? Do the X-rays alter or denature the antigenic determinants in the cercariae to make them more foreign to the host? Why is *S. japonicum* more immunogenic than *S. mansoni*? Could this be due to the "foreignness" of the antigenic determinants in *S. japonicum*? Kagan and Lee (1952) suggested that *S. japonicum* was a rodent schistosome. Is it a relatively new arrival in the host-parasite relationship of nonrodent vertebrates? These questions and the unanswered questions raised by Newsome (1956) with regard to mechanisms of immunity in schistosome infections require further study.

SUMMARY

Mechanisms for immunity in the host infected with the schistosome parasite have been under investigation for over three decades. The number of circulating antibodies described in experimental and natural infections, and the high sensitivity and specificity of serological tests for schistosomiasis led most investigators to equate circulating antibodies with some aspect of resistance in the host. In spite of much effort, there has been no conclusive evidence from passive transfer experiments and serological tests that bivalent antibodies mediate the immune response or serological tests reflect the immune status of the host. There is some evidence that resistance may be transferred with serum containing such antibodies (Sadun and Lin, 1959; Bruce and Sadun, 1964), but whether these antibodies are responsible for the resistance noted has not been conclusively shown.

An inability to readily demonstrate classical antibody mechanisms has led some workers to stress the importance of nonspecific factors in resistance (Kagan, 1953; Thompson, 1954; Hunter and Moore, 1964). Cellular mechanisms have been suggested which weaken and shorten the life span of the parasite in the host (von Lichtenberg and Sadun, 1963). Focal resistance in an organ such as the liver, which acts as the site of worm destruction in the immune host, was suggested by S. Y. Hsü et al. (1962) and Erickson and Caldwell (1965). Acquired immunity is believed to be related to tissue damage by the invading schistosomules (Jachowsky, 1962) or by "mesenchymal activation" (Magalhães Filho and Coutinho-Abath, 1961) of the spleen and other reticular organs. Stimulation of immunity by secretions and excretions and metabolic antigens of the parasite have also been suggested (Smithers, 1962a). All these suggestions are probably true, but they do not add up to a satisfactory explanation of all the data available on schistosome immunity. A significant breakthrough is the work of Ogilvie (1964), who suggested that reaginlike antibodies were responsible for stimulating immunity.

Does trematode immunity involve humoral factors with secondary cellular responses as suggested by Taliaferro (1940) for cestode and nematode immunity? The answer may still be "yes," but the evidence from a large number of studies suggests that the precipitin-type antibody that Taliaferro (1943) had in mind when he suggested the above hypothesis is not the antibody involved in trematode acquired immunity. In 1958 he stated that, although passive transfer of immunity for N. brasiliensis, a rat nematode, has been conclusively demonstrated, the antibody involved need not necessarily be a precipitin. He suggested that nonprecipitating antibodies may be responsible. Likewise, in trematode immunity the nonprecipitating reaginlike antibody reported by Ogilvie (1964) may be the activating agent which mediates the tissue response in the immune host. This is a challenging hypothesis and more work remains to be done before we arrive at a satisfactory stage in our understanding of the mechanisms in trematode immunity.

REFERENCES

Adler, S. (1964). Leishmania. *Advan. Parasitol.* **2**, 35-96.

Andrade, Z. A., Paronetto, F., and Popper, H. (1961). Immunocytochemical studies in schistosomiasis. *Am. J. Pathol.* **39**, 589-598.

Araki, M. (1959). Immunological studies of *Paragonimus ohirai* Miyazaki, 1939. *Fukuoka Acta Med.* **50**, 2180-2181 (summary in English).

Bénex, J., Raggal, M. H., and Deschiens, R. (1960). Aspects électrophorétiques des protéines du sérum sanguin dans les bilharzioses humaines. *Bull. Soc. Pathol. Exotique* **53**, 793-798.

Bruce, J. I., and Sadun, E. H. (1964). Passive resistance induced in rats by inoculation of serum from monkeys immunized against *Schistosoma mansoni*. *J. Parasitol.* **50**, Suppl., 23.

Bruce, J. I., Llewellyn, L. M., and Sadun, E. H. (1961). Susceptibility of wild mammals to infection by *Schistosoma mansoni*. *J. Parasitol.* **47**, 752-756.

Buck, A. A., Spruyt, D. J., Wade, M. K., Deressa, A., and Feyssa, E. (1964). Schistosomiasis in Adwa. A report on an epidemiological pilot study. *Ethiopian Med. J.* **3**, 93-106.

Caetano da Silva, L., and Guimarães Ferri, R. (1965). Immunodiffusion studies in human schistosomiasis mansoni II. Localization of antibodies by immunoelectrophoresis. *Rev. Inst. Med. Trop. Sao Paulo* **7**, 7-10.

Campbell, W. C. (1963). Attempts to demonstrate immunity to *Schistosoma mansoni* in mice previously subjected to chemically abbreviated infections. *J. Parasitol.* **49**, 824-829.

Cheever, A. W., DeWitt, W. B., and Warren, K. S. (1965). Repeated infection and treatment of mice with *Schistosoma mansoni*: Functional, anatomic and immunologic observations. *Am. J. Trop. Med. Hyg.* **14**, 239-253.

Clarke, H. V. de V. (1965). The relationship between acquired resistance and transmission of *Schistosoma* Weinland, 1858, in man, and its influences on the prevalence of *S. capense* (Harley, 1864) and *S. mansoni* Sambon, 1907, in Southern Rhodesia. Ph.D. Thesis, Rhodes University, South Africa.

Coker, C. M. (1957). Effect of cortisone on natural immunity to *Schistosoma mansoni* in mice. *Proc. Soc. Exptl. Biol. Med.* **96**, 1-3.

Coker, C. M., and Oliver-González, J. (1956). Studies on immunity to schistosomiasis—passive transfer of anti-egg antibody in humans. *Am. J. Trop. Med. Hyg.* **5**, 385.

Coutinho-Abath, E. (1962). Influence of protein intake on the penetration of cercariae of *Schistosoma mansoni* in the skin of normal and experimentally infected mice. *Rev. Inst. Med. Trop. Sao Paulo* **4**, 230-241.

Crandall, R. B., and Hunter, G. W., III. (1961). Some factors affecting "immunity" to *Schistosoma mansoni*. Infections in mice and the possible immunogenic role of the schistosome egg. *J. Parasitol.* **47**, Suppl., 49.

Damian, R. T. (1962). An analysis of some *Schistosoma mansoni* antigens including antigens in common with the mouse host. Ph.D. Thesis, Florida State University, Tallahassee, Florida.

Damian, R. T. (1964). Molecular mimicry: Antigen sharing by parasite and host and its consequences. *Am. Naturalist* **98**, 129-149.

Davis, J. R., Hsü, S. Y. Li, and Hsü, H. F. (1963). Comparative histopathological study on *Schistosoma japonicum* infection in immunized and non-immunized rhesus monkeys. *Z. Tropenmed. Parasitol.* **14**, 21-36.

Dawes, B. (1964). A preliminary study of the prospect of inducing immunity in fascioliasis by means of infection with X-irradiated metacercariae cysts and subsequent challenge with normal cysts of *Fasciola hepatica* L. *Parasitology* **54**, 369-389.

Dawes, B., and Hughes, D. L. (1964). Fascioliasis: The invasive stages of *Fasciola hepatica* in mammalian hosts. *Advan. Parasitol.* **2**, 97-168.

DeMorais, T. (1962). Frontiers in research in parasitism. 1. Cellular and humoral reactions in experimental schistosomiasis. Edited by D. R. Lincicome. *Exptl. Parasitol.* **12**, 238.

Dineen, J. K. (1963a). Immunological aspects of parasitism. *Nature* **197**, 268-269.

Dineen, J. K. (1963b). Antigenic relationship between host and parasite. *Nature* **197**, 471-472.

Erickson, D. G., and Caldwell, W. L. (1965). Acquired resistance in mice and rats after exposure to gamma-irradiated cercariae. *Am. J. Trop. Med. Hyg.* **14**, 566-573.

Fernex, M., and Fernex, P. (1963). Bilharziose et Mascocytose. Observations cliniques et expérience chez la souris. *Med. Afrique Noire* **4**, 1-4.

Fisher, A. C. (1934). A study of the schistosomiasis of the Stanleyville District of the Belgian Congo. *Trans. Roy. Soc. Trop. Med. Hyg.* **28**, 277-306.

Gothe, K. M. (1963). Beobachtungen über die Immunität bei *Schistosoma haematobium*-infektionen. *Z. Tropenmed. Parasitol.* **14**, 512-518.

Guerra, P., Mayer, M., and Di Prisco, J. (1945). La especificidad de las intradermorreacciones con antigenos de *Schistosoma mansoni* y *Fasciola hepatica* por el método de Prausnitz-Kuestner. *Rev. Sanidad Asistencia Social (Venezuela)* **10**, 51-63.

Hsü, H. F., and Hsü, S. Y. Li (1956). On the infectivity of the Formosan strain of *Schistosoma japonicum* in *Homo sapiens*. *Am. J. Trop. Med. Hyg.* **5**, 521-528.

Hsü, H. F., and Hsü, S. Y. Li (1962). *Schistosoma japonicum* in Formosa: A critical review. *Exptl. Parasitol.* **12**, 459-464.

Hsü, H. F., Davis, J. R. Hsü, S. Y. Li, and Osborne, J. W. (1963a). Histopathology in albino mice and rhesus monkeys infected with irradiated cercariae of *Schistosoma japonicum*. *Z. Tropenmed. Parasitol.* **14**, 240-261.

Hsü, H. F., Hsü, S. Y. Li, and Osborne, J. W. (1963b). Further studies on rhesus monkeys immunized against *Schistosoma japonicum* by administration of X-irradiated cercariae. *Z. Tropenmed. Parasitol.* **14**, 402-412.

Hsü, H. F., Hsü, S. Y. Li, and Tsai, C. T. (1964). Immunization against *Schistosoma japonicum* in rhesus monkeys by administration of cercariae of *Schistosomatium douthitti*. *Z. Tropenmed. Parasitol.* **15**, 435-440.

Hsü, S. Y. Li, and Hsü, H. F. (1961). New approach to immunization against *Schistosoma japonicum*. *Science* **133**, 766.

Hsü, S. Y. Li, and Hsü, H. F. (1964). Serum protein changes in rhesus monkeys during immunization and following challenge by *Schistosoma japonicum*. *Z. Tropenmed. Parasitol.* **15**, 43-56.

Hsü, S. Y. Li, Davis, J. R., and Hsü, H. F. (1962). Pathology in rhesus monkeys infected with the Formosan strain of *Schistosoma japonicum*. *Z. Tropenmed. Parasitol.* **13**, 341-356.

Hsü, S. Y. Li, Hsü, H. F., and Osborne, J. W. (1965). Immunizing effect of X-irradiated cercariae of *Schistosoma japonicum* in albino mice. *Z. Tropenmed. Parasitol.* **16**, 83-89.

Hunter, G. W., III, and Crandall, R. B. (1962). Studies on schistosomiasis. XIX.

Results of preliminary experiments on the antigenic significance of the schistosome egg. *Military Med.* **127**, 101-104.

Hunter, G. W., III, and Moore, D. V. (1964). Factors in resistance in white mice to schistosomiasis mansoni. *Proc. 7th Intern. Congr. Trop. Med. Malaria, Rio de Janeiro, 1963* Vol. 2, pp. 98-99.

Hunter, G. W., III, Weinmann, C. J., and Hoffmann, R. G. (1961). Studies on schistosomiasis. XVII. Non-reciprocal acquired resistance between *Schistosoma mansoni* and *Schistosomatium douthitti* in mice. *Exptl. Parasitol.* **11**, 133-140.

Hunter, G. W., III, Crandall, R. B., Zickafoose, D. E., and Purvis, Q. B. (1962). Studies on schistosomiasis. XVIII. Some factors affecting resistance to *Schistosoma mansoni* infections. *Am. J. Trop. Med. Hyg.* **11**, 17-24.

Hunter, G. W., III, Crandall, R. B., and Arean, V. M. (1963). Attempts to increase resistance to *Schistosoma mansoni* and *Schistosomatium douthitti* infection in mice by heterologous infections. *J. Parasitol.* **49**, Suppl., 55.

Jachowski, L. A. (1962). Frontiers in research in parasitism 1. Cellular and humoral reactions in experimental schistosomiasis. Edited by D. R. Lincicome. *Exptl. Parasitol.* **12**, 235.

Jachowski, L. A., and Bingham, G. A. (1961). Influence of trichinosis on *Schistosoma mansoni* in mice. *J. Parasitol.* **47**, 719.

Jachowski, L. A., Anderson, R. I., and Sadun, E. H. (1963). Serologic reactions to *Schistosoma mansoni*. I. Quantitative studies on experimentally infected monkeys (*Macaca mulatta*). *Am. J. Hyg.* **77**, 137-145.

Kagan, I. G. (1952). Acquired immunity in mice infected with *Schistosomatium douthitti*. *J. Infect. Diseases* **91**, 147-158.

Kagan, I. G. (1953). Experimental infections of rhesus monkeys with *Schistosomatium douthitti* (Cort, 1914). *J. Infect. Diseases* **93**, 200-206.

Kagan, I. G. (1958). Contributions to the immunology and serology of schistosomiasis. *Rice Inst. Pam.* **45**, 151-183.

Kagan, I. G., and Goodchild, C. G. (1961). Paper electrophoresis of sera from man and experimental animals infected with various helminths. *J. Parasitol.* **47**, 373-377.

Kagan, I. G., and Lee, C. L. (1952). Chemotherapy of experimental infections of mice with *Schistosomatium douthitti, Schistosoma mansoni* and *Schistosoma japonicum*. *J. Infect. Diseases* **91**, 224-230.

Kagan, I. G., and Levine, D. M. (1956). Studies on the serology of schistosomiasis. II. The *in vitro* activity of cercariae of *Schistosoma mansoni* in sera of normal and antigen-injected animals. *Exptl. Parasitol.* **5**, 48-60.

Kagan, I. G., and Meranze, D. R. (1955). The histopathology of immune and normal mouse skin exposed to cercariae of *Schistosomatium douthitti* (Trematoda: Schistosomatidae). *J. Infect. Diseases* **97**, 187-193.

Kagan, I. G., and Norman, L. (1963). Analysis of helminth antigens (*Echinococcus granulosus* and *Schistosoma mansoni*) by agar gel methods. *Ann. N.Y. Acad. Sci.* **113**, 130-153.

Kagan, I. G., and Pellegrino, J. (1961). A critical review of immunological methods for the diagnosis of bilharziasis. *Bull. World Health Organ.* **25**, 611-674.

Kawamura, R. (1932). The recent researches on schistosomiasis in Japan. *Compt. Rend. Congr. Intern. Med. Trop. Hyg.* **4**, 311-319.

Lee, C. L., and Lewert, R. M. (1960). The distribution of various reactants in human anti-*Schistosoma mansoni* serums fractionated by starch electrophoresis. *J. Infect. Diseases* **106**, 69-76.

Lengy, J. (1962). Studies on *Schistosoma bovis* (Sonsino, 1876) in Israel. II. The intra-mammalian phase of the life cycle. *Bull. Res. Council Israel* E10, 73-96.

Levine, D. M., and Kagan, I. G. (1960). Studies on the immunology of schistosomiasis by vaccination and passive transfer. *J. Parasitol.* 46, 787-792.

Lewert, R. M., and Mandlowitz, S. (1963). Innate immunity to *Schistosoma mansoni* relative to the state of connective tissue. *Ann. N.Y. Acad. Sci.* 113, 54-62.

Lincicome, D. R. (1962). Frontiers in research in parasitism: 1. Cellular and humoral reaction in experimental schistosomiasis. *Exptl. Parasitol.* 12, 211-240.

Liu, C., and Bang, F. B. (1950). The natural course of a light experimental infection of schistosomiasis japonica in monkeys. *Bull. Johns Hopkins Hosp.* 86, 215-233.

Loos, B. (1964). Über die Empfänglichkeit deutscher Kleinsäugetiere (Rodentia und Insectivora) für experimentelle Infektionen mit *Schistosoma mansoni*. *Z. Tropenmed. Parasitol.* 15, 56-94.

Magalhães Filho, A., and Coelho, R. B. (1957). Estudio histopathológico das penetração de cercárias de S. *mansoni* na pele de camundongos prèviamente infestados. *Anales Soc. Biol. Pernambuco* 15, 269-281.

Magalhães Filho, A., and Coutinho-Abath, E. (1961). Splenic reactions in Swiss albino mice to single and multiple infections with *Schistosoma mansoni*. *Am. J. Trop. Med. Hyg.* 10, 356-364.

Magalhães Filho, A. M., Krupp, I. M., and Malek, E. A. (1965). Localization of antigen and presence of antibody in tissues of mice infected with *Schistosoma mansoni* as indicated by fluorescent antibody technics. *Am. J. Trop. Med. Hyg.* 14, 84-99.

Meisenhelder, J. E., Olszewski, B., and Thompson, P. E. (1960). Observations on therapeutic and prophylactic effects by homologous immune blood against *Schistosoma mansoni* in rhesus monkeys. *J. Parasitol.* 46, 645-647.

Meleney, H. E., and Moore, D. V. (1954). Observations on immunity to superinfection with *Schistosoma mansoni* and S. *haematobium* in monkeys. *Exptl. Parasitol.* 3, 128-139.

Mendes, E., and Amato Neto, V. (1963). Alguns aspectos imunológicos relativos à esquistossomíase mausônica: Prova da transferência passiva de anticorpos e prova das precipitinas. *Hospital* (*Rio de Janeiro*) 64, 1289-1293.

Moore, D. V., Crandall, R. B., and Hunter, G. W., III. (1963). Studies on schistosomiasis. XX. Further studies on the immunogenic significance of *Schistosoma mansoni* eggs in albino mice when subjected to homologous challenge. *J. Parasitol.* 49, 117-120.

Nagamoto, T. (1959). Studies on *Clonorchis sinensis* II. Immunologic studies on *Clonorchis*. *J. Kurume Med. Assoc.* 22, 1399-1417.

Naimark, D. H., Benenson, A. S., Oliver-González, J., McMullen, D. B., and Ritchie, L. S. (1960). Studies on schistosomiasis in primates: Observations on acquired resistance (Progress Report). *Am. J. Trop. Med. Hyg.* 9, 430-435.

Nelson, G. S. (1959). *Schistosoma mansoni* infection in the West Nile District of Uganda. V. Host parasite relationships. *E. African Med. J.* 36, 29-35.

Newsome, J. (1956). Problems of fluke immunity: With special reference to schistosomiasis. *Trans. Roy. Soc. Trop. Med. Hyg.* 50, 258-274.

Ogilvie, B. M. (1964). Reagin-like antibodies in animals immune to helminth parasites. *Nature* 204, 91-92.

Okabe, K., and Tanaka, T. (1958). A new urine precipitin reaction for *Schistosoma japonica*. A preliminary report. *Kurume Med. J.* 5, 45-52.

Okabe, K., and Tanaka, T. (1961). Urine precipitin reaction for *Schistosoma japonica. Kurume Med. J.* **8**, 24-37.

Ovary, Z. (1958). Immediate reactions in the skin of experimental animals provoked by antigen-antibody interaction. *Progr. Allergy* **5**, 459-508.

Ozawa, M. (1930). Experimental studies on acquired immunity to schistosomiasis japonica. *Japan. J. Exptl. Med.* **8**, 79-84.

Pautrizel, R., Tribouley, J., Duret, J., and Couprie, M. (1964). Éosinopénie consécutive a l'injection intradermique d'antigène bilharzien, chez le subjet bilharzien. *Bull. Soc. Pathol. Exotique* **57**, 331-338.

Perlowagora-Szumlewicz, A. (1964). Studies on acquired resistance to *Schistosoma mansoni* in mice exposed to X-irradiated cercariae. *Bull. World Health Organ.* **30**, 401-412.

Perlowagora-Szumlewicz, A., and Olivier, L. J. (1963). *Schistosoma mansoni*: Development of challenge infections in mice exposed to irradiated cercariae. *Science* **140**, 411-412.

Radke, M. G., and Sadun, E. H. (1963). Resistance produced in mice by exposure to irradiated *Schistosoma mansoni* cercariae. *Exptl. Parasitol.* **13**, 134-142.

Raffel, S. (1961). "Immunity," 2nd ed. Appleton, New York.

Raslavicius, P. A. (1965). Schistosomiasis in parabiotic mice. Histopathological comparisons in infected mice and their uninfected partners. *Am. J. Trop. Med. Hyg.* **14**, 100-110.

Ritchie, L. S., Garson, S., and Erickson, D. G. (1962). Attempts to induce resistance against *Schistosoma mansoni* by injecting cercarial, adult worm, and egg homogenates in sequence. *J. Parasitol.* **48**, 233-236.

Ritchie, L. S., Frick, L. P., Knight, W. B., and Berrios-Duran, L. A. (1963a). Effect of the duration of *Schistosoma mansoni* infections on the degree of protection against subsequent exposures. *Trans. Roy. Soc. Trop. Med. Hyg.* **57**, 375-378.

Ritchie, L. S., Garson, S., and Knight, W. B. (1963b). The biology of *Schistosoma mansoni* in laboratory rats. *J. Parasitol.* **49**, 571-577.

Sadun, E. H. (1963). Immunization in schistosomiasis by previous exposure to homologous and heterologous cercariae by inoculation of preparations from schistosomes and by exposure to irradiated cercariae. *Ann. N.Y. Acad. Sci.* **113**, 418-439.

Sadun, E. H., and Bruce, J. I. (1964). Resistance induced in rats by previous exposure to and by vaccination with fresh homogenates of *Schistosoma mansoni. Exptl. Parasitol.* **15**, 32-43.

Sadun, E. H., and Lin, S. S. (1959). Studies on the host parasite relationships to *Schistosoma japonicum.* IV. Resistance acquired by infection, by vaccination, and by the injection of immune serum, in monkeys, rabbits and mice. *J. Parasitol.* **45**, 543-548.

Sadun, E. H., and Walton, B. C. (1958). Studies on the host parasite relationships to *Schistosoma japonicum.* II. Quantitative changes in the concentration of serum proteins in humans and rabbits. *Am. J. Trop. Med. Hyg.* **7**, 500-504.

Sadun, E. H., Yamaki, A., Lin, S. S., and Burke, J. C. (1961). Studies on the host-parasite relationships to *Schistosoma japonicum.* VI. Acquired resistance in mice and monkeys infected with the Formosan and Japanese strains. *J. Parasitol.* **47**, 891-897.

Sadun, E. H., Bruce, J. I., and Macomber, P. B. (1964). Parasitologic, pathologic and serologic reactions to *Schistosoma mansoni* in monkeys exposed to irradiated cercariae. *Am. J. Trop. Med. Hyg.* **13**, 548-557.

Smithers, S. R. (1962a). Acquired resistance to bilharziasis. *Ciba Found. Symp.*, *Bilharziasis* pp. 239-265.

Smithers, S. R. (1962b). Stimulation of acquired resistance to *Schistosoma mansoni* in monkeys: Role of eggs and worms. *Exptl. Parasitol.* 12, 263-273.

Smithers, S. R. (1962c). Immunizing effect of irradiated cercariae of *Schistosoma mansoni* in rhesus monkeys. *Nature* 194, 1146-1147.

Smithers, S. R., and Walker, P. J. (1961). Serum protein changes in monkeys infected with *Schistosoma mansoni*, with special reference to the metabolism of albumin. *Exptl. Parasitol.* 11, 39-49.

Soulsby, E. J. L. (1962). Antigen-antibody reactions in helminth infections. *Advan. Immunol.* 2, 265-308.

Soulsby, E. J. L. (1963). Diagnosis of helminth diseases. In "Clinical Aspects of Immunology" P. G. H. Gell, and R. R. A. Coombs, eds.), pp. 115-132. F. A. Davis, Philadelphia, Pennsylvania.

Stirewalt, M. A. (1956). Penetration of host skin by cercariae of *Schistosoma mansoni*. 1. Observed entry into skin of mouse, hamster, rat, monkey and man. *J. Parasitol.* 42, 565-580.

Stirewalt, M. A. (1963). Seminar on immunity to parasitic helminths. IV. Schistosome infections. *Exptl. Parasitol.* 13, 18-44.

Stirewalt, M. A., Kuntz, R. E., and Evans, A. S. (1951). The relative susceptibilities of the commonly used laboratory animals to infection by *Schistosoma mansoni*. *Am. J. Trop. Med. Hyg.* 31, 57-82.

Stirewalt, M. A., Shepperson, J. R., and Lincicome, D. R. (1965). Comparison of penetration and maturation of *Schistosoma mansoni* in four strains of mice. *Parasitology* 55, 227-235.

Taliaferro, W. H. (1940). The mechanisms of acquired immunity in infections with parasitic worms. *Physiol. Rev.* 20, 469-492.

Taliaferro, W. H. (1943). Antigen-antibody reactions in immunity to metazoan parasites. *Proc. Inst. Med. Chicago* 14, 358-368.

Taliaferro, W. H. (1958). The synthesis and activities of antibodies. *Rice Inst. Pam.* 45, 114-150.

Taliaferro, W. H., and Sarles, M. P. (1939). The cellular reactions in the skin, lungs and intestine of normal and immune rats after infection with *Nippostrongylus muris*. *J. Infect. Diseases* 64, 157-192.

Taliaferro, W. H., and Taliaferro, L. G. (1931). Skin reactions in persons infected with *Schistosoma mansoni*. *Puerto Rico J. Public Health* 7, 23-35.

Thompson, J. H., Jr. (1954). Host-parasite relationships of *Schistosoma mansoni*. *Exptl. Parasitol.* 3, 140-160.

Thorpe, E., and Broome, A. W. J. (1962). Immunity to *Fasciola hepatica* infection in albino rats vaccinated with irradiated metacercariae. *Vet. Record* 74, 755-756.

Urquhart, G. M., Mulligan, W., and Jennings, F. W. (1954). Artificial immunity to *Fasciola hepatica* in rabbits. *J. Infect. Diseases* 94, 126-133.

Vogel, H. (1949). Immunologie der Helminthiasen. *Zentr. Bakteriol., Parasitenk., Abt. I. Orig.* 154, 118-126.

Vogel, H. (1962). Beobachtungen über die erworbene Immunität von Rhesusaffen gegen Schistosoma-Infektionen. *Z. Tropenmed. Parasitol.* 13, 397-404.

Vogel, H., and Minning, W. (1953). Über die erworbene Resistanz von *Macacus rhesus* gegenüber *Schistosoma japonicum*. *Z. Tropenmed. Parasitol.* 4, 418-505.

von Lichtenberg, F. (1964). Comparative pathology of primates infected with *Schistosoma mansoni*. Unpublished data.

von Lichtenberg, F., and Sadun, E. H. (1963). Parasite migration and host reaction in mice exposed to irradiated cercariae of *Schistosoma mansoni*. *Exptl. Parasitol.* **13**, 256-265.

von Lichtenberg, F., Sadun, E. H., and Bruce, J. I. (1962). Tissue responses and mechanisms of resistance in schistosomiasis mansoni in abnormal hosts. *Am. J. Trop. Med. Hyg.* **11**, 347-356.

von Lichtenberg, F., Sadun, E. H., and Bruce, J. I. (1963). Host response to eggs of *Schistosoma mansoni*. III. The role of eggs in resistance. *J. Infect. Diseases* **13**, 113-122.

Weinmann, C. J. (1960a). Experimental infection of neonatal mice born of mothers infected with *Schistosoma mansoni*. *J. Parasitol.* **46**, 854.

Weinmann, C. J., (1960b). Studies on schistosomiasis. XV. Resistance to *Schistosoma mansoni* in mice immunized with *Trichinella spiralis*. *J. Parasitol.* **46**, Suppl., 37.

Weinmann, C. J., and Hunter, G. W., III. (1959). Studies on schistosomiasis. XIV. Effects of cortisone upon the *Schistosoma mansoni* burden in mice. *J. Parasitol.* **45**, Suppl., 16-17.

Weinmann, C. J., and Hunter, G. W., III. (1961). Studies on schistosomiasis. XVI. The effect of immune serum upon egg production by *Schistosoma mansoni* in mice. *Exptl. Parasitol.* **11**, 56-62.

Yoeli, M. (1956). Some aspects of concomitant infections of plasmodia and schistosomes. I. The effect of *Schistosoma mansoni* on the course of infection of *Plasmodium berghei* in the field vole (*Microtus guentheri*). *Am. J. Trop. Med. Hyg.* **5**, 988-999.

Yokogawa, M., Yoshimura, H., Oshima, T., and Kihata, M. (1957). Immunological study on paragonimiasis. III. Passive transfer (P-K) experiments in human skins. *Kiseichugaku Zasshi* **6**, 449-457.

Yokogawa, S., Cort, W. W., and Yokogawa, M. (1960). Paragonimus and paragonimiasis. *Exptl. Parasitol.* **10**, 81-137 and 139-205.

Immunity Mechanisms in Cestode Infections[1]

CLARENCE J. WEINMANN

Division of Parasitology, University of California, Berkeley, California

INTRODUCTION

The host may provide an unfavorable environment for a cestode for a wide range of reasons, most of them not well defined but usually considered as a conglomerate of factors under the heading of natural or innate immunity when independent of prior conditioning by parasite antigens. While these generally constitute the dominant or determining features of the environment with respect to a parasite, the mutability of this environment through immunological and other adaptive processes is equally important in certain tapeworm infections. This paper will be concerned only with acquired immunity to infection with tapeworms. Following a summary of the literature, two aspects will be considered in more detail; namely, the immunogenicity of adult worms, and observations on the *in vitro* effects of immune serum.

LITERATURE SUMMARY

Very little is known concerning acquired immunity in cestode infections of invertebrates or lower vertebrates (for the latter, see Bauer, 1959). Attention has focused mainly on the relatively few cestodes with a mammalian tissue phase during larval development (reviews by Culbertson, 1941; Larsh, 1951; Urquhart *et al.*, 1962; Soulsby, 1962). This is understandable, for when contrasted with the immunities induced in other helminth infections, these larval parasites appear to be unusually immunogenic. High, durable levels of acquired resistance to reinfection, sometimes bordering on absolute immunity, may be elicited by infection with relatively few parasites [for instance, *Hydatigera taeniaeformis* in rats (Miller, 1931b); *Hymenolepis nana* in mice (Hunninen, 1935a); *Taenia pisiformis* in rabbits (Kerr, 1935); *T. saginata* in cattle (Penfold

[1] This research was supported by grants AI-06104 and E-1384 from the Institute of Allergy and Infectious Diseases, National Institutes of Health, U. S. Public Health Service.

et al., 1936); *T. hydatigena* in sheep (Sweatman, 1957)]. Another unusual feature is the rapidity with which acquired immunity may develop to effective levels, a matter of 1 or 2 days (sometimes less) in the case of *H. nana* (Hearin, 1941) or *H. taeniaeformis* (Weinmann, 1964). Also, the persistence of high levels of immunity long after parasite removal (Miller and Massie, 1932; Hearin, 1941) is not typical of helminth infections. These features, however, do not appear to be characteristic of all larval cestode infections in mammals. Experimentally, *Echinococcus granulosus* in sheep is reported to elicit only moderate levels of acquired immunity, even after primary infections with large egg doses (Sweatman *et al.*, 1963). Field observations have shown that the incidence of *Echinococcus* in sheep and cattle tends to increase with host age (Pullar and Marshall, 1958; Froyd, 1960; Gemmell, 1961), findings that are not consistent with an unusually strong and durable immunity. On the other hand, observations of natural infections with *T. hydatigena* and *T. saginata* larvae tend to support experimental data showing high levels of acquired immunity (Froyd, 1960; Peel, 1961; Gemmell, 1961; Urquhart *et al.*, 1961). There is some evidence suggesting that calves may develop a degree of immunological tolerance if infected with *T. saginata* at or near birth and that they may later be reinfected (Urquhart, 1958; Soulsby, 1963).

In contrast to the marked immunogenicity of cestode larvae in mammalian tissues, tapeworms living exclusively in the intestinal lumen of their vertebrate hosts have been widely regarded as poorly immunogenic (for example, see Culbertson, 1941). Intradermal and serological tests have given varied results (Hacig *et al.*, 1959), while a number of observations have indicated that lumen-dwelling tapeworms do not evoke immune reactions which protect against reinfection (for example, Miller, 1932a; Luttermoser, 1938; Joyeux and Baer, 1939; Clapham, 1940; Vukovic, 1949; Heyneman, 1963). In experiments with *Hymenolepis diminuta* in rats, Chandler (1939) observed that inhibitory effects on challenge parasites were correlated with the primary worm mass and that removal or reduction of the latter relieved these effects. Parasite crowding and competition between worms, together with such factors as host age and nutrition, have in recent years been considered sufficient to account for most instances of apparent acquired resistance (for example, see Potemkina, 1959). However, it is known that worms residing in the intestinal lumen are not immunologically inert: they secrete antigens (Coleman, 1963) and elicit antibodies detectable by serological means (for example, see Coleman and deSa, 1964); they may incite immune reactions that have an inhibitory effect on challenge infections with cestode eggs (Weinmann, 1964) and they may themselves be inhibited in growth and longevity by the immunity evoked by prior infection with homologous or heterologous cestode larvae (Heyneman, 1962). Additional evidence pertaining to the immunogenicity of intestinal tapeworms will be presented in this paper.

In most helminth infections artificial immunization with nonliving antigens usually fails to evoke immune responses that are appreciably protective (Soulsby, 1962) but exceptions are found among larval cestodes. Repeated injection of antigens extracted from larval or adult worm tissues may stimulate significant levels of immunity to challenge with tissue-invading stages (see, for example, Miller, 1931a; Campbell, 1936; Larsh, 1944) although failures to enhance resistance have also been reported (by Moya and Blood, 1964, for instance). A measure of protection may even be afforded against challenge with lumen-dwelling stages as appears to be the case in *Echinococcus* in dogs (Gemmell, 1962b). Living antigens, when introduced parenterally in the form of eggs, cysts, or proglottids, have been found to stimulate a greater degree of protective immunity than nonviable antigens (for example, Miller, 1932b). In a series of crossinfection experiments with taeniid larvae in sheep and rabbits, Gemmell (1964, 1965a,b) determined that the intramuscular injection of active, artificially hatched oncospheres usually evoked a stronger protective immunity than viable (but unhatched) eggs and the latter were superior to dead eggs similarly injected. Protection was strongest against challenge with the homologous parasite but cross protection was marked in some cases. Immunization of mice by infection *per os* with X-irradiated eggs of *H. taeniaeformis* has been accomplished with high levels of infection immunity (Dow *et al.*, 1962). Preliminary results have indicated that calves may be similarly protected through infection with attenuated *T. saginata* eggs (Urquhart *et al.*, 1963). Higher complement-fixing antibody titers were obtained in rabbits inoculated intracerebrally with *T. solium* cysticerci than with eggs inoculated into the brain (Kepski *et al.*, 1963). These and other observations (Campbell, 1938c) suggest that the antigens functional in eliciting at least certain phases of immunity to infection are derived from actively metabolizing parasites. While a mosaic of functional antigens may be involved, some in common with other species or with different life cycle stages (for example, see Gemmell, 1964; Cramer and Dewhirst, 1965), the specificity of the immune response to homologous challenge (Weinmann, 1964) suggests that there are qualitative as well as quantitative requirements regarding functional antigens for the development of a full measure of acquired immunity. Group antigens among cestodes have long been known from serological and intradermal tests (for example, see Wharton, 1930; Vogel, 1953; Maddison *et al.*, 1961).

Humoral involvement in cestode immunity has been most directly indicated by the protective effects of serum from infected hosts following injection into normal recipients. Passive transfer of immunity has been demonstrated against several larval tapeworms: *H. taeniaeformis* in rats (Miller and Gardiner, 1934), *T. pisiformis* in rabbits (Kerr, 1935), *H. nana* in mice (Hearin, 1941). An unsuccessful attempt at passive immunization has recently been reported for *T. saginata* in calves (Froyd, 1964). There is evidence that a measure of passive immunity may be transferred from infected mothers to offspring in the case of *H. nana* in mice (Larsh, 1942) or *H. taeniaeformis* in rats (Miller, 1935). Sima (1937) was unable to show parental transfer of immunity with *T. pisiformis*. The studies of Campbell (1938a,b,c) have indicated that the protective properties of immune rabbit and rat serum in passive transfer tests change during the course of donor infection. Serum taken during the second week of infection (or after artificial immunization) with *T. pisiformis* and *H. taeniaeformis* was protective with primary effects against the establishment of challenge parasites (that is, "early immunity"). Protective potency could be removed from the serum by absorption *in vitro* with larval and adult worm tissues. Serum taken several weeks after infection was also protective but its main effects were considered to be associated with a marked increase in the destruction of established larvae (that is, "late immunity"). Artificial immunization did not produce this effect and the protective qualities of late serum were not absorbed *in vitro* by larval and adult worm tissues. These properties suggested that perhaps two types of protective antibody were formed during infection and that "late immunity" was probably stimulated by antigens released from growing larvae. Other investigators have noted quantitative changes in antibody titer, blood picture, or in serum protein components during the course of infection with cestode larvae (for instance, Kraut, 1956; Liebmann and Boch, 1960; Sweatman *et al.*, 1963). Soulsby (1962) reported that animals infected with *T. saginata* larvae showed a marked antibody response which had two main peaks of production, lasting over a period of 7 to 9 months. Kepski *et al.* (1963) detected complement-fixing antibodies as early as 3 days after intracerebral introduction of *T. solium* cysticerci into rabbits, with the first peak of antibody production occurring between the 10th and 15th days. This was followed by a second increase in complement-fixing antibodies which reached a peak on about the 35th day. Additional peaks were observed during days 50 to 150, with a gradual depression of antibody levels.

On the basis of experiments with *T. pisiformis* in rabbits, Leonard and Leonard (1941) suggested that immunity to infection with eggs involved two distinct phases, one parenteral and the other intestinal. It was observed that about the same number of larvae developed in the liver of nonimmune rabbits whether a standard egg dose was given *per os* or by inoculation into a mesenteric vein following artificial hatching. But in passively immunized rabbits, it was claimed that far fewer larvae developed in the liver after challenge *per os* than following intravenous challenge. The intestinal tract was regarded as the most likely site where the migrating parasites were arrested. Bailey (1951) found few *H. nana* larvae in histological sections of the intestinal wall of immune mice just 12 hours after heavy challenge with eggs. He concluded that the great majority of oncospheres were unable to invade the intestinal mucosa of previously infected animals. The few larvae that managed to do so were met by an accelerated host tissue response. It was suggested that the immunizing infection either produced some change in the epithelial tissue which inhibited invasion or that some action was exerted on oncospheres in the lumen of the intestine which rendered most of them incapable of penetrating into the intestinal wall. Bailey's observations have been confirmed (Weinmann, 1966): there was about a 10-fold reduction in *H. nana* larvae within the intestinal tissues of immune mice 4 and 12 hours after massive egg challenge. Larvae that succeeded in penetrating into the immune intestinal wall failed to develop into cysticercoids. Thus, a pattern of two or more phases in the immune response seems to generally prevail in larval tapeworm infections: the first either inhibits invasion of the intestinal mucosa (as in *H. nana*) or acts shortly thereafter to reduce establishment at sites of predilection, while the second phase affects primarily the established larvae. Froyd and Round (1960) were able to establish challenge *T. saginata* in immune calves by the parenteral inoculation of artificially hatched oconospheres even though the animals were highly resistant to reinfection *per os*. The observations of Gemmell (1962a) not only further indicate the importance of the early phase in acquired immunity but suggest that natural resistance is also partially effected at the intestinal level. The intestinal aspect of the early phase was less evident in rats immunized against *H. taeniaeformis* by infection with eggs attenuated through X-irradiation (Dow *et al.*, 1962). From histological examination of livers following challenge with normal eggs it appeared that fewer challenge larvae reached the liver and these were trapped and destroyed in the portal tracts. These workers pointed out the difficulties of obtaining accurate counts of the small focal lesions produced in livers by degenerating parasites.

While humoral and cellular elements have been shown to be operative in acquired immunity against larval cestodes, little is known concerning mechanisms of cellular action against these parasites. Monkeys immunized against *Spirometra mansonoides* were found to wall off challenge spargana in tough cysts while they were free in controls (Mueller and Chapman, 1937). Leonard (1940) reported accelerated cellular reactions in the livers of passively immunized rabbits following challenge with *T. pisiformis* eggs. In *H. nana* immune mice, challenge oncospheres encounter heightened host tissue reactions (Bailey, 1951) and abundant plasmocytes within the intestinal wall (Weinmann, 1966). Schwabe *et al.* (1959) stated that differences in susceptibility of mice to *Echinococcus* appeared to be related to the magnitude of the host's cellular response. Silverman and Hullard (1961) also observed an apparent correlation between the intensity of the cellular reaction around *T. saginata* cysticerci and reduced growth. Freeman (1964) noted a correlation between the rate at which eosinophilia developed and destruction of *T. crassiceps* cysticerci in mice. Some suggestive observations have be made concerning possible actions of the humoral factor. Heyneman and Welsh (1959) artificially immunized rabbits with *H. nana* adult homogenates and the resulting antiserum was tested *in vitro* against various living stages of this parasite. Some of the effects observed were precipitate formation within or about eggs, cysticercoids, and adults; a tendency for eggs to agglutinate; increased motility of adults in immune serum; and a marked decrease in the infectivity of eggs and cysticercoids when fed to mice after incubation. These responses were not observed with normal rabbit serum. Mueller (1961) incubated spargana of *Spirometra mansonoides in vitro* in serum from mice chronically infected with this worm. He observed immune precipitates around worms as well as a type of nonspecific precipitate, the latter presumably caused by coagulating glands in the scolices. Shults and Ismagilova (1962) reported that precipitates formed around the hydatid scolices of *Echinococcus granulosus* when these were incubated in immune rabbit, guinea pig, and sheep serum. Scolex motility was reduced earlier in the immune serum.

MATERIALS AND METHODS

All experiments on immunogenicity of adult cestodes were with Swiss albino mice (Berkeley Pacific Laboratories, California) while ICR Swiss mice (Dublin, Virginia) were used in the remainder except where indicated. Mice were males 6 to 15 weeks of age. The parasites utilized were species of *Hymenolepis* maintained routinely in this laboratory or in the Department of Biology, Rice University, Texas. Animals were exposed to infection with eggs or cysticercoids via stomach tube while under light ether anesthesia. Mice to be infected with *H. diminuta* were given morphine sulfate (19.2 mg/kg body weight) 15 minutes before exposure to slow intestinal emptying (Read and Voge, 1954). Cysticercoids of *H. nana* in mouse intestine were enumerated by the method of Hunninen (1935b). Adult worms were relaxed 1–3 hours in tap water before lengths were measured. Average wet and dry weights were based on *en masse* determinations for each group. Blood collection was by cardiac puncture and serum was used fresh or after overnight storage at 4°C without preservatives. Other procedures are described in the next section.

RESULTS

IMMUNOGENICITY OF ADULT CESTODES

Hymenolepis diminuta *in mice*

Preliminary study of *H. diminuta* growth in mice after single or 10 cysticercoid exposures yielded the following results (based on 148 mice): 81 percent of the parasites administered under morphine became established; almost all worms persisted for at least 7 days but few survived 10 days in multiple infections or 12 days in single worm infections; none survived 15 days or reached full maturity; single worms could be superimposed on one another without apparent effect on longevity during the first month.

Test mice were immunized by infection with *H. diminuta*, each receiving single cysticercoids three times at 10-day intervals. When challenged with *H. nana* eggs 10 or 20 days following the third immunizing exposure, there was a marked reduction in challenge parasite development in the intestinal villi (Table I, Exp. 1, 2). A distinct change in reactivity to challenge with beetle-reared cysticercoids of *H. nana* was also evident when these were administered 24 days after the last immunizing exposure. About half as many 7-day worms were present in immunized mice and these were considerably smaller than worms from controls exposed only to the challenge infection (Exp. 3). The results from an homologous challenge given 4 weeks after the final immunizing dose also showed a distinct difference between test and control groups. Each of the latter was infected with 7-day worms but not a single immunized mouse harbored parasites a week after challenge.

Hymenolepis citelli *in mice*

Each test mouse received a single dose of 10 cysticercoids. Controls for this exposure averaged 6.7 worms at 10 days. About a third of these was still present after 39 days. To remove the worms remaining, test mice were given an anthelmintic (Bayer 2353, Chemagro Corp., Kansas City, Missouri) on three successive days (from day 45) at a dosage rate

TABLE I

DEVELOPMENT OF HOMOLOGOUS AND HETEROLOGOUS CHALLENGE TAPEWORMS IN MICE WITH PRIMARY Hymenolepis diminuta OR H. citelli INFECTIONS

Exp. no.	Days from last primary to challenge exposure	Challenge parasite (dose/mouse)	Test			Control		
			No. mice	Average number worms (S.D.)[a]	Average worm length (cyst. age)	No. mice	Average number worms (S.D.)	Average worm length (cyst. age)
A. Primary Infection with H. diminuta, Single Cysticercoid Exposures, Three Times at 10-Day Intervals								
1.	10	500 H. nana eggs	10	0.2	(93 hr)	10	16.3 (4.8)	(93 hr)
2.	20	700 H. nana eggs	15	0.6	(90 hr)	12	28.0 (7.2)	(90 hr)
3.	24	10 H. nana cysticercoids	15	2.1[b] (1.2)	23.1 mm[d]	15	4.3[b] (2.1)	43.1 mm[d]
4.	28	10 H. diminuta cysticercoids	15	0[b]	0	15	5.9[b] (2.4)	33.2 mm
B. Primary Infection with H. citelli, 10 Cysticercoids, One Exposure								
5.	35	1100 H. nana eggs	11	17.4 (5.9)	(92 hr)	10	57.4 (12.1)	(92 hr)
6.	65	10 H. citelli cysticercoids	12	1.7[c] (1.5)	21.1 mm[e]	12	5.3[c] (1.2)	30.9 mm[e]
7.	92	850 H. nana eggs	12	6.7 (3.8)	(90 hr)	10	34.9 (7.8)	(90 hr)
8.	172	900 H. nana eggs	14	11.2 (3.1)	(93 hr)	12	46.1 (9.4)	(93 hr)
9.	181	8 H. citelli cysticercoids	10	3.4[c]	39.7 mm	9	3.2[c] (9.4)	34.3 mm

[a] Standard deviations.
[b] 7-Day-old worms.
[c] 10-Day-old worms.
[d] Average worm wet and dry weights: test, 0.52 and 0.13 mg; control, 1.91 and 0.4 mg (worms weighed en masse).
[e] Average worm wet and dry weights: test, 0.93 and 0.30 mg; control, 1.80 and 0.52 mg (worms weighed en masse).

of 250 mg/kg body weight. Uninfected control mice received the same treatment. No worms were found in eight test mice at necropsy five days after treatment.

Test animals showed significantly enhanced levels of resistance to infection with *H. nana* eggs when challenged 1 to 6 months after the primary infection (Table I, Exp. 5, 7, 8). In Exp. 5, primary worms were present in some mice at the time of challenge but their presence was not correlated with increased resistance to challenge. Homologous challenge 65 days after infection (and about two weeks after drug treatment) resulted in a significant reduction in worm establishment: only 17 percent of the administered parasites in test animals versus 53 percent in controls (Exp. 6). While the differences in mean worm lengths were not statistically significant, the worms in most of the test mice were distinctly smaller. However, several immunized mice harbored worms as large as any in the controls. Six months after the primary infection, there was no indication of acquired resistance to homologous challenge (Exp. 9). Thus, a persisting immunity to tissue invasion by oncospheres of *H. nana* was not accompanied by a durable immunity to the homologous parasite.

EFFECTS OF IMMUNE SERUM ON *Hymenolepis nana*

Passive Transfer Experiments

The protective potency of serum from mice infected with 1200 to 5000 eggs of *H. nana* 2 to 6 weeks prior to bleeding was tested in a series of experiments. In five of eleven experiments varying degrees of passive protection were obtained (Table II) but the remainder inexplicably

TABLE II

PASSIVE PROTECTION OF NONIMMUNE MICE WITH SERUM FROM MICE INFECTED WITH
Hymenolepis nana EGGS

Exp. no.	Number daily injections (0.5 ml, i.p.)	Interval: last injection to challenge	*H. nana* challenge (eggs/ mouse)	Average number cysticercoids (S.D.)[a] (no. mice)	
				Immune serum	Normal serum
1[c]	8	6 hr	1100	6.2 (3.2) (6)	127 (20.1) (7)
2	3	8 hr	1080	12.4 (4.3) (8)	55 (10.6) (8)
3	3	8 hr	1000	45 (11.9) (6)	90 (15.0) (6)
4	7	6 hr	3120	35 (5.5) (8)	142 (18.9) (8)
5[c]	7	6 hr	1025	34[b] (11.9) (8)	51 (11.5) (8)
	7	21 days	1150	21 (5.9) (8)	25 (6.7) (8)

[a] Standard deviation.
[b] $p < 0.05$.
[c] Heston C_3H mice (Univ. Calif. Cancer Genetics Lab., Berkeley).

failed to demonstrate a protective effect. Factors such as the duration or intensity of donor infection or the schedule and amount of serum administered did not seem to account for the variable results. No correlation was found between serum protective potency and complement-fixing antibody titer in the four experiments where these were compared. In one test (Exp. 5) the protective value of immune serum appeared to wane with time, suggesting a passive rather than active immunization. Unfortunately, the initial serum potency was quite low in this experiment.

In Exp. 4, a comparison was made between *H. nana* larvae within intestinal tissue 12 and 90 hours after *per os* challenge of mice previously inoculated with either normal or immune mouse serum. Procedures were as follows: Small intestines were rapidly removed and freed of mesenteries and then measured while under light tension. Five 1-cm long, nonadjacent pieces were cut from the second quarter of each intestine so that each piece was comparable between mice in distance from the anterior end. The pieces were slit and gently swirled in tap water to free loose debris and then allowed to undergo autolysis for three days at 4°C. After several washings, those tissues containing early larvae were stored in phenolized water until examined (within 2 weeks) as wet press mounts under 430×. With proper illumination and careful focusing through the relatively thick preparations, the oncosphere hooklets could be detected. The same individual searched each tissue for a comparable time. Results are shown in Table III. About four times as many cysticercoids developed in the normal serum group as in passively immunized mice; and in tissue samples, the 90-hour cysticercoid ratio was about 5 to 1. In the tissues taken only 12 hours after challenge exposure, almost

TABLE III

NUMBER OF PARASITES WITHIN INTESTINAL TISSUES OF PASSIVELY IMMUNIZED MICE 12 AND 90 HOURS AFTER CHALLENGE WITH *Hymenolepis nana* EGGS

	12 Hours after challenge		90 Hours after challenge	
	Immune serum	Normal serum	Immune serum	Normal serum
Number of mice	7	7	8	8
Number of tissue samples examined[a]	35	35	40	40
Parasites per mouse in tissue samples	4.0	15.3	5.1	26.6
Number of cysticercoids per mouse (average)[b]	—	—	35.2	142.0

[a] Refer to the above text for sampling procedure.
[b] See Table II, Exp. 4, for additional data.

four times as many larvae were detected in normal serum recipients as in mice inoculated with immune serum. These results indicate that the immune serum exerted its protective effect primarily during the initial phases of infection, probably by inhibiting intestinal invasion.

This conclusion is supported by another observation. In Exp. 2, a group of six mice did not receive immune serum until *after* the challenge infection. Serum which was protective when inoculated for 3 days prior to infection had little apparent effect when administered in similar amounts (0.5 ml intraperitoneally, 3 days) beginning 8 hours after exposure to challenge. An average of 48 cysticercoids (S.D., 8.9) occurred in test mice compared with 12.4 and 55 in mice treated before infection with immune and normal serum, respectively.

Effects of Immune Serum in Vitro

In a series of experiments various life stages of *H. nana* were incubated and observed in serum from mice immunized by infection with eggs and which were demonstrably resistant to reinfection. Most incubations were in essentially undiluted serum or serum diluted 1 : 4 with Ringer's solution. Replicate preparations were incubated at room temperature and 37°C. Eggs were either teased from gravid proglottids or isolated from feces; cysticercoids were removed from infected beetles, and immature worms were obtained from mice 3 to 24 hours after feeding massive numbers of cysticercoids.

Periodic microscopic examination of eggs and cysticercoids in immune and normal mouse serum for up to 48 hours did not reveal any apparent morphological changes, or precipitate formation, or a discernible tendency for eggs to agglutinate. Active oncospheres were occasionally seen but activity was inconsistent and usually short lived in both normal and immune serum. In two separate experiments eggs were given to mice following incubation in immune or normal serum for several hours at 37°C and overnight at 4°C. There was no effect on egg infectivity, even when immune serum was incorporated into the infecting dose. Cysticercoid infectivity was not tested.

A comparison was made between the effects of immune serum and an intestinal extract on immature worms. Both were from the same donors. The immune serum was found to be protective in a concurrent passive transfer experiment (Table II, Exp. 2) and representative donors were shown to have virtually absolute immunity against challenge with 145,000 eggs per mouse. Extracts were prepared as follows from immune and normal mice: a donor was killed by cervical separation and the small intestine removed to cold Ringer's solution where it was quickly flushed. Mucosal scrapings of the duodenum and jejunum were collected and homogenized by hand in a Potter-Elvehjem homogenizer with a loose-fitting teflon pestle in 1.0 ml of cold Ringer's solution per intestine. After centrifugation at 1200 rpm for 2 minutes, the opalescent super-natant material was diluted 1 : 2 and 1 : 4 with Ringer's solution and employed as the incubation medium. Three replicate preparations from different donors were utilized in each test. In each preparation 75 to 100 immature worms were incubated.

Observations during a 21-hour period (at room temperature) indicated that immune serum had little adverse effect on the worms. Differences between worms incubated in immune and normal serum were insignificant; both preserved the parasites so that motility as well as morphological integrity was retained and there was no mortality during the period of observation. In contrast, worms incubated in mucosal extracts, normal as well as immune, were markedly affected but there was a conspicuous difference in the rate at which this occurred. After 3 hours in normal mucosal extract (1 : 2 dilution) about 5 percent of the worms appeared dead. They were dark and granular in appearance and inactive. Another 15 percent showed only weak movements but 80 percent of the worms were relatively active and morphologically without gross distortion. Three hours in immune mucosal extract, however, was sufficient to cause a cessation of movements save feeble contractions of suckers in some worms. There was at least a 30 percent mortality, with worms on the verge of disintegrating. All worms were darkened and granular and by four hours a distinct membrane, reminiscent of the *Cercarien-hüllenreaktion,* could be seen around some of the still viable worms.

In a similar experiment, immature worms were incubated for 3 to 4 hours in normal and immune serum and mucosal extract and then fed to mice to test infectivity. Each mouse received by stomach tube 20 1-day-old worms from one of the preparations suspended in 0.1 ml of a bicarbonate buffer in Ringer's solution (pH 8.0). About 10 percent of the administered worms became established and 5 days later these were distributed as follows: in five of nine mice (normal serum), in six of ten mice (immune serum), in nine of ten mice (normal mucosal extract), in none of nine mice (immune mucosal extract). In this experiment, essentially the same *in vitro* effects were observed as before but the immune serum had little protective value in a passive transfer test.

DISCUSSION

The immunological features that set a number of larval tapeworm infections apart from other helminthiases are associated primarily with the early phases of the immune response, that is, those reactions which inhibit parasite invasion and curtail establishment at sites of predilection. The fate of the majority of challenge parasites is apparently determined soon after entry into the immune host, probably at the intestinal level, although direct evidence is lacking except in the case of *H. nana* (Bailey, 1951). Cross-protection experiments indicate a distinct element of specificity in the early response (Gemmell, 1964; Weinmann, 1964) but these and other immunization experiments (see Campbell, 1938a, for example) also suggest, from the diversity of sources of antigen, that the response is heterogeneous. Moreover, there appears to be some variability in the general pattern of host resistance to larval taeniids, for instance *Echinococcus* (Sweatman *et al.*, 1963), involving probably qualitative and (or) quantitative differences in functional antigens. But in most larval infections, the unusual efficacy of the early reactions against challenge suggests that the more important immunogens occur in the hexacanth embryos (for example, in the "penetration glands") although oncospheres in vertebrates may be particularly vulnerable, compared with intestinal nematodes, for example, to inhibition by a wide range of immune reactions. [In particular, one might speculate along these lines in the case of *H. nana* with its recently evolved direct life cycle (Shorb, 1933).] However, inflammation and other nonspecific alterations in the intestine (as evoked by bacterial endotoxins, for example) do not appreciably deter invasion by *H. nana* oncospheres in susceptible hosts (Weinmann, 1965). Subsequent phases of the immune response to cestode larvae are more in keeping with those in other helminth infections, that is, antibodies directed against products of actively metabolizing parasites and accelerated host cellular reactions which inhibit parasite growth, eventually isolating or destroying the larvae.

The rapid onset of acquired immunity in larval tapeworm infections may be part of an emerging pattern of immunity to enteric organisms, possibly involving a rapid, local stimulation of specific immune globulins with antiparasite activity (for example, Pierce, 1959; Straus, 1961; Freter, 1964). While serum antibodies have been detected serologically as early as 24 hours after implantation of adult *H. nana* in the mouse intestine (Coleman and deSa, 1964), local antibody production remains to be demonstrated. When the small intestine of mice was surgically sequestered and irradiated before implantation of *H. nana*, there was no inhibition of hemagglutination titer provided the rest of the body was shielded (Coleman *et al.*, 1965), suggesting that antibody was produced at sites other than the intestine. However, it is not yet clear whether serologically measured antibody is directly related to infection immunity or even if protective serum antibody is critically relevant to resistance to reinfection with *H. nana*.

In the present study, the protective effects of immune serum (when demonstrable) seemed to be exerted only during the initial phases of infection. Serum after infection was without apparent effect, perhaps because of the short duration of the tissue phase. Passive antibody has been reported to adversely affect established tapeworm larvae (Miller and Gardiner, 1934; Campbell, 1938b). The early action of immune serum probably was not directed against the hatching of eggs in the intestine since low but comparable numbers of eggs were occasionally hatched in normal and immune serum. The free oncosphere is the probable vulnerable stage. Silverman (1955) described several types of reaction about activated hexacanth embryos in immune serum while Chen (1950) was unable to observe an effect upon intact eggs. Since relatively large volumes of serum were administered to mice shortly before challenge, inhibition of oncosphere activity may have occurred in the intestinal lumen through extravasation of passive antibody. However, it seems more likely that the mucosal surface of the intestine was the site of inhibition. The demonstration of passive protection for days after the administration of relatively small amounts of immune serum (for example, see Campbell, 1938c) suggests that passive antibody may be absorbed or "fixed" to host tissues. Certain immune globulins have been shown to bind to skin, smooth muscle, and mucous membranes (Ovary *et al.*, 1963). The inconsistent results of the passive transfer experiments reported here may have been due to vagaries in the absorption and secretion of such antibody. Gemmell (1964) observed *in vitro* the fairly rapid digestion of hatched oncospheres by intestinal enzymes of the host and suggested that the immune mechanism might involve delay of penetration with subsequent digestion. Heyneman and Welsh (1959), using antiserum from artificially immunized rabbits, showed that serum antibodies *in vitro* can adversely affect all stages of *H. nana*, including the intact egg. But none of these effects were produced in the present study with serum from infected mice. Comparison by immunoelectrophoresis of sera from mice infected with *H. nana* and rabbits artificially immunized with adult worm homogenates have revealed different reactive systems (Coleman and Fotorny, 1962).

The influence of immune mucosal extract on immature worms *in vitro* was striking and to a degree the effects resembled those observed by Heyneman and Welsh (1959) in rabbit antiserum. Similar effects were produced whether or not the immune donor's serum contained protective antibody. The type of change produced in immature worms upon incubation *in vitro* also seemed to obtain *in vivo*. A marked difference was observed in the condition of freshly excysted worms several hours after feeding immune and nonimmune mice large numbers of cysticercoids

(Weinmann and Rothman, 1963). Those in immune mice were reduced in number, much less active, and had a darkened, granular appearance. Extracts of normal and immune intestines were both rapidly
deleterious to active oncospheres. The responsible factors in the immune mucosal extract remain to be characterized and the assay system
for antiparasitic activity requires standardization.

Substances inhibiting the development of intestinal nematodes have
been found in duodenal mucus (see Ackert, 1942, for example) and
precipitate formation has been described about the body openings of
parasitic nematodes incubated with intestinal extracts from immune
hosts (Douvres, 1962). Negative results have been reported in attempts
to demonstrate antibodies to nematodes in intestinal mucus (Soulsby,
1960). Recently, plasma cells of the human intestinal mucosa have been
found especially rich in γA-immunoglobulin, one of several types that
may occur in intestinal secretions (Crabbé et al., 1965). This globulin
in particular binds to mucous membranes and other tissues and the suggestion has been made that it may play a role in defending exposed body
cavities against invasion, presumably via release of histamine or other
substances following the local interaction of antigen and "fixed" antibody
(Uhr, 1964).

The immunogenicity of adult tapeworms poses many questions, some
pertinent to infection immunity. The results presented here show that
lumen-dwelling worms can, in time, evoke changes in host reactivity
sufficient to enhance resistance to infection with "normal" parasites of
the host, including lumen forms. Immunity to egg infection persisted
for months after loss of the primary worms while only a transitory immunity appeared to develop against lumen stages. That a degree of
resistance to homologous challenge developed is probably not surprising
considering the tenuous existence of the worms in their abnormal hosts.
Nevertheless, time and continuous or repeated exposure to infection
were apparently important to this effect. Sequential changes in reactivity
to challenge with lumen stages of H. nana have been observed in mice
immunized by egg infection (Weinmann and Rothman, 1963). Initially
no effects on challenge worms could be detected, then a stunting and
early loss of many worms, and eventually, after weeks of exposure, a
complete failure of challenge worms to survive more than a few hours
in immune hosts. Complications of parenteral infection aside, these observations further indicate the accumulative nature of the immune response and recall the remarks of Stoll (1948) on the importance of
reinfection for a comprehensive immunity to a helminth. However, the
intestinal milieu may become less favorable for adult worms for varied
reasons, with contributions from immune reactions apparently ranging

from inconsequential to significant (and usually being difficult to assess), depending upon the biologies of host and parasite. For example, *Moniezia expansa* seems to be profoundly affected by immune reactions although other factors undoubtedly contribute to the net effect (Seddon, 1931; Stoll, 1938; Hansen *et al.*, 1951). Adult cestodes would seem to be singularly suitable organisms (Read and Simmons, 1963) for studies concerned with the actions of antibody on physiological processes in parasites.

REFERENCES

Ackert, J. E. (1942) Natural resistance to helminthic infections. *J. Parasitol.* 28, 1-24.

Bailey, W. S. (1951). Host-tissue reactions to initial and superimposed infections with *Hymenolepis nana* var. *fraterna*. *J. Parasitol.* 37, 440-444.

Bauer, O. N. (1959). The ecology of parasites of freshwater fish. *Bull. State Sci. Res. Inst. Lake River Fisheries, Leningrad* 49, 3-215 [*Office Tech. Serv., U.S. Dept. Commerce*]. (English transl.)

Campbell, D. H. (1936). Active immunization of albino rats with protein fractions from *Taenia taeniaeformis* and its larval form *Cysticercus fasciolaris*. *Am. J. Hyg.* 23, 104-113.

Campbell, D. H. (1938a). The specific protective property of serum from rats infected with *Cysticercus crassicollis*. *J. Immunol.* 35, 195-204.

Campbell, D. H. (1938b). The specific absorbability of protective antibodies against *Cysticercus crassicollis* in rats and *Cysticercus pisiformis* in rabbits from infected and artificially immunized animals. *J. Immunol.* 35, 205-216.

Campbell, D. H. (1938c). Further studies on the "non-absorbable" protective property in serum from rats infected with *Cysticercus crassicollis*. *J. Immunol.* 35, 465-476.

Chandler, A. C. (1939). The effects of numbers and age of worms of the development of primary and secondary infections with *Hymenolepis diminuta* in rats. *Am. J. Hyg.* 29, 105-114.

Chen, H. T. (1950). The *in vitro* action of rat immune serum on the larvae of *Taenia taeniaeformis*. *J. Infect. Diseases* 86, 205-213.

Clapham, P. A. (1940). Studies on *Coenurus glomeratus*. *J. Helminthol.* 18, 45-52.

Coleman, R. M. (1963). Antigenicity of viable Hymenolepids maintained *in vitro*. *J. Parasitol.* 49, Sect. 2, p. 37.

Coleman, R. M., and de Sa, L. M. (1964). Host response to implanted adult *Hymenolepis nana*. *J. Parasitol.* 50, Sect. 2, p. 17.

Coleman, R. M., and Fortorny, N. M. (1962). *In vivo* isolation of *Hymenolepis nana* and antibody binding sites. *Nature* 195, 920-921.

Coleman, R. M., Fimian, W. J., and deSa, L. M. (1965). Effect of ionizing radiation on the immune response to implanted dwarf tapeworms. *J. Parasitol.* 51, Sect. 2, p. 64.

Crabbé, P. A., Carbonara, A. O., and Heremans, J. F. (1965). The normal human intestinal mucosa as a major source of plasma cells containing γA-immunoglobulin. *Lab. Invest.* 14, 235-248.

Cramer, J. D., and Dewhirst, L. W. (1965). Antigenic comparisons of adult and larval *Taenia saginata* with *Diphyllobothrium latum*. *J. Parasitol.* 51, 62.

Culbertson, J. T. (1941). "Immunity Against Animal Parasites," 274 pp. Columbia Univ. Press, New York.

Douvres, F. W. (1962). The in vitro cultivation of Oesophagostomum radiatum, the nodular worm of cattle. II. The use of this technique to study immune responses of host tissue extracts against the developing nematode. J. Parasitol. 48, 852-864.

Dow, C., Jarrett, W. F. H., Jennings, F. W., McIntyre, W. I. M., and Mulligan, W. (1962). The production of immunity to Cysticercus fasciolaris using X-irradiated oncospheres. Am. J. Vet. Res. 23, 146-149.

Freeman, R. S. (1964). Studies on responses of intermediate hosts to infection with Taenia crassiceps (Zeder, 1800) (Cestoda). Can. J. Zool. 42, 367-385.

Freter, R. (1964). Comparison of immune mechanisms in various experimental models of cholera. Bull. World Health Organ. 31, 825-834.

Froyd, G. (1960). Cysticercosis and hydatid disease of cattle in Kenya. J. Parasitol. 46, 491-496.

Froyd, G. (1964). The effect of post-infection serum on the infectability of calves with Taenia eggs. Brit. Vet. J. 120, 162-168.

Froyd, G., and Round, M. C. (1960). The artificial infection of adult cattle with Cysticercus bovis. Res. Vet. Sci. 1, 275-282.

Gemmell, M. A. (1961). Some observations on the differences in incidences between Echinococcus granulosus and Taenia hydatigena in the livers of sheep in New Zealand. New Zealand Vet. J. 9, 40-41.

Gemmell, M. A. (1962a). Natural and acquired immunity factors inhibiting penetration of some hexacanth embryos through the intestinal barrier. Nature 194, 701-702.

Gemmell, M. A. (1962b). Natural and acquired immunity factors interfering with development during the rapid growth phase of Echinococcus granulosus in dogs. Immunology 5, 496-503.

Gemmell, M. A. (1964). Immunological responses of the mammalian host against tapeworm infections. I. Species specificity of hexacanth embryos in protecting sheep against Taenia hydatigena. Immunology 7, 489-499.

Gemmell, M. A. (1965a). Immunological responses of the mammalian host against tapeworm infections. II. Species specificity of hexacanth embryos in protecting rabbits against Taenia pisiformis. Immunology 8, 270-280.

Gemmell, M. A. (1965b). Immunological responses of the mammalian host against tapeworm infections. III. Species specificity of hexacanth embryos in protecting sheep against Taenia ovis. Immunology 8, 281-290.

Hacig, A., Solomon, P., and Weinbach, R. (1959). Recherches sérologiques sur l'hyménolépidose. L'étude d'un antigène d'Hymenolepis diminuta sans les re-actions antigène-anticorps in vivo et in vitro. Arch. Roumaines Pathol. Exptl. Microbiol. 18, 611-625.

Hansen, M. F., Todd, A. C., Kelley, G. W., and Cawein, M. (1951). Effects of a pure infection of the tapeworm Moniezia expansa in lambs. Kentucky Agr. Expt. Sta., Bull. 556.

Hearin, J. T. (1941). Studies on the acquired immunity to the dwarf tapeworm Hymenolepis nana var. fraterna, in the mouse host. Am. J. Hyg. 33, 71-87.

Heyneman, D. (1962). Studies on helminth immunity. II. Influence of Hymenolepis nana (Cestoda: Hymenolepididae) in dual infections with H. diminuta in white mice and rats. Exptl. Parasitol. 12, 7-18.

Heyneman, D. (1963). Host-parasite resistance patterns—some implications from experimental studies with helminths. Ann. N.Y. Acad. Sci. 113, 114-129.

Heyneman, D., and Welsh, J. (1959). Action of homologous antiserum in vitro against life cycle stages of *Hymenolepis nana,* the dwarf mouse tapeworm. *Exptl. Parasitol.* **8,** 119-128.

Hunninen, A. V. (1935a). Studies on the life history and host-parasite relations of *Hymenolepis fraterna* (*H. nana* var. *fraterna* Stiles) in white mice. *Am. J. Hyg.* **22,** 414-443.

Hunninen, A. V. (1935b). A method of demonstrating cysticercoids of *Hymenolepis fraterna* (*H. nana* var. *fraterna* Stiles) in the intestinal villi of mice. *J. Parasitol.* **21,** 124-125.

Joyeux, C., and Baer, J. G. (1939). Recherche biologiques sur quelques cestodes Pseudophyllidae. *Jubilee Vol. Prof. Sadao Yoshida* **2,** 203-210.

Kepski, A., Szlaminski, Z., and Zapart, W. (1963). Serological tests in experimental cerebral cysticercosis in rabbits. *Acta Parasitol. Polon.* **11,** 133-143.

Kerr, K. B. (1935). Immunity against a cestode parasite, *Cysticercus pisiformis. Am. J. Hyg.* **22,** 169-182.

Kraut, N. (1956). An electrophoretic study of sera from rats artificially infected with and immunized against the larval cestode *Cysticercus fasciolaris. J. Parasitol.* **42,** 109-121.

Larsh, J. E., Jr. (1942). Transmission from mother to offspring of immunity against the mouse cestode, *Hymenolepis nana* var. *fraterna. Am. J. Hyg.* **36,** 187-194.

Larsh, J. E., Jr. (1944). Studies on the artificial immunization of mice against infection with the dwarf tapeworm, *Hymenolepis nana* var. *fraterna. Am. J. Hyg.* **39,** 129-132.

Larsh, J. E., Jr. (1951). Host-parasite relationships in cestode infections, with emphasis on host resistance. *J. Parasitol.* **37,** 343-352.

Leonard, A. B. (1940). The accelerated tissue response to *Cysticercus pisiformis* in passively immunized rabbits. *Am. J. Hyg.* **32,** 117-120.

Leonard, A. B., and Leonard, A. E. (1941). The intestinal phase of the resistance of rabbits to the larvae of *Taenia pisiformis. J. Parasitol.* **27,** 375-378.

Liebmann, H., and Boch, J. (1960). Untersuchungen an *Cysticercus pisiformis*-befallen Kaninchen. *Berlin. Muench. Tieraerztl. Wochschr.* **73,** 123-125.

Luttermoser, G. W. (1938). Susceptibility of chickens to reinfection with *Raillietina cesticillus* as determined by the presence of the original terminal segment. *J. Parasitol.* **24,** Sect. 2, pp. 14-15.

Maddison, S. E., Whittle, H., and Elsdon-Dew, R. (1961). The antigens of tapeworms. Preliminary note. *S. African J. Sci.* **57,** 273-277.

Miller, H. M., Jr. (1931a). The production of artificial immunity in the albino rat to a metazoan parasite. *J. Prevent. Med., Baltimore* **5,** 429-452.

Miller, H. M., Jr. (1931b). Immunity of the albino rat to superinfestation with *Cysticercus fasciolaris. J. Prevent. Med., Baltimore* **5,** 453-464.

Miller, H. M., Jr. (1932a). Superinfection of cats with *Taenia taeniaeformis. J. Prevent. Med., Baltimore* **6,** 17-29.

Miller, H. M., Jr. (1932b). Further studies on immunity to a metazoan parasite, *Cysticercus fasciolaris. J. Prevent. Med., Baltimore* **6,** 37-46.

Miller, H. M., Jr. (1935). Transmission to offspring of immunity against infection with a metazoan (cestode) parasite. *Am. J. Hyg.* **21,** 456-461.

Miller, H. M., Jr., and Gardiner, M. L. (1934). Further studies on passive immunity to a metazoan parasite, *Cysticercus fasciolaris. Am. J. Hyg.* **20,** 424-431.

Miller, H. M., Jr., and Massie, E. (1932). Persistence of acquired immunity to *Cysticercus fasciolaris* after removal of the worms. *J. Prevent. Med., Baltimore* **6,** 31-36.

Moya, V., and Blood, B. D. (1964). Actividad immunogénica de un producto biológico ensayado como vacuna contra la hidetidosis ovina. *Bol. Chileno Parasitol.* **19**, 7-10.

Mueller, J. F. (1961). The laboratory propagation of *Spirometra mansonoides* as an experimental tool. V. Behavior of the sparganum in and out of the mouse host, and formation of immune precipitates. *J. Parasitol.* **47**, 879-883.

Mueller, J. F., and Chapman, O. D. (1937). Resistance and immunity reactions in infections with *Sparganum mansonoides*. *J. Parasitol.* **23**, 561-562.

Ovary, Z., Benacerraf, B., and Bloch, K. J. (1963). Properties of guinea pig 7S antibodies. II. Identification of antibodies in passive cutaneous and systemic anaphylaxis. *J. Exptl. Med.* **117**, 951-964.

Peel, C. (1961). The influence of the age factor in *Cysticercus bovis* infestations in West Africa N'Dama cattle. *J. Trop. Med. Hyg.* **64**, 239-242.

Penfold, W. J., Penfold, H. B., and Phillips, M. (1936). Acquired active immunity in the ox to *Cysticercus bovis*. *Med. J. Australia* **1**, 417-423.

Pierce, A. E. (1959). Specific antibodies at mucous surfaces. *Vet. Rev. Annotations* **5**, 17-36.

Potemkina, V. A. (1959). Study of the reinfection and age susceptibility of sheep to *Moniezia*. *Byul. Nauchn.-Tekhn. Inform. Vses. Inst. Gelmintol.* **5**, 78-82 (in Russian).

Pullar, C. P., and Marshall, W. K. (1958). The incidence of hydatids in Victorian cattle. *Australian Vet. J.* **34**, 193-201.

Read, C. P., and Simmons, J. E., Jr. (1963). Biochemistry and physiology of tapeworms. *Physiol. Rev.* **43**, 263-305.

Read, C. P., and Voge, M. (1954). The size attained by *Hymenolepis diminuta* in different host species. *J. Parasitol.* **40**, 88-89.

Schwabe, C. W., Schinaza, L. A., and Kilejian, A. (1959). Host-parasite relationships in echinococcosis. II. Age resistance to secondary echinococcosis in the white mouse. *Am. J. Trop. Med. Hyg.* **8**, 29-36.

Seddon, H. R. (1931). The development in sheep of immunity to *Moniezia expansa*. *Ann. Trop. Med. Parasitol.* **25**, 431-435.

Shorb, D. A. (1933). Host-parasite relations of *Hymenolepis fraterna* in the rat and the mouse. *Am. J. Hyg.* **18**, 74-113.

Shults, R. S., and Ismagilova, R. G. (1962). A new immunological reaction in hydatidosis. *Vestn. Sel's. Kokhoz. Nauki, Alma-Ata.* **6**, 45-49 (in Russian).

Sima, I. A. (1937). A Taenia és *Cysticercus pisiformis*. elleni immunitas. *Allatorv. Lapok.* **60**, 1-4.

Silverman, P. H. (1955). A technique for studying the *in vitro* effect of serum on activated taeniid hexacanth embryos. *Nature* **176**, 598-599.

Silverman, P. H., and Hullard, T. J. (1961). Histological observations on bovine cysticercosis. *Res. Vet. Sci.* **2**, 248-252.

Soulsby, E. J. L. (1960). The use of haemagglutination technique for the detection of antibodies in gastro-intestinal nematode infections of sheep. II. The red cell-linked antigen test. *Brit. Vet. J.* **116**, 315-321.

Soulsby, E. J. L. (1962). Antigen-antibody reactions in helminth infections. *Advan. Immunol.* **2**, 265-308.

Soulsby, E. J. L. (1963). Immunological unresponsiveness to helminth infections in animals. *Proc. 17th World Vet. Congr., 1962* Vol. **1**, pp. 761-767.

Stoll, N. R. (1938). Tapeworm studies. XII. Variations in pasture infestation with *Moniezia expansa*. *J. Parasitol.* **24**, 527-545.

Stoll, N. R. (1948). Comments on a paper in *Proc. 4th Intern. Congr. Trop. Med. Malaria, Washington, D.C., 1948* Vol. 2, pp. 981-983.

Straus, E. K. (1961). Occurrence of antibody in human vaginal mucus. *Proc. Soc. Exptl. Biol. Med.* **106**, 617-621.

Sweatman, G. K. (1957). Acquired immunity in lambs infected with *Taenia hydatigena. Can. J. Comp. Med. Vet. Sci.* **21**, 65-70.

Sweatman, G. K., Williams, R. J., Moriarty, K. M., and Henshall, T. C. (1963). On acquired immunity to *Echinococcus granulosus* in sheep. *Res. Vet. Sci.* **4**, 187-198.

Uhr, J. W. (1964). The heterogeneity of the immune response. *Science* **145**, 457-464.

Urquhart, G. M. (1958). The production of experimental cysticercosis in calves in Kenya. *Bull. Epizootiol. Diseases Africa* **6**, 385-393.

Urquhart, G. M. (1961). Epizootiological and experimental studies on bovine cysticercosis in East Africa. *J. Parasitol.* **47**, 857-869.

Urquhart, G. M., Jarrett, W. F. H., and Mulligan, W. (1962). Helminth immunity. *Advan. Vet. Sci.* **7**, 87-129.

Urquhart, G. M., McIntyre, W. I. M., Mulligan, W., Jarrett, W. F. H., and Sharp, N. C. C. (1963). Vaccination against helminth disease. *Proc. 17th World Vet. Congr., 1963* Vol. 1, pp. 769-774.

Vogel, H. (1953). A serological study of some helminth relations. *J. Immunol.* **70**, 503-506.

Vukovic, V. (1949). L'infection et surinfection du chien par *Taenia hydatigena. Arch. Sci. Biol. Belgrade* **1**, 258-261.

Weinmann, C. J. (1964). Host resistance to *Hymenolepis nana.* II. Specificity of resistance to reinfection in the direct cycle. *Exptl. Parasitol.* **15**, 514-526.

Weinmann, C. J. (1965). Bacterial endotoxin and host resistance to *Hymenolepis nana. J. Parasitol.* **51**, 560.

Weinmann, C. J. (1966). Unpublished data.

Weinmann, C. J., and Rothman, A. H. (1963). Unpublished data.

Wharton, D. R. A. (1930). Immunological studies with tapeworm antigens. *Am. J. Hyg.* **12**, 511-536.

Immunity Mechanisms to Protozoa

G. A. MAEKELT

Departamento de Inmunologia, Instituto de Medicina Tropical,
Facultad de Medicina, Universidad Central de Venezuela,
Caracas, Venezuela

ANALYSIS AND CLASSIFICATION OF IMMUNITY MECHANISMS OF THE VERTEBRATE HOST

The immunity mechanisms to protozoal infections are complex and varied, so that rules and general laws can be applied only to more general phenomena. The virulence of the parasite, the penetration, multiplication, dissemination, and self-protection mechanisms on one side, and innate resistance[1] and acquired immunity of the host on the other, determine the relation between the parasite and the host. This relationship is never stable, but there exists a dynamic equilibrium that may end in the death of the parasite and survival of the host or vice versa or result in compromise and mutual coexistence. This mutual and intimate relationship between parasite and host also explains the fact that the defense mechanisms of the host are always determined in part by parasite factors and cannot be considered separately. The mechanisms of host defense can be classified as follows:

(a) *Innate resistance.* This is an expression of defense mechanisms that are operative during the first contact with the parasite. Usually they are nonspecific, but they may have specificity against certain species or development stages of parasites, particularly in experimental infections in abnormal hosts.

(b) *Active acquired immunity.* This is an expression of specific defense mechanisms, developed after a previous contact with parasite substances foreign to the host. Acquired immunity is always superimposed upon a certain degree of innate resistance and the mechanisms of both are often very difficult to separate. The defense mechanisms can inhibit parasite invasion but once a parasite has invaded a host, they act

---

[1] The term "natural immunity" is avoided to prevent confusion with acquired immunity mechanisms.

in several ways. Thus reproduction may be inhibited, toxins neutralized, and organisms agglutinated, immobilized, lysed, and disintegrated or phagocytosized. At one time active acquired immunity was considered residual ("sterilizing"), if it persisted after complete elimination of the parasite, but the advent of more refined methods (for example, subinoculations of blood in susceptible animals, or splenectomy), has shown a residuum of parasites in hosts which had appeared to have eliminated them. Consequently an increasing number of parasitologists believe that acquired immunity is, in the majority of cases, related to the persistence of parasites in the host, which continue to release antigen and thus stimulate antibody formation. That is called *premunition* ("nonsterilizing," infection immunity) (Sergent *et al.*, 1924).

While premunition exists, superinfection with the homologous strain of parasite is inhibited or attenuated. It seems that the superinfecting strain can survive together with the original strain. Moshkovsky (1937) called it "the principle of re-inoculation." Kagan and Norman (1962) demonstrated this possibility by superinfection of mice with a virulent strain of *Trypanosoma cruzi* and recovery of this strain by subinoculation. It is probable that the great majority of immunity mechanisms to protozoa are of the premunition type; exceptions are the residual immunity observed in infections of *Plasmodium cynomolgi* in monkeys (Garnham, 1963), *Plasmodium berghei* in rats (Corradetti, 1950), *Theileria parva* in cattle (Barnett, 1963), and *Leishmania tropica* in man (Manson-Bahr, 1963a).

Differences occur in the degree, duration, and specificity of immunity both for innate resistance and acquired immunity. The degree of protection may be complete, resulting in a refractory state or nonsusceptibility without parasitism, or incomplete with a parasitic tolerance causing parasitism with localized lesions, followed by recovery or parasitism with lesions, or chronic or acute disease to be followed by recovery. Intermediate states consist of parasitism with acute or chronic lesions with acute or delayed death. The duration of protection may be for life, years, months, or a few days or hours, being independent of the degree of protection. The specificity of protection may be directed only against certain development stages of a certain strain, against one homologous strain of a certain species, against all strains of a species, against heterologous species of a genus, or against other genera. Common antigens of different species may provoke cross immunity, but on the other hand, the development stages of a parasite may have such a specific antigenic composition that immunity may be produced only against that development stage, but not against other stages of the same strain [for example, human beings previously infected with a homologous strain of *P. vivax* can support normal schizonts in liver cells, but failed to develop a parasitemia (Shortt and Garnham, 1948)]. Specificity may also be related to the host; thus the affinity of coccidia for epithelial cells of the intestine or *L. tropica* for skin tissues may be related to host factors which favor a better development environment for parasites, and specific "histotropism" [for instance, of different strains of *T. cruzi* (Pizzi, 1957)] is probably not only related to the parasite, but also to the host.

Active immunity can be acquired by natural infection via the arthropod vector or induced by artificial infection or immunization with nonliving vaccines. Infection with living parasites generally produces a more marked immune response than inoculation of dead parasites, presumably since the multiplication of living parasites in the host gives rise to a greater and more prolonged antigenic stimulation. The number of parasites may play an important role in the stimulation of the immune response since the more frequent the infection, the more rapid and pronounced the response will be. A single infection seldom poduces the same effect as multiple infections with the same parasite.

Living vaccines can be prepared from parasites of low natural virulence, or virulent parasites, artificially attenuated (for example, by drugs or biological techniques): they can be homologous or heterologous parasites and the latter can produce cross immunity. For example, in premunition of cattle against piroplasmosis a combination of an initial infection with a mild strain followed 2 months later by a superinfection with a virulent strain is used (Barnett, 1963). Infection with a virulent strain followed by treatment with drugs may confer satisfactory protection for several years [for example, cattle infected with *Trypanosoma brucei* (Smith, 1958); cattle infected with *Trypanosoma congolense* (Fiennes, 1950)]. Greater virulence of the parasite does not necessarily imply a greater immune response and generally no antigenic variation can be noted between strains of a homologous parasite which shows different degrees of virulence.

The inoculation of dead parasites provokes the appearance of a large number of different humoral antibodies but generally, they are not related to the state of immunity and up to the present time, it has not been possible to achieve good acquired immunity with nonliving vaccines prepared from *Piroplasma*, *Leishmania*, *Toxoplasma*, or *Coccidia*. Certain advances were achieved with dead vaccines prepared from *Plasmodium* (Powell and Brewer, 1964) and *Trypanosoma* (Kligler and Berman, 1935; Soltys, 1963).

Nonliving vaccines can be prepared from endo- or exoantigens. Endoantigens are suspensions of parasites killed by chemical substances or by heat, or they can also be homogenates of the whole parasite, disintegrated by physical methods (ultrasonication, for instance), or they may be chemical fractions of the organisms. Exoantigens are metabolic substances, excreted or secreted by the parasites into an artificial medium [for example, *T. cruzi* culture medium (Tarrant *et al.*, 1965)] or into a natural one [for example, blood plasma of mice infected with *T. brucei* (Weitz, 1963)]. Endoantigens of *T. vivax* and *T. brucei* ("bound-antigens") produced cross immunity in infections with both parasites (Weitz, 1963), but cross immunity was not observed with soluble exoantigens of *T. vivax* and *T. brucei*, liberated into the blood plasma during parasitemia. These antigens probably consisted of metabolic parasite substances and acted only in the presence of a serum protein component, and thus can probably be considered as incomplete antigens.

An increase in an immunization effect can be expected by using a vaccine prepared from disintegrated parasites, rather than from whole organisms [for example, vaccines of *T. cruzi* (Goble *et al.*, 1964)], while better effects are also observed by the use of adjuvants (Powell and Brewer, 1964), which gives a prolongation of antigen stimulus. Stage specificity of immunity may be indicated when vaccines prepared from certain development stages, such as sporozoites or blood forms, will only protect against infections by the same developmental stages. For prophylaxis of human malaria, the use of nonliving vaccines prepared from sporozoites of several species and strains ("polyvalent vaccine") together with an adjuvant, has been recommended to obtain prolonged protection against natural infection by mosquitoes (Powell and Brewer, 1964).

In passive acquired immunity protective humoral antibodies may be acquired prenatally by transplacental transmission to the fetus [for example, in human beings infected with *Plasmodium falciparum* (Bruce-Chwatt, 1952)] or postnatally via colostrum and milk to the offspring [for instance, in ungulates (Bruce-Chwatt, 1963), in *T. lewisi* infection in rats (Culbertson, 1939), or *T. cruzi* infection in rats (Kolodny, 1939)]. Passive immunity may also be induced artificially. Natural immune serum generally has less effect than hyperimmune serum obtained by artificial immunization, while the use of protective antibodies in the form of 7S gamma globulin of serum has an additional advantage as illustrated by the work of Cohen and McGregor (1963), who found a good protective effect against trophozoites of *P. falciparum* infection in man with such fractions. Passive immunization is of doubtful value in infection with blood trypanosomes owing to the rapidly changing antigenic nature of these parasites.

Self-protection mechanisms of the parasite may play an important role in acquired immunity of certain parasites. Examples are the antigenic changes of "antibody resistant strain" or "relapse strains" of *T. brucei* in mice (Ritz, 1914). This may be the reason that acquired immunity to blood trypanosomal infection has never been demonstrated in man (Manson-Bahr, 1963b). The cyst wall formation partly by *T. gondii* in man (Kikkawa and Gueft, 1964), or the pseudocysts formation of *T. cruzi* in the heart muscle of man, may be an expression of another type of self-protection mechanisms against humoral antibodies (Maekelt, 1965). A tissue-blood barrier may protect the exo-erythocytic stage of *Plasmodium* against humoral antibodies (Coulston and Huff, 1948) while escape of trypanosomes to deep microcirculation in vessels, which show a shunting mechanism, may protect them against humoral antibodies (Ormerod, 1963).

FACTORS AFFECTING INNATE RESISTANCE OF THE VERTEBRATE HOST

These may be properly interpreted only if all factors related to the parasite are well known. An increase in resistance may be related to the age of the host (age resistance). Thus generally greater susceptibility of the young in comparison with the adult has been observed in *T. cruzi* in mice (Kolodny, 1940), in *Leishmania infantum* in man (Taub, 1956), and in *Eimeria meleagrimitis* in turkeys (Augustin and Ridges, 1963). However, the greater resistance of calves to an infection of *Babesia* than adults is an exception to the general rule and the mechanism of this phenomenon is not yet fully clarified (Riek, 1963). A decrease of resistance may be provoked by hormonal influences. Thus, male mice are more susceptible to *T. cruzi* infection than the female (Hauschka, 1947) and cortisone decreases resistance of mice against infection by *T. cruzi* (Pizzi *et al.*, 1952) or *Toxoplasma gondii* (Beattie, 1963). Folliculin may also produce earlier death in mice infected with *T. gondii* (Kozar and Sozka, 1956).

It is not well understood whether the rapid decrease in the capacity to produce sexual forms of some parasites in abnormal or natural hosts is caused by mechanisms of innate resistance. This phenomenon has been observed during multiple passages of *P. berghei* in white mice (Garnham, 1963), and of *T. annulata* in calves (Barnett, 1963).

Certain races (strains) of host species may have greater resistance to infection by protozoa than others, for example, the greater resistance of East African zebu against *T. parva* (Barnett, 1963) or of N'Dama cattle of western Africa against *T. vivax* and *T. congolense* (Chandler, 1952). Genetic abnormalities, such as deficiencies in certain metabolic substances in the host, are illustrated by the presence of hemoglobin-S, which is responsible for the sickle-cell trait (Allison, 1963) and may suppress an infection by *P. falciparum* in man and contribute to an increase in resistance. It has been considered that the presence of *Thalassemia* and fetal hemoglobin may have a similar influence (Allison, 1963). Recent research by Powell and Brewer (1965) did not provide evidence supporting the hypothesis that glucose-6-phosphate dehydrogenase deficiency (Motulsky, 1964) confers a biological advantage against *falciparum* malaria. Deficiencies of *p*-aminobenzoic acid during a milk diet of rats suppressed a *P. berghei* infection (Maegraith *et al.*, 1952; Hawking, 1954), while milk diet to the rhesus monkey suppressed *P. cynomolgi* infection (Bray and Garham, 1953). Malnutrition and vitamin deficiency may considerably decrease the resistance of the host, for instance, deficiency of thiamin, pantothenate, pyridoxine, and vitamin A in the diet of mice infected with *T. cruzi* (Yaeger and Miller, 1963). Superimposed parasitic infection may decrease the resistance; thus pigs highly resistant to *T. brucei* become susceptible if there is an intercurrent parasitic infection (Soltys, 1963).

If a natural host, in which the whole cycle of the parasite normally develops, is substituted by an abnormal one, resistance of different degrees, duration, and specificity may arise; thus nonsusceptibility has been observed in baboons to trypanosome infection (Manson-Bahr, 1963b), in rhesus monkeys to *P. vivax* (Garnham and Bray, 1956), in African buffalos to *Theileria annulata* (Barnett, 1963), in man to *T. brucei, T. congolense,* and *T. vivax* (Soltys, 1963), and in birds to *T. cruzi* (Dias, 1934). This information has been used to isolate *Anaplasma* from cattle with concomitant infection with *Babesia*. When blood infected with both parasites is inoculated into sheep or goats, the *Babesia* disappear since they cannot develop in these hosts (Diaz-Ungria, 1960).

Partial resistance against certain development stages of the parasite may be observed. Cebus monkeys inoculated with *P. cynomolgi* only show immunity to blood forms of the parasite and not to the tissue forms (Garnham, 1963). The same observation has been made in chimpanzees inoculated with *P. falciparum* (Bray, 1958). Parasite tolerance may be observed in bats infected with *P. berghei* (Corradetti *et al.*, 1959) and in rats infected with *T. gondii* (Eyles, 1952).

Nonspecific humoral factors of the host, such as complement, properdin, and "nonimmune" gamma globulin, etc., probably are of great importance in the defense mechanisms. Thus Gronroos (1955) suggested that mothers infected with *T. gondii* who showed properdin deficiency were more likely to bear a child with congenital toxoplasmosis. Complement of nonimmune sera destroys the crithidial but not the metacyclic and trypanosomal forms of *T. cruzi* (Muniz and Boriello, 1945) and also causes a lytic effect with merozoites of *E. meleagrimitis* (Augustin and Ridges, 1963). Nonspecific factors related to reproduction inhibition of intracellular parasites, comparable to "interferon" in virus infections, might play a part in innate defense mechanisms against intracellular protozoa. Nonspecific cellular factors such as phagocytic activity may also play an important role in protection mechanisms.

Various manipulations can decrease innate resistance. Thus abnormal hosts that are resistant may become susceptible after splenectomy, for example, the chimpanzee for *Babesia divergens* (Garnham and Bray, 1959) and the man for *Babesia* (Skrabalo and Deanovic, 1957). X-Irradiation may reduce resistance, for example in mice infected with *Trypanosoma duttoni* (Jaroslow, 1959), while other artificial methods of reducing resistance include blockade or destruction of the lymphoid-macrophage system with India ink or palmitic acid (Garnham, 1963).

The provision of substances on which the parasite is dependent may allow development in an abnormal host as illustrated by the maintenance of *T. vivax* in rats by the inoculation of sheep serum (Desowitz and Watson, 1951).

FACTORS CONCERNED IN ACQUIRED IMMUNITY OF THE VERTEBRATE HOST

Many factors affect the development, degree, duration, and specificity of acquired immunity which may be related to the parasite or to the host. Lysins, ablastins, opsonins, immobilizing cytoplasm-modifying antibodies, and those that alter the parasite's metabolism should be considered as humoral protective antibodies. They are generally independent of the antibodies which are used in immuno diagnosis, such as precipitins, agglutinins, complement fixation, and fluorescent antibodies, or delayed skin reactions. The behavior of humoral antibodies is frequently related to nonspecific humoral substances, such as complement or properdin, and so forth.

Cellular protective antibodies are intimately related to the mesenchymal cell system, called by Taliaferro and Mulligan (1937) the lymphoid-macrophage system (LMS). This cell system shows ability for a hyperproduction of humoral antibody-forming cells, such as lymphocytes and plasma cells, which are the chief producers of immune globulins and antibodies. It reacts at the same time with a generalized hyperplasia and accelerated multiplication of highly active fixed tissue and wandering blood and lymph stream macrophages, characterized by their ability to take up, engulf, digest, and remove the parasite and its residuals. Cellular and tissue factors are mainly responsible for acquired immunity to intracellular parasites and almost exclusively in *T. cruzi* infections (Pizzi, 1957) and *Leishmania* infection (Manson-Bahr, 1963a).

Lysis of organisms involves the fixation of complement; thus unheated immune serum has a higher lytic effect for merozoites of *E. meleagrimitis* than inactivated immune serum (Augustin and Ridges, 1963) while in the dye test, employed for the diagnosis of toxoplasmosis (Sabin and Feldman, 1948) or Chagas disease (Scorza *et al.*, 1959), the lytic effect of humoral antibodies together with the properdin system on the intra-cytoplasmatic structures of the parasite is well illustrated by electron microscopic examination (Thalhammer, 1957; Ludvik and Piekarski, 1963). Notwithstanding the knowledge that humoral antibodies are the main cause for immune protection from African trypanosomes and that trypanocidal lysin of serum, which is a 19S gamma globulin of high molecular weight (D'Alesandro, 1959), removes trypanosomes from the blood, the trypanolysin has not been convincingly demonstrated *in vitro* (Soltys, 1963). Tests used in studies of immune hemolysis need to be applied to protozoa in an endeavor to clarify the importance of immuno-lytic mechanisms.

Taliaferro (1924) was the first to demonstrate an acquired reproduc-tion inhibition substance, named ablastin, in rats infected with *Trypano-soma lewisi*. This is associated with a passively transferable serum factor of 7S gamma globulin (D'Alesandro, 1959). The antibody produces marked metabolic effects without being immediately lethal. Thus it does not physically injure the parasites, since they reproduce normally when they are washed and transferred to a nonimmune host; they do not lose their mobility and viability, but change their glucose metabolism from an assimilative type to one of maintenance (Moulder, 1948); their nucleic acid and protein synthesis is inhibited and decreases progres-sively for several weeks (Taliaferro and Pizzi, 1960); and their lactic dehydrogenase enzyme level is three times decreased (D'Alesandro and Sherman, 1964). The most remarkable property of ablastin, which dis-tinguishes it from other antibodies, is that it apparently cannot be ab-sorbed *in vitro* by homologous trypanosomes (Taliaferro, 1932; Thillet and Chandler, 1957). This phenomenon is not well understood. Ormerod (1963) believes that the ablastin effect of humoral antibodies principally causes a selective trypanolytic activity against developing forms of tryp-anosomes and not against adult stages, which may have a different an-tigen structure. The two antigens suggested by Ormerod (1963) could also explain why ablastin neither can be absorbed by adult trypano-somes, nor can desensitize them, these retaining their infectivity. No such acquired ablastin has been demonstrated in blood trypanosome infection of man.

It is suspected that immune serum factors play a part in the highly increased phagocytosis in acquired immunity of most protozoa infections. The opsonizing effect of hyperimmune chicken serum on *Plasmodium gallinaceum* in an *in vitro* test with macrophages was shown by Zuckerman (1963). Opsonins probably act on the parasite to change the surface properties or the surface of parasitized host cells, thus increasing their susceptibility to adherence and agglutination and facilitating phagocytosis. Opsonization mechanisms of protozoa have not been well studied and there is an urgent need for better tests.

Antimetabolic humoral antibodies are those of the ablastin type. Desowitz (1956) reported that reduction in oxygen uptake by *T. vivax* occurred if homologous immune serum was present and the same respiratory inhibiting effect of antibodies against *T. gondii* was reported by Fulton and Spooner (1960). Antimetabolic antibodies probably play an important role in lowering the virulence of parasites and decrease the invading capacity of intracellular protozoa. Thus, Augustin and Ridges (1963) supposed that antibodies may act against an invasive proteolytic enzyme produced by the sporozoites of coccidia.

Hyperplasia of the LMS is of great importance for cellular immunity against protozoa though in visceral leishmaniasis proliferation of lymphoid cells does not necessarily lead to immunity. This cell system has the principal function to remove the parasites and their residuals from the blood stream by active phagocytosis. The spleen, which contains a large number and concentration of cells of the LMS, plays an important role in immunity mechanisms. Thus, splenectomy generally produces relapse of chronic latent protozoal infection; however, in some cases of kala azar resistant to treatment with all drugs splenectomy leads to cure of the disease (Manson-Bahr, 1963b).

Immunity mechanisms against intracellular parasites may be involved in order to counter-attack the reproductive capacity of these protozoa. Vischer and Suter (1954) showed that living macrophages obtained from immunized animals are able to inhibit *T. gondii* infection. Thus, it may be supposed that intracellular antibodies can participate in immunity mechanisms. It is not known whether they are reproduction inhibition antibodies or intracellular lysins or both. The observation was made that in the chronic phase of Chagas disease "latent" pseudocysts are much more frequent than the "active" pseudocysts. It was suggested that antibodies that inhibit the transformation from the leishmanial stage to the blood trypanosome stage may be involved (Maekelt, 1965). Cyst wall formation produced in part by the host against *T. gondii* in the chronic phases of infection probably may be related to cellular immunity mechanisms.

Tissue hypersensitivity may play an additional role in immunity mechanisms. These inflammatory reactions usually act independently from humoral protective antibodies by inhibition of parasite dissemination. However, they can be harmful to the host if they are localized in certain vital tissues (for instance, in chorioretinitis caused by toxoplasmosis, or chronic Chagas' myocarditis with blockage of the intracardial conduction system). Hypersensitivity may be of the delayed type, being associated with cell-bound antibodies, or of the immediate type. The latter can be an immediate type of sensitivity, related to the presence of reagins, or an Arthus phenomenon, related to the presence of precipitins.

Haptens of parasites may combine with body proteins of the host and then can be a stimulus to produce autoantibodies against the host's own cells or tissues. Thus destruction of normal red blood cells may occur following antibody production against red cells parasitized by malarial parasites (Zuckerman, 1963). It is not clear whether these autoantibodies are cytotoxic and if they can really produce autoaggression, or if they are nonharmful and only a consequence of a tissue immune reaction.

REFERENCES

Allison, A. C. (1963). Inherited factors in blood conferring resistance to protozoa. In "Immunity to Protozoa" (P. C. C. Garnham, A. E. Pierce, and I. Roitt, eds.), pp. 109-122. Blackwell, Oxford.

Augustin, R., and Ridges, A. P. (1963). Immunity mechanisms in *Eimeria meleagrimitis*. In "Immunity to Protozoa" (P. C. C. Garnham, A. E. Pierce, and I. Roitt, eds.), pp. 295-335. Blackwell, Oxford.

Barnett, S. F. (1963). The biological races of the bovine *Theileria* and their host-parasite relationship. In "Immunity to Protozoa" (P. C. C. Garnham, A. E. Pierce, and I. Roitt, eds.), pp. 180-195. Blackwell, Oxford.

Beattie, C. P. (1963). Immunity to toxoplasma. In "Immunity to Protozoa" (P. C. C. Garnham, A. E. Pierce, and I. Roitt, eds.), pp. 253-258. Blackwell, Oxford.

Bray, R. S. (1958). Studies on malaria in chimpanzees. VI. *Laverania falcipara*. Am. J. Trop. Med. Hyg. 7, 20-24.

Bray, R. S., and Garnham, P. C. C. (1953). Effect of milk diet on *P. cynomolgi* infections in monkeys. Brit. Med. J. I, 1200-1201.

Bruce-Chwatt, L. J. (1952). Malaria in African infants and children in Southern Nigeria. Ann. Trop. Med. Parasitol. 46, 173-200.

Bruce-Chwatt, L. J. (1963). Congenital transmission of immunity in malaria. In "Immunity to Protozoa" (P. C. C. Garnham, A. E. Pierce, and I. Roitt, eds.), pp. 89-108. Blackwell, Oxford.

Chandler, R. L. (1952). Comparative tolerance of West Africa N'Dama cattle to trypanosomiasis. Ann. Trop. Med. Parasitol. 46, 127-134.

Cohen, S., and McGregor, I. A. (1963). Gamma-globulin and acquired immunity to malaria. In "Immunity to Protozoa" (P. C. C. Garnham, A. E. Pierce, and I. Roitt, eds.), pp. 123-159. Blackwell, Oxford.

Corradetti, A. (1950). Particolari fenomeni immunitari nell' infezione da *Plasmodium berghei*. Riv. Parassitol. 11, 201-209.

Corradetti, A., Verolini, F., and Rostirolla, M. (1959). Durate della soprovivenza di *Plasmodium berghei* nel pipistrello insettivoro italiano Minopterus shreibersii. *Riv. Parassitol.* **20**, 255-257.

Coulston, F., and Huff, C. G. (1948). Symposium on exoerythrocyte forms of malaria parasites. IV. The chemotherapy and immunology of pre-erythrocytic stages in avian malaria. *J. Parasitol.* **34**, 290-299.

Culbertson, J. T. (1939). The immunization of rats of different age groups against *Trypanosoma lewisi* by the administration of specific antiserum *per os. J. Parasitol.* **25**, 181-182.

D'Alesandro, P. A. (1959). Electrophoretic and ultracentrifugal studies of antibodies to *Trypanosoma lewisi. J. Infect. Diseases* **64**, 217-240.

D'Alesandro, P. A., and Sherman, I. W. (1964). Changes in lactic dehydrogenase levels of *Trypanosoma lewisi* associated with appearance of ablastin immunity. *Exptl. Parasitol.* **15**, 430-438.

Desowitz, R. S. (1956). Effect of antibody on the respiratory rate of *Trypanosoma vivax. Nature* **177**, 132.

Desowitz, R. S., and Watson, H. J. C. (1951). Studies on *Trypanosoma vivax*. I. Susceptibility of white rats to infection. *Ann. Trop. Med. Parasitol.* **45**, 207-219.

Dias, E. (1934). Etudos sobre o *Schizotrypanum cruzi. Mem. Inst. Oswaldo Cruz* **28**, 1-110.

Diaz-Ungria, C. (1960). "Parasitologia Venezolana," Vol. I. Sociedad de Ciencias Naturales LaSalle, Caracas, Venezuela.

Eyles, D. E. (1952). Toxoplasma in the Norway rat. *J. Parasitol* **38**, 226-229.

Fiennes, R. N. T. W. (1950). The cattle trypanosomiases: Cryptic trypanosomiasis. *Ann. Trop. Med. Parasitol.* **44**, 222-237.

Fulton, J. D., and Spooner, D. F. (1960). Metabolic studies on *Toxoplasma gondii. Exptl. Parasitol.* **9**, 293-301.

Garnham, P. C. C. (1963). An introduction to protozoal immunity. In "Immunity to Protozoa" (P. C. C. Garnham, A. E. Pierce, and I. Roitt, eds.), pp. 3-21. Blackwell, Oxford.

Garnham, P. C. C., and Bray, R. S. (1956). Influence of immunity upon stages (including late exo-erythrocytic schizonts) of mammalian malaria parasites. *Rev. Brasil. Malariol. Doenças Trop.*, **8**, 151-160.

Garnham, P. C. C., and Bray, R. S. (1959). The susceptibility of the higher primates to piroplasms. *J. Protozool.* **6**, 352-355.

Goble, F. C., Boyd, J. L., Grimm-Welmco, M., and Konrath, M. (1964). Vaccination against experimental Chagas' disease with homogenates of culture tissues of *Trypanosoma cruzi. J. Parasitol.* **50**, 19.

Gronroos, P. (1955). The action of properdin on *Toxoplasma gondii*. A preliminary report. *Ann. Med. Exptl. Biol. Fenniae* (*Helsinki*) **33**, 310-315.

Hauschka, T. S. (1947). Sex of host as a factor in Chagas' disease. *J. Parasitol.* **33**, 399-404.

Hawking, F. (1954). Milk, *p*-aminobenzoate and malaria of rats and monkeys. *Brit. Med. J.* **I**, 425-429.

Jaroslow, B. N. (1959). The effects of X or neutron irradiation, India ink blockade, or splenectomy on innate immunity against *Trypanosoma duttoni* in mice. *J. Infect. Diseases* **104**, 119-129.

Kagan, I. G., and Norman, L. (1962). Immunological studies on *Trypanosoma cruzi*. IV. Serial transfer of organisms from immune to non-immune mice. *J. Parasitol.* **48**, 584-588.

Kikkawa, Y., and Gueft, B. (1964). *Toxoplasma* cysts in the human heart, and electron microscopic study. *J. Parasitol.* **50**, 217-225.

Kligler, I. J., and Berman, M. (1935). Susceptibility and resistance to a trypanosome infection. X. Specific character of the immunity produced in rats by the injection of suspensions of dead trypanosomes. *Ann. Trop. Med. Parasitol.* **29**, 457-461.

Kolodny, M. H. (1939). The transmission of immunity in experimental trypanosomiasis (*Trypanosoma cruzi*) from mother rats to their offspring. *Am. J. Hyg.* **30**, 19-39.

Kolodny, M. H. (1940). Studies on age resistance against trypanosome infection. VII. The influence of age upon the immunological response of rats to infection with *Trypanosoma cruzi. Am. J. Hyg.* **31**, 1-8.

Kozar, Z., and Soszka, S. (1956). Hormonal factors in the development of *Toxoplasma* infection. *Bull. State Inst. Marine Trop. Med. Gdánsk, Poland* **7**, 168.

Ludvik, J., and Piekarski, G. (1963). Einfluss der Antikörper auf die Toxoplasmazellen im Elektronenmikroskop. *Proc. 1st Intern. Congr. Protozool, Prague, 1961* p. 369. Czech. Acad. Sci. Prague.

Maegraith, B. G., Deegan, T., and Jones, E. S. (1952). Suppression of malaria (*P. berghei*) by milk. *Brit. Med. J.* **II**, 1382-1384.

Maekelt, A. (1965). "El diagnóstico parasito-inmunológico de la infección chagásica," Monograph of the School of Medicine, Central University, Caracas, Venezuela.

Manson-Bahr, P. E. C. (1963a). Active immunization in leishmaniasis. *In* "Immunity to Protozoa" (P. C. C. Garnham, A. E. Pierce, and I. Roitt, eds.), pp. 246-252. Blackwell, Oxford.

Manson-Bahr, P. E. C. (1963b). Immunity in the prophylaxis of the protozoal diseases. *In* "Clinical Aspects of Immunology" (P. G. H. Gell and R. R. A. Coombs, eds.), pp. 759-775. Blackwell, Oxford.

Moshkovsky, C. D. (1937). On the rules governing immunity in infectious diseases (the principle or reinoculation). *Med. Parazitol.* (*Mosk.*) **6**, 291.

Motulsky, A. G. (1964). Hereditary red cell traits and malaria. *Am. J. Trop. Med. Hyg.* **13**, 147-158.

Moulder, J. W. (1948). Changes in the glucose metabolism of *Trypanosoma lewisi* during the course of infection in the rat. *J. Infect. Diseases* **83**, 42-49.

Muniz, J., and Borriello, A. (1945). Etudo sobre a ação lítica de diferentes soros sobre as formas de cultura e sanguicolas do *Schizotrypanum cruzi* en crithidias. *Rev. Brasil. Med.* **2**, 994-998.

Ormerod, W. E. (1963). The initial stages of infection with *Trypanosoma lewisi*; control of parasitemia by the host. *In* "Immunity to Protozoa" (P. C. C. Garnham, A. E. Pierce, and I. Roitt, eds.), pp. 213-227. Blackwell, Oxford.

Parrot, L. (1955). Sur l'immunité dans les paludismes. *Arch. Inst. Pasteur Algérie* **33**, 223-225.

Pizzi, T. (1957). "Inmunologia de la Enfermedad de Chagas," Monograph of the University of Santiago, Chile.

Pizzi, T. P., Rubio, D. M., Prager, R. S., and Silva, R. C. (1952). Accion de la cortisona en la infeccion experimental por *Trypanosoma cruzi. Bol. Inform. Parasitas. Chilenas* **7**, 22-24.

Powell, R. D., and Brewer, G. J. (1964). Active immunization against malaria. *Am. J. Trop. Med. Hyg.* **13**, 228-232.

Powell, R. D., and Brewer, G. T. (1965). Glucose-6-phosphate dehydrogenase deficiency and *falciparum* malaria. *Am. J. Trop. Med. Hyg.* 14, 358-362.

Riek, R. F. (1963). Immunity to babesiosis. In "Immunity to Protozoa" (P. C. C. Garnham, A. E. Pierce, and I. Roitt, eds.), pp. 160-179. Blackwell, Oxford.

Ritz, H. (1914). Über Rezidive bei experimenteller Trypanosomiasis. *Deut. Med. Wochschr.* 40, 1355-1358.

Sabin, A. B., and Feldman, H. A. (1948). Dyes as microchemical indicators of a new immunity phenomenon affecting a protozoan parasite (*Toxoplasma*). *Science,* 108, 660-663.

Scorza, J. V., Alvarez, A., Ramos, I., Dagert, C., Diaz Vasquez, A., and Torrealba, F. R. S. (1959). Nuevo metodo rapido para el diagnostico de la enfermedad de Chagas en su fase cronica. *Arch. Venezolanos Med. Trop.* 3, 121-135.

Sergent, E., Donatien, A. L., Parrot, F. C., Plantureux, E., and Rougebief, H. (1924). Études expérimentales sur les piroplasmosis bovines d'Algérie. *Ann. Inst. Pasteur* 38, 273.

Shortt, H. E., and Garnham, P. C. C. (1948). The pre-erythrocytic development of *Plasmodium cynomolgi* and *Plasmodium vivax. Trans. Roy. Soc. Trop. Med. Hyg.* 41, 785-795.

Skrabalo, Z., and Deanović, A. (1957). Piroplasmosis in man. *Doc. Med. Geograph. Trop.* 9, 11-16.

Smith, I. M. (1958). The protection against trypanosomiasis conferred on cattle by repeated doses of Antrycide alone or with *Trypanosoma congolense. Ann. Trop. Med. Parasitol.* 52, 391-401.

Soltys, M. A. (1963). Immunity in African trypanosomiasis. *Bull. World Health Organ.* 28, 753-761.

Taliaferro, W. H. (1924). A reaction product in infections with *Trypanosoma lewisi* which inhibits the reproduction of the trypanosomes. *J. Exptl. Med.* 39, 171-190.

Taliaferro, W. H. (1932). Trypanocidal and reproduction-inhibiting antibodies to *Trypanosoma lewisi* in rats and rabbits. *Am. J. Hyg.* 16, 32-84.

Taliaferro, W. H., and Mulligan, H. W. (1937). The histopathology of malaria with special reference to the function and origin of the macrophages in defense. *Indian Med. Res. Mem.* 29, 138.

Taliaferro, W. H., and Pizzi, T. (1960). The inhibition of nucleic acid and protein synthesis in *Trypanosoma lewisi* by the antibody ablastin. *Proc. Natl. Acad. Sci. U.S.* 46, 733-745.

Tarrant, C. J., Fife, E. H., Jr., and Anderson, R. I. (1965). Serological characteristics and general chemical nature of the "in vitro" exoantigens of *T. cruzi. J. Parasitol.* 51, 277-285.

Taub, J. (1956). The effect of normal human serum on *Leishmania. Bull. Res. Council Israel* E6, 55-57.

Thalhammer, O. (1957). "Die Toxoplasmose bei Mensch und Tier." Wilhelm Maudrich, Wien-Bonn, Germany.

Thillet, C. F., Jr., and Chandler, A. C. (1957). Immunization against *Trypanosoma lewisi* in rats by infections of metabolic products. *Science* 125, 346-347.

Vischer, W. A., and Suter, E. (1954). Intercellular multiplication of *Toxoplasma gondii* in adult mammalian macrophages cultured "in vitro." *Proc. Soc. Exptl. Biol. Med.* 86, 413-419.

Weitz, B. (1963). The antigenicity of some African trypanosomes. *In* "Immunity to

Protozoa" (P. C. C. Garnham, A. E. Pierce, and I. Roitt, eds.), pp. 196-203. Blackwell, Oxford.

Yaeger, R. G., and Miller, O. N. (1963). Effect of lysine deficiency on Chagas' disease in laboratory rats. *J. Nutr.* **81**, 169-174.

Zuckerman, A. (1963). Immunity in malaria with particular reference to red cell destruction. *In* "Immunity to Protozoa" (P. C. C. Garnham, A. E. Pierce, and I. Roitt, eds.), pp. 78-88. Blackwell, Oxford.

Author Index

Figures in italics refer to the pages on which references are listed.

A

Abadie, S., 44, 57, *121*
Abramov, I. V., 18, *30, 31*
Ackert, J. E., 88, 97, 101, *120*, 315, *316*
Adler, S., 137, *141*, 290, *293*
Akamatsu, T., 221, *224*
Alcock, S. J., *254*
Alexander, A. E., 102, *120*
Alicata, J. E., 90, *97, 98*
Alifanov, V. I., 76, *82*
Allan, B., 217, *224*
Allen, R. W., *141*
Allison, A. C., 150, 151, *151*, 326, *330*
Almeida, A. F., 51, *58*
Alvarado, R., 103, *120*
Alvarez, A., *333*
Amato Neto, V., 283, *296*
Anand, R. S., *181*
Andersen, F. L., 10, *12*
Anderson, N., 263, *273*
Anderson, R. I., *295, 333*
Andrade, Z. A., 288, *293*
Andrews, J. S., 92, 97, 162, 163, 169, *181*
Andrews, W. H., *253*
Anson, M. L., 34, *38*
Anthony, D. W., 134, *140*
Apitz, R. J., 151, *152*
Araki, M., 289, *293*
Arbogast, F. M., *183*
Arean, V. M., *295*
Armour, J., *273*
Arthur, D. R., 75, *82*, 229, *235*
Asami, K., 215, *224*
Ashton, N., *224*
Augustin, R., 270, *273*, 325, 327, 328, 329, *330*
Austen, K. F., 272, *273*
Azevedo, A. P., 246, *254*

B

Baer, J. G., 302, *318*
Bailey, K. P., 137, *139*
Bailey, W. S., 169, *181*, 305, 306, 313, *316*

Baker, A. D., 88, *97*
Baker, N. F., 96, *97*, 162, 163, 166, 167, 168, 170, 172, 174, 175, 180, *181, 182*
Baldone, J. A., 219, *224*
Bang, F. B., 287, *296*
Barnett, S. F., *31*, 128, 134, 135, 137, 138, *139*, 322, 323, 325, 326, *330*
Bartley, J. C., *181*
Bauer, O. N., 301, *316*
Baxter, J. H., *253*
Beames, H. W., *122*
Beattie, C. P., 325, *330*
Beaver, P. C., 96, 97, 216, 217, 218, 219, 222, 223, *224, 225*
Becker, E. R., 243, *252*
Beckett, E. B., 103, *120*
Bell, E. J., 146, *151*
Benacerra, B., *319*
Benenson, A. S., *296*
Benex, J., 278, *293*
Benjamini, E., 233, 234, *235, 236*
Berman, M., 323, *332*
Berntzen, A. K., 146, 147, *151*
Berrios-Duran, L. A., *297*
Bingham, G. A., 287, *295*
Bingham, M. L., 200, 210, 213, *213*
Björkman, N., 103, 104, 110, 111, *120*
125
Black, A. L., 170, *181*
Bloch, E., *253*
Bloch, K. J., *319*
Blood, B. D., 303, *319*
Blumenfeld, N., *182*
Boatman, P. A., *12*
Boch, J., 304, *318*
Bogitsh, B. J., 108, *120*
Bolin, D. W., *183*
Bonneville, M. A., 50, *58*
Booth, V. H., 188, *196*
Boothroyd, B., 103, *120*
Borriello, A., 326, *332*
Boughton, I. B., 162, *181*
Boyd, J. L., *331*
Brain, L., 217, *224*

Subject Index

A

Ablastin
  effect on nucleic acid synthesis, 328
  in *T. lewisi*, 328
Absorption mechanisms, in
  Ascaridia galli, 102
  Ascaris suum, 102
  cestodes, 105
  Fasciola hepatica, 103
  Hymenolepis citelli, 115
    diminuta, 105
  nematodes, 101
  Raillietina cesticillus, 105
Amino acids, absorption by
  Acanthocephala, 119
  Ascaridia, 109
  Ascaris, 101, 102, 110
  Callibothrium verticillatum, 118
  Fasciola hepatica, 103
  Hymenolepis spp., 111 *et seq.*
  Macracanthorhynchus, 119
  Moniliformis, 119
Anaplasma marginale, 133, 137
Ancylostoma
  braziliense
    incidence of, 218
    larval stages, parasitic of, 94
    visceral larva migrans, due to, 218
  caninum
    larval stages, parasitic, of, 89, 93
    pigmentation in, 151
    visceral larva migrans, due to, 219
  ceylanicum
    visceral larva migrans, due to, 218
  duodenale, larval stages, parasitic, of,
    90
  tubaeforme, visceral larva migrans, due
    to, 218
Anemia, associated with
  autoimmunization, 132
  Babesia spp., 132 *et seq.*
  erythrophagocytosis, 133
  Haemonchus contortus, 162
    genesis of, 163 *et seq.*

helminth infection, 155 *et seq.*
  hypochromic, 161
  macrocytic, 158
  microcytic, 161
  normocytic, 160
hookworm infection, 161
  Strongylus vulgaris, 212
  Trichostrongylus spp., 169
Angiostrongylus cantonensis
  larval stages of, 95
Antigen(s)
  eclipse, 291
  of *Babesia* spp., 130
    chemical nature of, 131
    physical properties of, 132
    protamine sulfate precipitated, 130
  of gastro-intestinal nematodes, 258, 268
  of schistosomes, 280, 291
  of *Theileria* spp., 137
  of *Trypanosoma lewisi*, 132
Arthus reaction, in helminth infection,
  270
Ascaridia galli
  absorptive mechanisms in, 102
  larval stages of, 88
Ascaris
  columnaris, larval stages of, 95
  lumbricoides
    hatching of eggs, 35
    moulting in, 85
    pigment in, 150
  mustelarum, larval stages of, 95
  suum
    absorptive mechanisms of, 102
    effect on *S. mansoni*, 287
      S. douthitti, 287
    larval stages of, 89
    visceral larva migrans, due to, 221
Aspicularis tetraptera, larval stages of, 88
Autoimmunization
  in anaplasmosis, 133
    Babesia rhodhaini, 132
    babesiosis, 132
    Plasmodium berghei, 133

B

Babesia
  argentina
    development in *Boophilus,* 19 *et seq.*
    effect of temperature on, 20
  bigemina
    ticks, development in, 16, 73
      effect of temperature, 74
      stages in, 15 *et. seq.*
      transovarian transmission in, 17
      transmitting, 64
  bovis
    in man, 62
    in ticks, development in, 73
  caballi, 128 *et seq.*
    ticks transmitting, 75
  canis, 133
    ticks, development in, 17
  divergens
    in chimpanzee, 62
    ticks, transmission in, 73
      transmitting, 73, 74
    in wild ruminants, 62
  equi, 128
    ticks, transmitting, 75
    transovarian transmission in, 80
  ovis
    development in ticks, 18
  pitheci, 62
  rodhaini, 81, 132, 241
  spp.
    developmental cycle of
      in mammals, 127
      in ticks, 15 *et seq.*
    electron microscopy of, 129
    from wild rodents, 62
    in horses, 128 *et seq.*
      in Florida, 128
    host specificity of, 62, 81
    immunity to, 327
    innate resistance to, 327
    pathogenesis of, 240
    protamine sulfate precipitated antigen of, 130
    serological features of, 132
    ticks transmitting, 63 *et seq.*
Biology, environmental of
  H. contortus, 186 *et seq.*
  Ostertagia spp., 188

Blood, alterations in helminth infections, 155 *et seq.*
Boophilus
  annulatus
    distribution, 72
  decoloratus
    distribution, 71
Brugia
  malayi, 94
  pahangi, 94
Bunostomum phlebotomum, immune response to, 265

C

Caenorhabditis briggsae, 150
  rhabditin in, 150
Callibothrium verticillatum
  absorptive mechanisms in, 112 *et seq.*
Cell inclusions, *see N. braziliensis*
Cercarienhüllenreaktion, 278
Chlorambucil, effect on immunity to nematodes, 262
Climate, effect on infective larvae, 7
Cobamide, in coelomocytes, 148
Cooperia
  curticei
    larval stages of, 91
  spp.
    anemia due to, 169
Cortisone
  effect on immunity to
    gastro-intestinal nematodes, 262
    Toxoplasma, 325
    Trypanosoma cruzi, 325
Culicoides, histamine in, 230
Cultivation, *in vitro,* 143
  cellular changes in
    cobamide, 148
    pigments, 148
    sperm morphology, 147
  of *Dirofilaria immitis,* 147
  of *Echinococcus granulosus,* 145
    multilocularis, 145
  of *Haemonchus contortus,* 147
  of helminths, 143 *et seq.*
    advantages of, 144
  of *Nippostrongylus braziliensis,* 147 *et seq.*
  of *Theileria* spp., 137
  of *Trichinella spiralis,* 145

exo-antigens of, 323
pathogenesis of, 241
' *vivax,* antimetabolic antibodies of, 329

U

Uncinaria stenocephala, 218

V

Visceral larva migrans
due to
Ancylostoma braziliense, 218
caninum, 218
ceylanicum, 218
tubaeforme, 218
Ascaris suum, 221
Balantidium spp., 215
Dipetalonema reconditum, 222
Dirofilaria immitis, 222
tenuis, 222
Oesophagostomum spp., 218
Strongyloides spp., 218
Toxocara canis, 215
cati, 217

Uncinaria stenocephala, 218
Vitamin B$_{12}$
absorption by Ascaris, 102, 110
in helminth anemias, 158

W

Wuchereria bancrofti, 94

Z

Zoonoses due to
Ancylostoma caninum, 218
braziliense, 218
ceylanicum, 218
tubaeforme, 218
Ascaris suum, 221
Balantidium spp., 215
Dirofilaria immitis, 222
tenuis, 222
Dipetalonema reconditum, 222
Oesophagostomum spp., 215
Strongyloides spp., 215
Toxocara canis, 215 *et seq.*
cati, 217

AF